STUDIES IN FOSSIL BOTANY

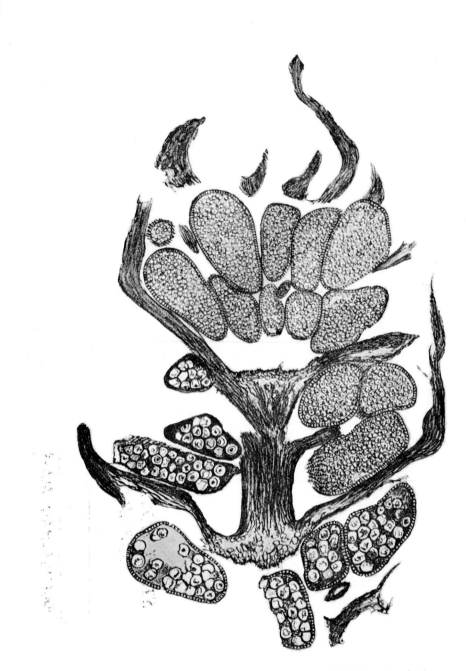

FIG. 1.—*Calamostachys Casheana.* Longitudinal section of heterosporous cone, showing microsporangia above and megasporangia below. × about 18. From Williamson's original drawing. See p. 48.

Frontispiece.

STUDIES

IN

FOSSIL BOTANY

BY

DUKINFIELD HENRY SCOTT

M.A., LL.D., D.SC., PH.D., F.R.S., F.L.S., F.G.S., F.R.M.S.

LATELY HONORARY KEEPER OF THE JODRELL LABORATORY, ROYAL BOTANIC
GARDENS, KEW

AUTHOR OF 'AN INTRODUCTION TO STRUCTURAL BOTANY,'
'THE EVOLUTION OF PLANTS,' ETC.

" Nous devons donc envisager l'état présent de l'univers comme l'effet
de son état antérieur."—*Laplace.*

VOL. I

PTERIDOPHYTA

THIRD EDITION

CONTAINING 190 ILLUSTRATIONS

HAFNER PUBLISHING COMPANY
NEW YORK
1962

Originally published in 1920-1923 by

A. & C. BLACK, LTD.

REPRINTED BY ARRANGEMENT

Published by

HAFNER PUBLISHING CO., INC.
31 East 10th Street
New York 3, N. Y.

LIBRARY OF CONGRESS CATALOG CARD NUMBER: 61-16861

Printed in the U.S.A.
Noble Offset Printers, Inc.
New York 3, N.Y.

PREFACE TO THIRD EDITION
VOLUME I

THE third edition of these " Studies " has needed quite as thorough a revision as the second, owing to the continued advance of the subject during the last dozen years.

In the earlier chapters of the present volume, however, the changes have been comparatively small; further information is given, for example, on the leaves of Calamites (p. 36) and the roots of *Sphenophyllum* (p. 87), but perhaps the most important addition, up to Chapter VII., is the new account of the remarkable Lycopodineous fructification, *Mazocarpon*, described by Dr. Margaret Benson (p. 213).

When we reach the Ferns the alterations become considerable. The true nature of the root-zone in *Psaronius* is now cleared up, thanks to the work of the late Count Solms-Laubach (p. 274). The geological history of the Osmundaceae has been successfully traced by Kidston and Gwynne-Vaughan, and a summary of their important results is given (p. 278).

The rapid growth of our knowledge of the Primofilices, owing to the investigations of Paul Bertrand, Kidston and Gordon, has rendered necessary a complete recasting of Chapter IX. (Botryopteridaceae), with very considerable additions.

Lastly, a wholly new chapter has been added, on the Psilophytales, a class of early Devonian Cryptogams,

v

only recently recognised (Chapter X.). The discoveries, chiefly those of Kidston and Lang, recorded in this chapter, are among the most fundamental yet made in the palæontological history of plants. The liberality of the authors mentioned has enabled me to illustrate the new group fully, by reproductions of many of the original photographs.

The present volume contains sixty-six new figures. The frontispiece is reproduced from Williamson's original drawing (one of those kindly placed at my disposal by Mrs. Williamson) of his heterosporous cone of *Calamostachys*. The other new illustrations are the following : Figs. 11, 15, 37, 43, 79, 83, 90, 103-106, 121, 124, 126-129, 132, 133, 136-143, 146, 150, 152, and 156-190, including all those for the new chapter. In a few cases some old figures have been superseded by the new.

The work of preparing the Index has again been undertaken by my wife, Mrs. D. H. Scott, F.L.S.

D. H. SCOTT.

28th July 1920.

PREFACE TO SECOND EDITION
VOLUME I

THE exceptionally rapid progress of Fossil Botany during the last eight years has rendered necessary a very thorough revision of this book, and the rewriting of considerable portions. At the same time care has been taken to maintain the original character of the " Studies " as a first introduction to " those results of palæontological inquiry which appear to be of fundamental importance from the botanist's point of view." No attempt has been made to extend the scope of the book, which now, as before, is concerned essentially with the morphological and evolutionary aspects of Palæobotany, but in every chapter new results of research have been incorporated.

The volume now issued (Chapters I.-IX.) covers the Pteridophyta, *i.e.* those groups of Vascular Plants which may still be considered as, on the whole, Cryptogamic. The second volume (Chapters X.-XIV.) will contain the Spermophyta, so far as they are dealt with, together with the chapter on " General Results."

The boundary between Pteridophyta and Spermophyta, though no longer a " scientific frontier," happens to serve as a convenient limit between the two volumes.

The heading " Chapter " now replaces " Lecture," for, except perhaps in the Introduction, little trace of the original lecture form survives.

The first three chapters have been slightly rearranged,

so as to give a somewhat more logical division of the
subject - matter. The substantial changes in these
chapters are not great, Mr. Hickling's new observations
on *Palaeostachya* and M. Halle's investigation of Mesozoic
Equisetales being the chief novelties.

In Chapter IV. some account is given of a new type
of fructification in *Sphenophyllum*, and Professor Nathorst's discovery of the group Pseudoborniales is shortly
noticed.

In Chapter V. the changes are only in details, but
Chapter VI. has received important additions; in
particular, the curious seed-like fructifications of certain
Palæozoic Lycopods, only shortly referred to in the
first edition, have demanded fuller consideration.

In Chapter VII. a considerable advance in our knowledge both of *Sigillaria* and *Stigmaria* has been placed on
record, and a short section on the herbaceous forms
(Lycopoditeae) has been added, based on recent researches
from French and Swedish sources.

The treatment of the Ferns (Chapters VIII. and IX.)
has of necessity been profoundly changed by the discovery (due to Oliver, Kidston, Grand'Eury, White,
and others) that so large a proportion of the supposed
Palæozoic Ferns were, in reality, seed-bearing plants.
Chapter IX., in which the now prominent family of
the Botryopterideae is described, has been more extended
than any other in the volume.

Volume I. contains 27 additional figures, besides a few
cases in which new illustrations have been substituted
for old. The figures now added are : 11, 27, 42, 47,
48, 76, 77, 78, 80, 81, 82, 83, 84, 94, 95, 103, 106, 114,
117, 120, 122, 123, 124, 125, 126, 127, and 128.

The new figures signed " R. S." are by my wife, Mrs.
D. H. Scott, F.L.S., who has also made the Index.

D. H. SCOTT.

12th March 1908.

PREFACE TO FIRST EDITION

THESE *Studies in Fossil Botany* are founded on a special course of lectures, given, under the same title, at University College, London, in the year 1896.

The lecture form has been retained, but the number of lectures, into which the course is divided, has increased from eleven to fourteen. The introductory lecture preserves something of its original character, but all the rest have been completely recast, and most of them wholly rewritten.

At the present day, happily, fossil botany is an eminently progressive branch of science, and thus the mere lapse of time, since the lectures were delivered, has necessitated the introduction of much new matter and of many new points of view. A certain number of unpublished observations are also embodied in the book.

My object has by no means been to write a manual of fossil botany, a superfluous undertaking, in view of the excellent publications of the last few years. To mention only the very latest works, we have Mr. Seward's extensive treatise on *Fossil Plants*, now in course of publication, Professor Potonié's concise *Lehrbuch der Pflanzen-palæontologie*, and, within the present year, M. Zeiller's *Éléments de Paléobotanique*, all of them, in their several ways, admirable hand-books for the student of palæobotany.

My purpose has been quite a different one, namely, to present to the botanical reader those results of palæontological inquiry which appear to be of fundamental importance from the botanist's point of view. Such far-reaching results have, at present, related almost entirely to two of the vegetable Sub-kingdoms, the Pteridophytes and the Gymnosperms, and it is to these Sub-kingdoms that the " Studies " are confined.

Within these limits, the value of the fossil evidence already available is manifest, though as yet hardly realised by botanists. The last few years, however, have seen a considerable advance in this respect, and we may hope that the palæontological record will no longer be ignored by students of the evolution of plants.

The present book, while it assumes no previous knowledge of fossil plants, presupposes a general acquaintance with recent botany, and with the rudiments, though only the rudiments, of geology. The terminology employed will be familiar to the botanical student ; in the few cases where new or less usual terms are introduced, their explanation is given. Only two points seem to require notice here. The term *tracheae* is used in the wide sense adopted by De Bary, to cover both the *vessels* of the wood (arising by cell-fusion) and the *tracheides* (consisting of single cells).[1] Other authors have used the word in more restricted senses, but a general term for the water-conducting elements is indispensable, and De Bary's usage answers every purpose.

As in my *Introduction to Structural Botany*, the form *megaspore* is used throughout, in preference to *macrospore*, on the ground that the former term is more correct, and less liable to verbal confusion with microspore.

More than a third of the illustrations are new, and of these the majority (over forty in number) were drawn for me by Mr. Gwilliam, as indicated by his initials, G. T. G. In addition, a considerable number of the borrowed figures were redrawn by the same artist, to whose skill the book is much indebted.

---

[1] De Bary, *Comparative Anatomy of the Phanerogams and Ferns.* English edition, 1884, p. 155.

Of the figures which are not new, a great many are taken from memoirs by the late Dr. W. C. Williamson, F.R.S., by myself, or by both of us, jointly. The source of all figures borrowed from other authors is of course acknowledged. I have to thank the Royal Society for permission to reproduce a large number of figures from the *Philosophical Transactions*, and the Linnean Society for a similar permission in the case of that Society's publications.

Mr. W. Carruthers, F.R.S., has kindly allowed me to make use of some illustrations from his well-known memoir on fossil Cycadean stems.

The restoration of *Lyginodendron Oldhamium*, forming the frontispiece, is the work of Mr. J. Allen, who has carried out a difficult task with much ability.

For various photographic illustrations I am indebted to Dr. E. C. Bousfield, and to my colleague, Mr. L. A. Boodle.

Wherever possible, I have given the number of the section or specimen illustrated, in the collection to which it belongs. The abbreviation " Will. Coll." indicates the Williamson Collection (now in the British Museum, Natural History Department), while " S. Coll." refers to my own collection. In other cases the name is given in full.

The progress of scientific fossil botany has been greatly advanced by the skilled and intelligent work, in collecting petrified specimens and preparing sections, of such men as Mr. J. Lomax, Mr. G. Wild, and their colleagues, now deceased, Mr. J. Butterworth, Mr. J. Spencer, and others.

The references to the literature make no pretence to being exhaustive ; I hope, however, that the works of chief importance to the botanical reader have been cited, and that justice has in all cases been done to those who have laid the foundations of our knowledge.

D. H. SCOTT.

20th June 1900.

CONTENTS OF VOLUME I

PAGE

PREFACE TO THIRD EDITION, VOLUME I . . . v

PREFACE TO SECOND EDITION, VOLUME I . . vii

PREFACE TO FIRST EDITION ix

CHAPTER I

INTRODUCTION 1

CHAPTER II

EQUISETALES—VEGETATIVE STRUCTURE

Calamites ; Arthrodendron ; Calamodendron ; Protocalamites

1. The Calamarieae 13
2. The Stem of Calamites 17
3. Branching 27
4. Other Types of Stem 29
5. The Leaves 33
6. The Roots 37
7. The Medullary Casts 41

CHAPTER III

EQUISETALES—FRUCTIFICATIONS AND CLASSIFICATION

Calamostachys ; Palaeostachya ; Cingularia ; Archaeocalamites ; Macrostachya ; Classification of Calamarieae ; Mesozoic Equisetales

1. The Fructifications 43

	PAGE
2. Calamostachys	44
3. Palaeostachya	54
4. Cingularia	59
5. Archaeocalamites	62
6. Macrostachya	64
7. Classification	65
8. Mesozoic Equisetales	72

CHAPTER IV

SPHENOPHYLLALES

Sphenophylleae ; Cheirostrobeae ; Pseudoborniales

I. Sphenophylleae	75
1. Sphenophyllum—Vegetative Organs . . .	75
2. Fructifications of Sphenophyllum—S. Dawsoni Type	88
3. Bowmanites Römeri, Sphenophyllum fertile, S. majus	
and S. trichomatosum	96
II. Cheirostrobeae	102
4. Cheirostrobus	102
III. Pseudoborniales	110
5. Pseudobornia	110

CHAPTER V

LYCOPODIALES

Lepidodendron and Lepidophloios

Introductory Remarks	111
1. Habit	112
2. Stem	118
3. Leaves	138
4. Branching	143

CHAPTER VI

LYCOPODIALES—*continued*

Ulodendron and Halonia ; Fructifications of Lepidodendreae ;
Bothrodendron ; Pinakodendron

PAGE

1. Ulodendron and Halonia 147
2. Lepidostrobus 155
3. Spencerites 169
4. The Seed-like Lycopodiaceous Fructifications . 173
5. Bothrodendron 179
6. Pinakodendron 183

CHAPTER VII

LYCOPODIALES—*continued*

Sigillaria and Stigmaria ; Lycopoditeae

I. Sigillaria   184

1. Habit and External Characters. . . . 184
2. Anatomical Structure 193
3. Fructifications 208
4. Mazocarpon 213

II. Stigmaria   217

1. Habit and External Characters. . . . 217
2. Anatomical Structure 221
3. Morphology 236

III. Lycopoditeae   239

Conclusion 241

CHAPTER VIII

THE FERNS

Fronds ; Fructifications ; Anatomy

Introductory Remarks 244

PAGE

1. Fronds 246
2. Fructifications 250
3. Anatomy—Psaronius 268
4. Osmundaceae 278

CHAPTER IX

THE FERNS—*continued*

The Botryopteridaceae—Summary on the Ferns

I. Botryopteridaceae   287

A. *Zygopterideae*   288

1. Ankyropteris 289
2. Clepsydropsis 303
3. Asterochlaena 306
4. Asteropteris 309
5. Dineuron 311
6. Metaclepsydropsis 312
7. Diplolabis 316
8. Zygopteris 318
9. Botrychioxylon 319
10. Etapteris 322
11. Corynepteris 328
12. Stauropteris 329
Relationships of the Genera 336

B. *Botryopterideae*   337

Botryopteris 337
Other Genera 350

C. *Anachoropterideae*   352

Affinities of the Order 356

II. Summary   365

CHAPTER X

THE PSILOPHYTALES

Early Devonian Pteridophytes

PAGE

Rhynia 371

Relation of Rhynia to Psilophyton . . . 382

Hornea 387

Sporogonites 395

Asteroxylon 397

Affinities of Asteroxylon 409

Arthrostigma 417

General Relations of the Psilophytales . . 419

INDEX 423

LIST OF ILLUSTRATIONS

FIGURE   PAGE

1. *Calamostachys Casheana.* Cone . . . . . *Frontispiece*
2. *Calamites Suckowii.* Medullary cast 15
3.   ,,   ,,   Medullary cast 16
4. *Calamites,* sp. Part of a transverse section of a young stem . 18
5.   ,,   sp. Transverse section of a very young twig . . 19
6.   ,,   sp. Part of a radial section through primary wood . 20
7.   ,,   sp. Radial section of a decorticated stem . . . 22
8. *Calamites communis.* Tangential section of wood . . . 23
9.   ,,   ,,   Tangential section of wood showing a branch 27
10. *Calamodendron intermedium.* Part of transverse section of stem . 30
11. *Protocalamites pettycurensis.* Transverse section . . . 32
12. *Calamites,* sp. Transverse fracture through a node showing leaf-
    sheath 33
13. *Calamites,* sp. Part of a transverse section close to a node . 34
14.   ,,   sp. Transverse section of a bud 35
15. Calamite leaves in transverse section 36
16. *Calamites,* sp. Part of a transverse section of a large root . . 38
17.   ,,   sp. Transverse section of small tetrarch rootlet . . 40
18. *Calamostachys Binneyana.* Radial section of part of cone . . 44
19.   ,,   ,,   Transverse section of cone . . 45
20.   ,,   ,,   Transverse section of axis of cone . 46
21.   ,,   ,,   A single peltate sporangiophore . 48
22.   ,,   ,,   Part of tangential section of cone . 49
23.   ,,   ,,   A single sporangium. A-D, spores . 50
24. *Calamostachys Casheana.* Tangential section 51
25. A. *Palaeostachya.* Radial section of cone. B. *Archaeocalamites
    radiatus.* Part of cone showing axis bearing sporangiophores 54
26. *Palaeostachya pedunculata* 55
27. *Palaeostachya vera.* Transverse section of cone . . . 57
28.   ,,   ,,   Diagrammatic longitudinal section of cone . 58
29. *Cingularia typica.* Part of branch 60
30.   ,,   ,,   Enlarged diagram of a verticil of the cone . 61
31. *Archaeocalamites radiatus.* Branch bearing whorled leaves . . 63
32.   ,,   ,,   Single leaf 63
33. *Macrostachya infundibuliformis.* Cone borne laterally on a branch 65
34. *Annularia brevifolia.* Twigs bearing whorled leaves . . . 66
35. *Asterophyllites densifolius.* Branch bearing distichously arranged
    twigs 68
36. *Sphenophyllum,* sp. Branched stem bearing leaves and cone . 76
37. *Sphenophyllum saxifragaefolium,* showing the whorled leaves . 77
38. *Sphenophyllum quadrifidum.* A. Radial section through a node.
    B. Transverse section of same stem. C. Transverse section
    through a node. D. Transverse section of a portion of secondary
    wood 79

FIGURE   PAGE

39. *Sphenophyllum plurifoliatum.* Transverse section of stem through
    whorl of leaves   80
40. *Sphenophyllum plurifoliatum.* Transverse section of older stem .   81
41.   „   „   Radial section through part of
    secondary wood   82
42. *Sphenophyllum insigne.* Transverse section of rather young stem .   84
43. *Sphenophyllum,* sp. Root, transverse   87
44. *Sphenophyllum Dawsoni.* A. Diagram of cone in longitudinal
    section. B. Stele of axis in transverse section. C. Spores in
    superficial aspect   90
45. *Sphenophyllum Dawsoni.* Longitudinal section of cone . .   91
46.   „   „   Transverse section of cone . . .   93
47.   „   „   Sporangiophore and its sporangium .   95
48. *Bowmanites Römeri.* Part of transverse section of cone . .   97
49.   „   „   A. Lamina of sporangiophore. B. Longi-
    tudinal section through upper part of sporangiophore . .   98
50. *Sphenophyllum fertile.* Diagram A. Node in radial section.
    B. One lobe of sporophyll   100
51. *Sphenophyllum majus.* Forked sporophyll bearing four sporangia .   101
52. *Cheirostrobus pettycurensis.* Diagram. Transverse and radial
    section   103
53. *Cheirostrobus pettycurensis.* Part of radial section . . .   105
54.   „   „   Transverse section of axis of cone .   106
55. *Lepidodendron elegans.* Restoration of tree   113
56. *Lepidodendron Ophiurus.* A. Fragment of stem-surface. B.
    Leafy branch bearing a cone   114
57. *Lepidodendron Veltheimianum.* Portion of surface of stem . .   115
58. *Lepidodendron.* Leaf-base   116
59. *Lepidodendron Harcourtii.* A. Transverse section of stem. B.
    Stele of same   123
60. *Lepidodendron (Lepidophloios ?) Wunschianum.* Transverse section
    from outer part of stele   127
61. *Lepidodendron brevifolium.* Transverse section of stem . .   128
62. *Lepidodendron selaginoides.* Transverse section of young branch .   129
63.   „   „   Transverse section of stele . .   130
64.   „   „   Part of radial section . . .   135
65. *Lepidophloios,* sp. A. Tangential section from the outside of a
    stem. B. A single leaf-base   139
66. *Lepidophloios,* sp. Radial section of a leaf-base . . .   141
67. *Lepidodendron Hickii.* Transverse section of leaf . . .   143
68.   „   „   Epidermis of leaf, with stomata . .   143
69. *Lepidodendron selaginoides.* Transverse section showing the two
    steles of a bifurcating stem   144
70. *Ulodendron.* Surface of branch   148
71. *Lepidophloios scoticus.* A. Bifurcating Halonial branch. B. Leaf-
    cushions enlarged   151
72. *Lepidophloios fuliginosus.* Transverse section of a young shoot .   153
73. *Lepidostrobus Hibbertianus.* Compressed specimen of an almost
    perfect cone   156
74. *Lepidostrobus.* Diagram of heterosporous cone in radial section .   157
75. *Lepidostrobus Veltheimianus.* Transverse section of cone through
    microspore-region   163
76. *Lepidostrobus Veltheimianus.* Transverse section of cone through
    megaspore-region   164
77. *Lepidostrobus Veltheimianus.* Longitudinal section of cone . .   165
78. Spores of Lepidodendreae. A. and B. *Spencerites insignis.* C.
    Lepidostrobus Veltheimianus. D. A single megaspore . .   166
79. *Lepidostrobus foliaceus.* Sporangium   167
80.   „   „   Megaspore   167

FIGURE / PAGE

81. *Lepidostrobus Veltheimianus.* Megaspore in section showing prothallus 168
82. *Mazocarpon.* Isolated megaspore showing prothallus . . 168
83. *Lepidostrobus Veltheimianus.* Archegonium 169
84. *Spencerites insignis.* Somewhat diagrammatic radial section . 171
85. *Lepidocarpon Lomaxi.* Sporangium and sporophyll . . . 174
86. ,, ,, Upper part of integumented " seed " . 175
87. ,, ,, Diagrammatic section of " seed " . . 176
88. *Miadesmia membranacea.* Approximately transverse section of seed-like organ 177
89. *Miadesmia membranacea.* Radial section of seed-like organ . 178
90. *Bothrodendron mundum.* Sporophyll and sporangium . . 181
91. Stump and roots (*Stigmaria ficoides*) of a Lycopodiaceous tree . 186
92. *Sigillaria tessellata (Favularia* type). Surface of stem . . 187
93. *Sigillaria mamillaris (Rhytidolepis* type). Surface of stem . 188
94. *Sigillaria Brardi (Leiodermaria* type). Part of surface of stem . 189
95. *Sigillaria Menardi (Clathraria* type). Section and surface . . 194
96. *Sigillaria spinulosa.* Part of transverse section of stem . . 198
97. ,, ,, Part of wood more highly magnified . 198
98. ,, ,, A. Tangential section of outer cortex. B. Leaf. C. *Sigillaria latifolia.* Transverse section of leaf . 200
99. *Sigillaria (Rhytidolepis* type). Segment of stem in transverse section 204
100. *Sigillaria scutellata.* Transverse section of a portion of the wood . 206
101. *Sigillariopsis sulcata.* Transverse section of leaf . . . 207
102. *Sigillariostrobus rhombibracteatus.* A. Part of cone. B. *S. ciliatus.* Part of axis with sporangia. C. Megaspores . . 211
103. *Mazocarpon.* Diagram 213
104. *M. shorense.* Section of megasporangium 214
105. ,, ,, Section showing four megaspores . . . 215
106. ,, ,, Detached portion of fragmented megasporangium . 215
107. *Stigmaria ficoides.* Part of surface 218
108. ,, ,, Transverse section of a small specimen . 222
109. ,, ,, Part of tangential section through wood . 224
110. ,, ,, Part of transverse section with rootlet . 225
111. ,, ,, Transverse section of rootlet . . . 229
112. ,, ,, Part of transverse section of rootlet . . 230
113. ,, ,, Transverse section of rootlet showing vascular system 232
114. *Stigmaria ficoides.* Transverse section of central part of rootlet . 233
115. ,, ,, Transverse section of rootlet showing dichotomy 234
116. *Stigmaria,* sp. Transverse section of an axis with centripetal wood 235
117. *Pecopteris (Dactylotheca) dentata.* Part of a frond . . . 247
118. *Ptychocarpus unitus.* Fructification. A. Part of a fertile pinnule. B. Synangia in side view. C. A synangium . . . 253
119. Group of Palaeozoic fructifications of Ferns or Pteridosperms. A. *Asterotheca.* B. *Renaultia.* C. *Dactylotheca.* D. *Sturiella.* E. *Oligocarpia.* F. *Crossotheca.* G. *Senftenbergia.* H. *Hawlea.* J. *Urnatopteris* 255
120. *Scolecopteris polymorpha.* A. Lower surface of a fertile pinnule. B. Transverse section of half a pinnule showing synangium . 257
121. *Pteridotheca Williamsonii.* A. Two sporangia. B. Sporangium in transverse section 265
122. *Pteridotheca Williamsonii.* Group of annulate sporangia . . 266
123. *Psaronius brasiliensis.* Transverse section of stem . . . 272
124. *Psaronius,* from Brazil. Root-zone 275
125. *Psaronius Renaulti.* Part of transverse section of stem . . 277

FIGURE   PAGE

126. *Osmundites skidegatensis.* Inner margin of vascular ring . . 280
127. *Thamnopteris Schlechtendalii.* Transverse section . . . 282
128.   „   „   Portion of stele in transverse section 283
129. *Thamnopteris Schlechtendalii.* Diagrams illustrating departure of leaf-trace 285
130. *Ankyropteris Grayi.* Transverse section of stem . . . 290
131.   „   „   Transverse section of stele . . . 291
132.   „   „   Undivided leaf-trace 293
133.   „   „   Separation of the axillary stele . . 294
134. *Ankyropteris corrugata.* Transverse section of an " Aphlebia " . 297
135. *Ankyropteris westphaliensis.* Transverse section of a petiole . 298
136. *Ankyropteris corrugata.* Transverse section of a dichotomous stem 302
137. *Asterochlaena laxa.* General transverse section . . . 307
138.   „   „   Leaf-trace 309
139. *Asteropteris noveboracensis.* Transverse section of stem . . 310
140. Diagrams showing the foliar bundles of various Zygopterideae . 313
141. *Metaclepsydropsis duplex.* Transverse section of rachis . . 316
142. *Botrychioxylon paradoxum.* Transverse section of stele . . 320
143. *Etapteris Scotti.* Transverse section of rachis 324
144. *Etapteris Lacattei.* 1. Group of four sporangia. 2. Sporangia enlarged. 3. Group of sporangia in transverse section . ֹ 326
145. *Stauropteris oldhamia.* Transverse section of vascular bundle of main rachis 330
146. *Stauropteris oldhamia.* A. Diagram of primary rachis. B. Corresponding diagram of a secondary rachis 331
147. *Stauropteris oldhamia.* A, B, C. Three sporangia . . . 332
148.   „   „   Four germinating spores . . . 334
149. *Botryopteris hirsuta.* Transverse section of stem . . . 338
150. *Botryopteris ramosa.* Transverse section of stem . . . 339
151. *Botryopteris hirsuta.* Transverse section of vascular bundle of young petiole 340
152. *Botryopteris forensis.* Transverse section of vascular bundle of petiole 342
153. *Botryopteris forensis.* Group of sporangia 343
154. *Botryopteris*, sp. Group of sporangia 344
155.   „   Sporangium in transverse section . . . 345
156. *Botryopteris cylindrica.* α form. A. Transverse section showing unequal dichotomy. B. Transverse section of stem and petiole 346
157. *Botryopteris cylindrica.* β form. Transverse section . . 347
158. *Anachoropteris rotundata.* Transverse section of petiole . . 353
159. *Chorionopteris gleichenioides.* Synangium 354
160. *Rhynia Gwynne-Vaughani.* External view of a portion of stem . 373
161. *Rhynia major.* Transverse section of aerial stem · . . 374
162. *Rhynia Gwynne-Vaughani.* Longitudinal section of stem . . 375
163.   „   „   „   Transverse section of aerial stem, showing dichotomy 376
164. *Rhynia Gwynne-Vaughani.* Part of epidermis, showing stoma . 377
165.   „   „   „   Part of transverse section of aerial stem 378
166. *Rhynia Gwynne-Vaughani.* Tracheides in longitudinal section . 379
167.   „   „   „   Superficial tissues of aerial stem . 380
168.   „   „   „   Transverse section of aerial stem bearing an adventitious branch 381
169. *Rhynia major.* Longitudinal section of a sporangium . . 382
170.   „   „   Transverse section of sporangium . . . 383
171.   „   „   Spores 384
172. *Psilophyton princeps.* Dawson's original restoration . . . 385

FIGURE PAGE

173. *Hornea Lignieri.* Large protocormous rhizome . . . 387
174. ,, ,, Flat, broad rhizome, showing rhizoids . . 388
175. ,, ,, Stele of stem, in transverse section . . 389
176. ,, ,, Stele in longitudinal section 390
177. ,, ,, Two well-preserved sporangia . . . 391
178. ,, ,, Portion of sporangium, enlarged . . . 392
179. ,, ,, Spores in tetrads 393
180. *Asteroxylon Mackiei.* Transverse section of rhizome . . 398
181. ,, ,, Transverse section of large aerial stem . 399
182. ,, ,, Longitudinal section of aerial stem . . 400
183. ,, ,, Transverse section of stellate xylem . 401
184. ,, ,, Transverse section of an arm of the stellate
wood 402
185. *Asteroxylon Mackiei.* Longitudinal section of xylem . . 403
186. ,, ,, Stoma 404
187. ,, ,, Fertile axes in transverse section . . 405
188. ,, ,, Other fertile axes 406
189. ,, ,, Longitudinal section of a sporangium . 407
190. *Arthrostigma gracile.* Stem, bearing the falcate leaves . . 417

STUDIES IN FOSSIL BOTANY

CHAPTER I

INTRODUCTION

IT is a general rule, applying to knowledge of every kind, that we cannot hope to understand any group of phenomena without a study of its antecedents. In political inquiries, no student would attempt to make himself acquainted with the existing constitution of a country, without seeking to gain a knowledge of the historical events by which it has been built up. In like manner, we cannot obtain any adequate idea of the present state of an art, such as sculpture or painting, unless we are prepared to study the history and development of the art in past times. Again, to come nearer to our own subject, scientific geography is impossible without geology, that is to say, without a knowledge of the past changes, to which the surface of the earth owes its present configuration. *Vere scire est per causas scire*, and causation is only known to us by the succession of events.

The same principle holds good for the special case of biology, the science of which botany is a part. Botany, on its morphological side, consists in the application of the comparative method to the study of plants, with a view to the determination of their relationships. In these days, most of us, when we speak of relationship among

I

organisms, mean to imply a real affinity, that is to say, a blood-relationship, so that, on this view, the ultimate object of morphological inquiry is to build up the genealogical tree of the organic world. Many attempts at the construction of genealogical trees have been failures, but still this is the object, however remote, which we have ultimately before us when we devote ourselves to morphological studies.

Existing organisms are related to each other more or less as brothers or cousins are related. All the species living at the present day belong, as it were, to the present generation. By the study of living organisms alone, it must necessarily be a matter very much of conjecture to decide which of them, in any given group, stands nearest to the old family stock. As regards some of the main taxonomic divisions, it is true, there can be no doubt. We should all agree, for example, that the Green Algae are, on the whole, much more primitive than the Flowering Plants ; but when we come to more difficult questions, such, for example, as the relative position of the various families of Vascular Cryptogams, we find the most different opinions prevailing, and the conclusion at which we may arrive is largely a matter of subjective interpretation.

The only direct evidence which is possible in questions of descent among plants is from the ancient plants themselves. Fortunately, the rocks afford us a considerable amount of such direct evidence. I need not say that the estimation of this evidence is in itself beset with the greatest difficulties, difficulties which those best appreciate who have themselves worked at fossil remains. The construction of a pedigree of the Vegetable Kingdom is a pious desire, which will certainly not be realised in our time ; all we can hope to do is to make some very small contributions to the work. Yet we may at least gather up some fragments from past chapters in the history of plants, and extend our view beyond the narrow limits of the present epoch, for the flora now living is after all nothing but one particular stage in the evolution of the Vegetable Kingdom. The old plants are well worth knowing for their own sake, apart from theoretical considerations.

There is a phrase in the introduction to the late Count Solms-Laubach's classical *Fossil Botany* [1] which I think very appropriate to our purpose. The author says that our object in studying fossil plants is " the completion of the natural system." That is the point of view which we shall take up in this book. I shall endeavour to bring before the reader those discoveries in fossil botany which already contribute something towards the completion of the natural system. If this be our purpose, it is evident that only well-characterised fossils have any interest for us. A specimen which may be an Alga, or perhaps a worm-track, or possibly even a wave-mark, is no doubt a curiosity, but will not help us much towards the end in view. Such specimens we shall leave severely alone !

Fossil botany at one time incurred a certain degree of not wholly undeserved contempt, from the excessive prominence given to doubtful objects, from which no conclusions of botanical interest could possibly be drawn.

The purpose which we have in view necessitates a botanical arrangement of our subject-matter, but it is essential for us also to bear constantly in mind the geological horizon of the remains with which we are dealing. In botanical history dates are just as important as in human history. In the former, however, absolute dates are unattainable, and only relative ages come into question.

The imperfection of the geological record is a familiar subject, and I need not dwell upon it here. We naturally find that vegetable remains are by no means evenly distributed throughout the series of strata. From some formations they are almost absent, while in others they

[1] *Introduction to Fossil Botany*, English edition, 1892.

are relatively abundant. Thus, beginning at the top, the Miocene is rich in such remains, especially in Switzerland ; so also is the Oligocene, as shown in the Isle of Wight, and the Eocene, to which the very rich leaf-beds in the Isle of Mull probably belong. All these Tertiary plants bear, as we should expect, a general resemblance to families now living.

Passing to the Secondary system, the Cretaceous formation is of special interest, for the first well-characterised Angiosperms make their appearance in these rocks. The remains from the Lower Greensand, however, are mostly of a different type, and often have their structure well preserved ; they include some of the most remarkable of fossil forms. The Wealden, which some geologists reckon with the Cretaceous, and some with the Jurassic formation, yields abundant remains, with which we have become better acquainted through the work of Prof. Seward of Cambridge. Ferns, Cycadophyta, and Conifers are the most characteristic forms of this period. The Oolitic strata, specially the Purbeck beds at the top of the system, also abound in Cycad-like remains, though most of the Mesozoic plants with the habit of Cycads were very different from any members of the family as now existing. The Lower Cretaceous and Upper Jurassic of the United States are extraordinarily rich in Cycadophyta, investigated, with brilliant results, by Dr. Wieland of Yale. Such remains as we have from the Trias, e.g. the New Red Sandstone, have a still more old-world character (including strange and gigantic Horsetails and Lycopods), and prepare us for the Palaeozoic system.

When we descend to the Permian we find ourselves at once among the characteristic Palaeozoic families— especially the Sigillarias and Calamites, together with extinct Spermophytic types. This brings us to the Carboniferous formation, the flora of which is the richest and most perfect which the rocks have preserved for us. The Carboniferous formation includes many other strata besides those of the Coal-measures, which belong to its upper part. The Coal-measures themselves reach a thickness of 12,000 feet, and represent a prodigious period of time. Fortunately, however, we are not limited for our specimens to this part of the formation, extensive as it is, for there are productive beds down to the base of the Lower Carboniferous rocks ; when we find well-preserved plants much older than the Coal-measures, we may think ourselves specially fortunate. The plant-remains of the next great formation, the Devonian, though scanty compared with those of the Carboniferous, are of the greatest interest, for this is the earliest period from which clearly recognisable land-plants have come down to us. Of the two Devonian Floras, the Upper bears a considerable resemblance to the Lower Carboniferous vegetation, including well-characterised Vascular Cryptogams and probable Seed Plants. The older (Middle and Lower) Devonian Flora contains some highly remarkable and relatively primitive forms, some of which, from the Middle Old Red Sandstone of Scotland, have recently been fully investigated (see Chapter X.). In addition, some much higher types, probably already seed-bearing plants, are recorded, from similar horizons. As regards the Silurian, there is little to say. Most remains from it are very doubtful, though there are one or two remarkable and well-preserved specimens, which have been shown on good evidence to belong to the Algae ; the evidence for the existence of Vascular plants is doubtful.

To us, in these studies, the older formations will be the most interesting, for it is from them that we may expect to fill up gaps among the main groups of the natural system, and it is only with main groups that the limits of the book will allow us to deal. Also, I think that the investigation of the earlier formations (the Palaeozoic and the Lower Mesozoic) has really been more fertile in results, up to the present time, than that of the later deposits, though no doubt from them also we may expect brilliant revelations in the future. The centre of gravity of our work will lie in the Carboniferous formation. The wealth of material which has come down to us from this period is marvellous, as every one knows. It is true, however, that the Coal-flora, rich as it is, is a very special one, although it extended with a certain degree of uniformity over a large part of the earth's surface. It is essentially a swamp-flora, and we know little or nothing of the vegetation of the uplands. If we obtained all our knowledge of the existing flora from plants growing in such localities as the Great Dismal Swamp near the coast of the Southern United States, or from the mangrove-vegetation of tropical shores, our ideas would evidently be one-sided. On the other hand, when it is argued that on the hills of the Coal-period there may have been flowers and trees and shrubs of the higher Angiospermous families, that, surely, is a wild imagination. The flora of swamps, however peculiar, is made up of plants belonging to the same main groups as those of other habitats, and in so far as main groups alone are in question, we may take the Coal-flora, such as it has come down to us, as fairly representative of its period.

Before beginning our detailed work, we must say something as to the modes of preservation of fossil plants, without some knowledge of which we can form no idea of the relative value of the evidence before us.

There are two different modes of preservation, which we must keep perfectly distinct in our minds. These have been termed *incrustation* and *petrifaction*. Incrusted remains include almost all the specimens of fossil plants familiar to the general public. In the case of incrustation, the parts of plants were merely incased in the mineral substance, and any of the larger cavities they contained were filled with it. Their organic tissue became converted into structureless coal, if it did not previously decay altogether. Hence, incrusted specimens give us impressions or casts, which may reproduce with the greatest beauty an external or internal surface, but which tell us little of organised structure. The beautiful Fern-like fronds, so frequent in the Coal-measures, are perhaps more familiar to the ordinary observer than any other specimens of fossil plants. In them we have essentially the print of the frond on the shale lying above and below it. The finer the mineral material was when deposited, the more perfect will be the impression. The substance of the frond is reduced to a layer of coal in which there is comparatively little structure to be traced, though the more resistant parts, such as spores or cuticle, will have left recognisable remains, observable on appropriate chemical treatment.

Other comparatively familiar fossils are the stems of the *Lepidodendra* and *Sigillariae*. In many of these specimens the markings of the surface, as characterised by the bases and scars of the leaves, are preserved exactly as in nature (see Figs. 57 and 92, pp. 115 and 187). Where this is the case the whole substance of the plant has been replaced by mineral matter. In other instances we have a *mould* of the external surface, elevations being repre-sented by depressions, and *vice versa*. The markings, in all these cases, will necessarily depend on the state of preservation of the specimen when incrustation took place. Thus in *Lepidodendron* we have quite different superficial markings according to the condition of the specimen, whether all its tissues were intact, or the epidermis had been stripped off, or a thin or thick layer of the cortex had also been lost. At least four different " genera " have been founded on these different states of preservation of one and the same plant (see Chapter V. p. 117).

Among internal casts the most important examples are those which filled the medullary cavity of the Cala-mites or arboreal Horsetails ; these casts, reproducing exactly the internal surface of the woody cylinder, constitute the most familiar remains of this group of plants, and were long confused with the stems themselves.

Seams of coal have been regarded as a case of incrustation on a great scale.[1] Here it is not single specimens, but whole masses of vegetable remains which have been incrusted by mineral matter. The remains themselves have been converted into the greatly altered carbonaceous material which we call coal, but on the upper and lower shales we find impressions of the plants which happen to have been in contact with the adjacent mineral deposits. The coal itself has undergone great chemical changes, the organic substance having been largely converted into various degradation - products. In certain cases, however, sufficient structure has been preserved to enable us to form some idea of the kinds of plants and tissues to which the coal owed its origin.[2]

We now come to the other great mode of preservation, *petrifaction*, in which the whole of the organised substance has been completely saturated by mineral matter in solution, which has subsequently been precipitated in a solid form. In this case alone is the structure thoroughly preserved. There have been many petrifying agents ; the two most important for us are silicic acid (H_4SiO_4), and calcium carbonate ($CaCO_3$). The most interesting vegetable remains showing structure belong to these two classes. So far as the Carboniferous formation is concerned, silicified specimens are characteristic of the French fossil flora, while calcified remains prevail in the English coal-fields. The former have become classic through the investigations of Brongniart and Renault, the latter through those of Witham, Binney, Williamson, and others. In good specimens of both kinds, the whole microscopic

---

[1] Solms-Laubach, *l.c.* chap. i.

[2] See M. C. Stopes and R. V. Wheeler, *Monograph on the Constitution of Coal*, Dept. of Scientific and Industrial Research, 1918, with a full Bibliography of Coal literature.

structure is often preserved with marvellous perfection. It has been alleged that the French silicified specimens are the more perfect of the two, but, beautiful as they are in many cases, the calcareous petrifactions are on the whole superior to them in the preservation of structure. In the calcified specimens the actual organic substance remains, though chemically altered. The entire network of cell-walls, sometimes showing even their most delicate markings, traverses the matrix ; in the cavities some remains of the cell-contents are often preserved.

The following analyses, which the authors have kindly permitted me to reproduce, are from a paper by Dr. M. C. Stopes and Mr. D. M. S. Watson [1] :—

	Seam near Bacup. Upper Foot Mine.	New Horizon at Stalybridge.	Burntisland, Lower Carboniferous.
Calcium Carbonate, $CaCO_3$.	51.188	87.827	80.192
Magnesium Carbonate, $MgCO_3$.	42.820	6.212	3.967
Ferrous Carbonate, $FeCO_3$.	2.342	1.026	0.825
Ferric (?) Oxide, Fe_2O_3 .	..	..	traces
Manganous Carbonate, $MaCO_3$.	0.521	0.853	1.146
Alumina, Al_2O_3 . . .	traces	traces	traces
Calcium Phosphate, $Ca_3P_2O_8$.	0.525	traces	traces
Iron Pyrites, FeS_2 . . .	0.339	1.430	..
Silicate of Alumina (Clay) .	0.119	0.000	10.492 [2]
Carbonaceous Matter . .	1.855	2.579	3.051
Free Moisture	0.264	0.100	0.305
	99.973	100.027	99.978 [3]

[1] " On the present distribution and origin of the calcareous concretions in coal-seams, known as 'Coal Balls' " (*Phil. Trans. Royal Soc.* B, vol. 200, 1908).

[2] Taken together with all the inorganic residues.

[3] The figures are practically percentages, according to weight. The first two columns give the analyses of "coal-balls" from the Lower Coal-measures of Lancashire. The third column relates to the plant-bearing calcareous deposit near Burntisland, in Scotland, at a much lower horizon. The most important variation is in the amount of Magnesium Carbonate, which in many of the coal-balls is nearly equal to that of the Calcium Carbonate.

The carbonaceous material in these analyses is specially interesting, because it represents the actual tissue preserved in the petrifaction. In some silicious specimens, however, the organic substance has entirely perished, and the cell-walls are represented by a system of minute crevices in the matrix. Though all the essential features of the structure may be thus marked out, they may still be very difficult to see. In such cases M. Renault made use of stains, by which the cracks representing the cell-walls were injected. He thus obtained a coloured image of the structure, and so for the first time succeeded in staining a fossil section. Other substances, such as calcium sulphate and phosphate, have played a part in petrifaction, and so too, among organic products, has amber. In a few cases, fine clay has penetrated vegetable substances sufficiently to cause an effectual petrifaction ; one important specimen, to which we shall have occasion to refer, is preserved in this way (see Chapter IV. p. 96).

The calcified remains of the English Coal-measures occur largely in the form of calcareous nodules or coalballs, stony masses which are found in certain localities, especially in Yorkshire and Lancashire, in the actual productive coal-seams, and also in the " roof " above them. The former represent, as it were, parts of the raw material of coal which have been saved by petrifaction from carbonisation, and have consequently retained their structure. These nodules are literally crowded with vegetable remains of all kinds. The calcareous material, of which these nodules are formed, may have been derived from the shells of marine Mollusca, which lived 'and died on the old forest ground when sunk once more beneath the sea, or the lime normally contained in sea-water may have sufficed.

We can form a good idea of the sort of material which these nodules contain, if we notice the deposits of vegetable debris left on the banks of a tidal river. There we find miscellaneous fragments of plants heaped together in utter confusion, bits of reeds and rushes, rhizomes of water-lilies and aquatic grasses, twigs and scraps of bark from river-side trees, seeds, nuts, and cones. If we imagine a handful of such a conglomeration, saturated and fixed by some petrifying substance, we shall have a very fair idea of the kind of material a coal-ball consists of.

The question whether coal was formed *in situ* in the actual forest itself, or from vegetable drift carried by currents to a distance, has been much disputed. The accumulations represented by the nodules in the coal must have been formed within the forest region, for the remains that they contain are penetrated in all directions by the rootlets of the trees which grew there. The roof-nodules, however, contain drifted fragments, representing a somewhat different Flora.

Coal-balls of this kind are limited to certain horizons, and are by no means of general occurrence, even in the Lancashire and Yorkshire district. Naturally, these stony lumps do not improve the value of the coal, and unfortunately for the palaeobotanist, the mines which produce them tend to go out of working. At Shore, Littleborough, in Lancashire, however, a mine was purposely reopened by the late owner, Mr. W. Sutcliffe, F.G.S., for the sake of the petrifactions in which this locality is peculiarly rich.

For the purposes of the botanist, the petrified remains showing structure are the most important, and will form the main basis of our work, though it is always necessary to correlate them, as far as possible, with specimens which exhibit the external characters.

In the classification of recent plants, systematic botanists, so far at least as the Flowering Plants are concerned, are accustomed to rely chiefly on the morphology of the reproductive organs, and usually on their more external, as distinguished from their microscopic features. Such characters, however, are often absent in fossil specimens, and it becomes necessary to make use of other means of discrimination. In the case of the Cryptogams, which play so important a part among plants of the earlier periods, few conclusions can be drawn, even where the fructifications are preserved, without the use of microscopic characters. Still more is this the case when vegetative organs alone are preserved. Among the plants of the more ancient formations, necessarily very remote from any now living, little reliance can be placed on the mere external vegetative characters, while experience has shown that anatomical structure affords a much more trustworthy clue, when interpreted with proper care and judgment. Hence the study of the more minute structure, which is beginning to take a more prominent place in recent taxonomy also, is relatively of far greater importance when we are dealing with fossil specimens. The most favourable cases for investigation are of course those in which the fructification is itself well preserved, and, fortunately, specimens of this nature are tolerably frequent.

In selecting examples of fossil plants for our consideration, I propose to begin with the Vascular Cryptogams. It is among these plants, together with the Fern-like Spermophyta and the Gymnosperms, that palaeobotany has so far made its most important contributions towards the completion of the natural system, and to these Sub-kingdoms our studies will be devoted. As we proceed we shall find that the data afforded by the study of fossil plants demand considerable modification of the current system of classification.

CHAPTER II

Calamites ; Arthrodendron ; Calamodendron ;
Protocalamites

1. *The Calamarieae.*—We know that among living
Pteridophyta we can distinguish three great classes or
phyla : the Ferns, the Lycopods, and the Horsetails.
The last-mentioned group, though manifestly quite as
distinct a stock as the other two, is now represented
only by the single genus *Equisetum*, the species of which
exhibit but small variety of structure. We might
naturally suppose that in *Equisetum*, a group at once
so isolated and so limited, we have the last surviving
remnant of a once more extensive family. Fossil botany
affords the most remarkable proofs of the truth of this
hypothesis, and indeed shows that in the Carboniferous
period the Horsetail stock was among the best-represented
divisions of the Vegetable Kingdom. In fact, we may
safely say that any adequate knowledge of the Equisetales
must be derived to a much greater extent from the study
of the extinct forms than from that of the few surviving
representatives. In saying this, I am assuming that all
the Palaeozoic plants known as Calamarieae were of
Equisetaceous affinities. Though at one time some
botanists hesitated to accept this conclusion, we shall
find that it is now supported by irresistible evidence.
It is a matter of indifference whether, with Zeiller, we
name the whole group *Equisetineae*, after its sole living

representatives, or term it, with Endlicher, *Calamarieae*, after its more important fossil members. The form Equisetales will be adopted in this book, as indicating a group of higher than ordinal rank.

Many of the Calamarieae attained the dimensions of trees. It is not possible to give the complete measurements of any specimen, but the following facts may afford some indication of the size attained. Mr. G. Wild found in the roof of a coal-mine in Lancashire a medullary cast of a Calamite 30 feet long ; the diameter of the pith amounted to about 6 inches in the thickest part. This cast must have represented a portion only of the main trunk. In some of M. Grand'Eury's specimens the cast of the pith is over a foot in diameter ; if the whole tree were in proportion, it must have been of an immense size. In other specimens of his, a height of 9 feet from the base scarcely takes us above the region where the roots are given off. M. Grand'Eury estimated the height of the stem in many of these Calamarian trees at from 20 to 30 metres.[1]

As already mentioned, the most common mode of preservation of Calamites is in the form of casts of the medullary cavity (see Figs. 2 and 3). The marks which they show correspond, not to any features of the external surface, but to the print of the inner surface of the wood. Hence the superficial resemblance of these specimens to the ribbed stem of an *Equisetum* is fallacious, except that in both cases the marks on the surface are related to the course of the vascular bundles. In some specimens the tissue of the stem surrounding the medullary cast is preserved, and the true cortical surface shown. The latter is either smooth, or, if ribbed, the ribs do not correspond to those of the medullary casts.[2] The char-

---

[1] *Flore carbonifère du Département de la Loire*, 1878, p. 29 ; *Bassin houiller du Gard*, 1890, p. 210.

[2] The external surface of the *wood*, however, in decorticated petrified specimens, is sometimes ribbed, and may bear a deceptive resemblance to that of a medullary cast.

acters which first suggested Equisetaceous affinities having proved to a certain extent deceptive, the whole question had to be reconsidered, and the systematic position of these fossils has now been determined by arguments of quite a different kind, drawn from the fructifications and from the anatomy of specimens with their structure preserved.

The most conspicuous markings on a Calamitean cast consist of longitudinal ridges and furrows, the former usually broader than the latter. The specimens are distinctly jointed, the joints being marked by zigzag

FIG. 2.—*Calamites Suckowii.* Medullary cast, showing three nodes, on one of which the cast of a branch is borne. Below each node, and between the furrows, the prints of the infranodal canals are seen. About ⅔ of natural size. After Stur.

commissural furrows. It has always been recognised that these joints represent the nodes. Often, but not invariably, the ridges and furrows of successive internodes are alternate with one another. Many of the specimens taper towards one end, which, as we shall subsequently show, corresponds to the base of the branch (see Fig. 2). Above the nodes we often find more or less circular scars, of relatively large size, which there is reason to believe mark the position of the lateral branches. In well-preserved casts it is usual to find a small circular or elliptical elevation on the surface of each ridge, just below the node (see Fig. 2, Fig. 3, *i.c.*). In most of these fossils the tissue of the stem enclosing the cast has become reduced to a comparatively thin coaly rind. In a few cases the anatomical structure of the wood and the cast

FIG. 3.—*Calamites Suckowii.* Medullary cast, bearing the cast of a branch larger than that of the main stem. *i.c.*, the prints of the infranodal canals below a node. ⅔ of natural size. From a photograph by Dr. R. Kidston, F.R.S., taken from a specimen in his collection, found at the Oaks Colliery, Barnsley; Middle Coal-measures.

of the pith are preserved in the same stem,[1] and such specimens afford the best evidence for the identification of the two classes of remains. We will defer a full explana-

[1] See, for example, Williamson, " Organisation of the Fossil Plants of the Coal-measures," Part i., *Phil. Trans. Roy. Soc.* 1871, Plate xxvi. Fig. 21.

tion of the markings on the cast until we have considered
the anatomical structure.

2. *The Stem of Calamites.*—Petrified specimens of the
various parts of plants belonging to the Calamarieae
are common in the calcareous nodules of the Lower Coal-
measures of Britain and among the silicious remains in the
Upper Coal-measures and Permian of France, as well as
at other horizons. The anatomical structure of all the
organs has thus become known, though the correlation
of the fragmentary remains has presented great difficulties.

We will now go on at once to the anatomical description of the first type to be considered in detail, namely
the genus *Calamites*. Included in this group there are
many so-called species, though they are very difficult of
distinction. As to the sense in which the name *Calamites*
is used here, the characteristics of the genus will become
evident as we go on, and I will only mention now that
Calamites, as the name is employed in the present book,
is equivalent to the *Arthropitys* of many palaeobotanists,
especially in France.

If we examine, by means of sections, the ordinary
form of stem of a typical Calamite in the petrified condition, with well-preserved structure, we find the following characters : the pith is generally hollow, only its
outer zone being preserved, and the definite internal
limit which we often find to this persistent zone leads us
to believe that the pith was fistular during life, and that
the cavity is not merely the result of decay. In Fig. 4
part of a transverse section of a Calamitean stem is
shown. The pith, as usual, was hollow, but only the
persistent layers of the external part are represented.
Around the pith is a ring of collateral vascular bundles ;
here, as in the great majority of specimens, a considerable
mass of secondary tissue has already been formed, so
that each of the bundles has assumed a more or less
regular wedge-like form. On the inner limit of each

we find, with the rarest exceptions, a definite canal, so that the whole appearance recalls very much that of a section of the stem of one of the living *Equiseta*. The question whether this appearance indicates a real identity of structure is one which we shall have to consider presently. In most specimens everything outside the wood has perished, but in a minority the cortex is preserved (see Fig. 4).

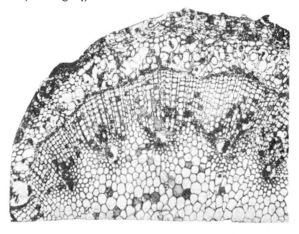

Fig. 4.—*Calamites*, sp. Part of transverse section of a young stem, showing pith, cortex, and five vascular bundles, each with a canal at its inner edge. In some of the canals remains of the spiral tracheides can be seen. Beyond the secondary wood, and next the cortex, are traces of the phloëm. × about 40. From a photograph by Prof. J. B. Farmer, F.R.S. Will. Coll. 1553.

We will defer for the moment the consideration of the wood, which we will take more in detail afterwards, and pass on to the cortex. This consists of two zones, the inner formed of a rather thin-walled tissue, some cells in which contain very dense black carbonaceous matter, and have been supposed to represent secretory organs, while the outer zone consists of smaller cells, with thicker walls. In some exceptional cases we find in this zone regular fibrous ribs alternating with parenchymatous bands. In fact, we have, in such specimens, very much the same mechanical arrangement as we find in the stems of recent Equisetaceae. In a few instances we have been so fortunate as to find stems preserved at the very commencement, or even before the commencement, of secondary growth, as shown in Fig. 5. This is a comparatively rare stage to find, and when it is found, it is nearly always in a small twig. The larger stems of *Calamites* are rarely, if ever, met with at so early a stage of development. In a twig in this early condition, before secondary thickening has begun, the pith is often persistent (though fistular in the specimen figured), and round it we find a ring of primary vascular bundles, in

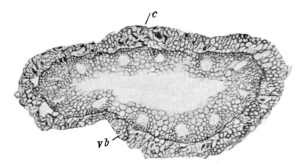

FIG. 5.—*Calamites*, sp. Transverse section of a very young twig, showing primary structure. *c*, cortex ; *v.b.*, vascular bundles, of which there are twelve, each with its canal. × nearly 40. *Phil. Trans.*, W. and S. Will. Coll. 1561.

which the wood is but little developed, and then the cortex. The whole structure is strikingly like that of the stem of an *Equisetum*.[1] Now one of the most important questions to be settled, bearing on the comparison with recent Equisetaceae, was this : Are these canals in *Calamites* really homologous with the carinal canals of an *Equisetum*, or are they of a different nature ; perhaps, as some observers formerly thought, representing the phloëm ?

It has been observed that, in many cases, in the transverse section of a stem, the canals are not perfectly

[1] Cp. Scott, *Structural Botany*, Part II. Fig. 39, showing the transverse section of a small stem of *Equisetum arvense*.

empty, but that they contain minute rings adhering to their edges, as indicated in Fig. 4. This suggests very strongly the position of the annular and spiral tracheides in *Equisetum*, which are often found within the carinal canal. To determine the true state of the case, however, a very detailed examination was necessary. There are now many sections showing these canals quite clearly, and proving that they contain the first-formed woody elements, or protoxylem, of the vascular bundles.

FIG. 6.—*Calamites*, sp. Part of radial section through primary wood. *px*, disorganised spiral and annular tracheides in the canal; *sc*, scalariform tracheides of the more external primary wood. On the left is the pith. × about 160. *Phil. Trans.*, W. and S. Will. Coll. 20 A.

Fig. 6 represents a radial section passing through the canal of one of the bundles. On the inner side of the canal is pith; on the outer side wood. We notice that the canal is to a great extent occupied by the disorganised tracheae. It is a point of some importance that the disorganisation is found to be greatest on the inner side of the canal, while, as we approach its outer edge, the tracheae become more continuous. We know that the disorganisation of the tracheae is constantly greatest in that part of the primary wood which is differentiated before the growth in length is completed. Hence we may infer that the innermost elements, being the most disorganised, were the earliest formed ; and we thus obtain a proof that the development of the primary wood was strictly centrifugal.

The elements of the primary wood, other than those in the canal, present no special interest. We find the spiral and annular tracheae of the protoxylem replaced by other elements (scalariform or pitted) as we get beyond the canal. I have spoken of these bundles as collateral. In the very best preparations, we can satisfy ourselves that on the inner side of the vascular bundle there are no traces of phloëm ; the canal abuts directly on the pith. On the other hand, in very fortunate cases, where the preservation is exceptionally good, we find, on the outer side of the wood, strands of delicate tissue made up of small thin-walled elements ; these we can only interpret as phloëm-groups ; we find, further, between these groups and the wood, remnants of cells of the cambium itself. Some traces of these tissues will be recognised in Fig. 4, immediately outside the secondary wood.[1]

We thus see that the structure of the young stem of a Calamite is in all essentials similar to that of an Equisetaceous stem. Surrounding the usually fistular pith, interrupted at every node by a persistent diaphragm (see Fig. 7), we have a ring of collateral vascular bundles, with centrifugally developed wood ; at the inner border of each is a canal containing the disorganised tracheae of the protoxylem.[2] Thus, the Calamite, so far as anatomy goes, is simply an *Equisetum* with secondary thickening. In order to carry the comparison further, we must settle one or two points, especially the course of the vascular bundles. In *Equisetum* itself their course is exceedingly simple : a single vascular bundle enters the stem from each leaf, and passes straight down through one internode only. At the node next below, the bundle

[1] For special figures of the phloëm and cambium, see Williamson and Scott, " Further Observations on the Organisation of the Fossil Plants of the Coal-measures," *Phil. Trans.* vol. 185, B, 1894, Plate lxxviii. Figs. 12-14.

[2] In a Calamarian stem of Lower Carboniferous age, from the Burntisland deposits, named *Protocalamites pettycurensis*, groups of centripetally developed wood are present on the inner side of the canals. This is a point of interest, as tending to connect the Calamarieae with the Sphenophyllales, in which the primary wood is centripetal (see pp. 32 and 78).

forks, and its branches attach themselves to the adjacent
alternating vascular bundles passing out at that node.
This type is often found in the Calamites also, but on the
whole, the bundle-system of the latter is less regular and
more complicated. Sometimes the bundles of successive
internodes are not alternate, but run on in the same
straight line. Where this is the case, the forks of the
bundle, as we trace it down, instead of attaching them-

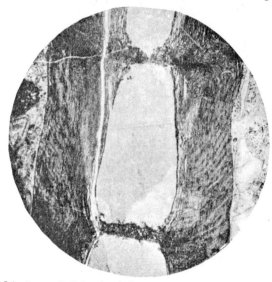

Fig. 7.—*Calamites*, sp. Radial section of a decorticated stem, with fairly thick wood, showing
the fistular pith, crossed by diaphragms at the nodes. × 9. From a photograph.
Phil. Trans., W. and S. Will. Coll. 1937.

selves to the alternate bundles at the node below, con-
verge again on the other side of the outgoing leaf-trace,
so as to form a loop, through which the trace passes out,
and the bundle below the loop continues in the same
straight line as before. This straight course of the
bundles and absence of alternation between those of
successive internodes is specially characteristic of one
very ancient type of the Calamarieae, namely the genus
Archaeocalamites, which occurs in the Lower Carboniferous
and possibly in the Upper Devonian formation (see p. 62).

Secondly, we may find a greater complexity in the vascular system.   In this case the bundle may run down through more than one internode, and pass on to the second node below (Fig. 8).   It follows that here the number of vascular bundles in each internode may be double that of the leaves in a whorl.   Where a bundle

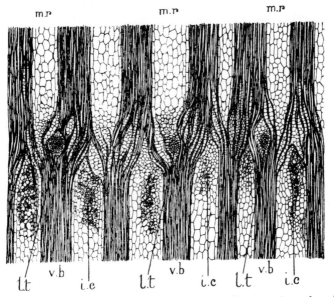

Fig. 8.—*Calamites communis.*   Tangential section of wood, passing through a node, and cut near the pith.   *v.b.*, vascular bundles of the stem (six shown).   *l.t.*, leaf-traces cut transversely as they turn outward at the node.   Note that they are only half as numerous as the bundles of the stem.   *m.r.*, primary medullary rays.   *i.c.*, small-celled tissue of the rays below the node, corresponding to Williamson's " infranodal canals."   × 12.   S. Coll. 897.   (G. T. G.)

passes between the outgoing traces at the node, it may either be connected with them by lateral strands or remain free.   The former case is illustrated by Fig. 8, from a large and perfectly preserved stem.   We may therefore express the general characteristics of the Calamarian vascular system by the statement that the whole arrangement is of the type of *Equisetum*, but more varied, and sometimes more complex.   I may further mention that these variations may even occur side by side in different parts of one and the same specimen.

The following considerations serve to identify the leaf-traces. We constantly find in all specimens of *Calamites*, that at every joint a whorl of small and uniform bundles passes out, and though it is only in the very rarest cases that we are able to trace out these bundles continuously into the leaf, yet there is no doubt that these outgoing bundles are really the leaf-traces. For one thing, their arrangement precisely corresponds with the arrangement of the leaves, as shown in certain specimens which have retained their foliage, and we know that each of these whorled leaves actually received a single bundle from the stem (see Fig. 12). Secondly, the outgoing bundles form the direct continuation of those which traverse the internode below, precisely as is the case with the leaf-traces of *Equisetum*. And then again we have the argument of exclusion. If these bundles are not leaf-traces, what are they ? They must in that case be either traces of branches or of roots. But as we shall see below, the connection of these organs with the stem is now well known, and is quite independent of the bundles in question. By all these considerations the interpretation of these outgoing bundles as leaf-traces is now fully established. If a section be cut tangentially through the wood, it intersects these bundles transversely (see Figs. 8 and 9). They also appear (cut longitudinally) in the transverse sections of the stem, which pass exactly through a node. A radial section in the plane of the outgoing strand shows that the primary bundle passes out as a whole on its way to the leaf, and can be followed through the secondary wood. The whole course of the leaf-traces is thus made clear from every point of view.[1]

The next point to be considered is the structure of the secondary wood. We find that the wood as a whole

[1] For further illustrations of all these points, see the memoir by Williamson and Scott, above cited.

is divided up into the bundles, and the principal rays between them. The behaviour of these rays in passing through the wood is a matter of some importance, for great emphasis has been laid on it in discriminating species. It is obviously desirable to aim at establishing species on anatomical lines, and if possible to correlate them with the various forms of casts. A great many attempts have been made in that direction, but at present with imperfect success. We find, however, the following variations, whatever may be their taxonomic value. In comparatively few cases we can trace the ray in undiminished width throughout the whole thickness of the wood. That seems to be the characteristic of the type which the French authorities call *Arthropitys bistriata,* a form of *Calamites.* Then we may have the opposite extreme ; the ray may come to an end almost immediately, and thus be shut off by interfascicular wood ; or, again, it may gradually die out, becoming encroached upon laterally by the wood, and cut up by strands of intercalated tracheae. This last is the commonest form among English Calamites (*Calamites communis,* Binney). It is not very easy to determine how this mode of enclosing a ray by the wood was brought about, because the tracheae are very long and the ray-cells which they replace very short, and yet the radial arrangement of the elements is not disturbed. The only explanation appears to be that the growth must have taken place in the cambial cells themselves, rather than in their products.

I have hitherto spoken of tracheae, using the word in its widest sense, so as to leave open the question as to the true nature of the woody elements. First of all, were they tracheides, derived from single cells, or vessels, arising by cell-fusion ? We constantly find that they have tapering ends, with no evidence of perforation ; but there is this difficulty, that every now and then there are distinct traces of transverse walls in these elements. This, however, is very inconstant, and where these apparent transverse walls appear, they seem to be perfect septa, and not merely annular ridges such as we are accustomed to find in vessels, marking the limits of their constituent cells. I am disposed to think that the elements of the wood in *Calamites* were occasionally septate, unlike true tracheides, but there is no proof that they ever arose by cell-fusion, and we cannot therefore regard them as vessels in De Bary's sense. There is evidence that the pits, which were either scalariform or of the rounder, multiseriate type, were closed.

The disposition of the pits is of some interest. Throughout the whole of the secondary wood they are limited to the radial walls. The general arrangement was thus very much like that in the Coniferae of the present day, and the mechanism of water-conduction must have been similar. The cells of the medullary rays have this peculiarity, that they are generally longer vertically than in any other direction, and thus the rays have not the muriform appearance which is general, though not universal, among recent plants. Some of the rays are very small, and may even consist of a single radial row of cells.

I have already given the principal facts about the primary cortex. In the few cases in which we find the cortex well preserved in an old stem, there is an enormous development of periderm, as shown by a specimen in the Williamson Collection, which has secondary wood two inches thick, and bark of even greater thickness.[1]

Occasionally, in comparatively young stems, we find tangential divisions beginning in the inner cells of the cortex, and it is highly probable that this was the first commencement of the periderm-formation which attained such a great extent in the older stems. The trunks of the larger Calamites must have had a regular bark, like

---

[1] Figured in Williamson, "Organisation of Fossil Plants of the Coal-measures," Part ix., *Phil. Trans.* 1878, Part ii. Plate xx. Figs. 14 and 15 ; also in Seward's *Fossil Plants*, vol. i. Fig. 78.

that of our forest-trees, but thicker than in most of the latter.

3. *Branching.*—The next question to be considered

FIG. 9.—*Calamites communis.* Tangential section of wood, passing through a node, as in Fig. 8, but showing the base of a branch, inserted between and above two of the leaf-trace bundles. *f*, vascular bundles of stem ; *m*, leaf-traces (three shown) ; *c*, medullary rays. × 20. After Williamson, *Phil. Trans.* Will. Coll. 90.

is that of the branching of the stem. It is very common to find the bases of branches in connection with the main axis. The section represented in Fig. 9 is a tangential one, passing through the base of a branch, where it joins the primary wood, so that its tissues are shown in continuity with those of the stem which bears it. The

insertion of these branches is very regular. They are
always placed immediately above the node, and usually
between two of the outgoing leaf-trace bundles (Fig. 9).
Sometimes a branch may be nearly or quite as large as
the main stem, repeating all the characteristics of the
latter ; in other cases we find lateral branches which
are very small in comparison with the main stem ; [1]
such lateral shoots often occur in considerable numbers
in a verticil. It is an interesting point that these little
branches were in many cases abortive, as shown by the
fact that we often find their bases completely enclosed
in the wood. At the same time that this was proved
for the English specimens, Renault came to exactly the
same conclusion independently, from the study of the
French material. These observations show that very
often the small lateral branches were cast off early, a
fact which admits of two explanations. The branch
may either have been abortive altogether, or, which is
still more likely, it may have been caducous, forming a
limited shoot of temporary duration, comparable to the
spurs which bear the needles in *Pinus*.

The position of the branches with reference to the
nodes and leaf-traces was precisely the same in *Calamites*
as in the recent *Equisetum*. The pith of the branch
tapered towards the point of attachment, so that its
actual junction with the pith of the main stem was
effected by a slender neck of tissue. This fact is shown
quite clearly by sections of specimens passing through
the junction of stem and branch, and explains one of
the most characteristic forms of Calamitean casts, which
in a great many cases are tapered towards one end.
Figs. 2 and 3 each show the medullary cast of a branch
in connection with that of the stem, and confirm the
evidence, derived from sections, that the pith became
gradually smaller towards the point of attachment.

[1] The medullary casts shown in Figs. 2 and 3 illustrate these two
cases.

Some of the older observers thought that the tapered end was the apex, thus turning the specimen wrong way upwards.[1] The root-bearing base of the main stem was also tapered.

4. *Other Types of Stem.*—The type which I have been describing so far is, as I have already said, the *Arthropitys* of the French authors, and this is the least complex of the Calamarian stems. We have seen that the structure of the wood is, after all, very simple. It consists essentially of the tracheae and the medullary rays—including both primary and secondary rays. The differentiation is about on a level with that of the simplest Coniferous woods of the present day, as, for example, that of the Yew.

There are certain other Calamarian types of stem-structure, some of which have long been distinguished. There is one form which became known to us by the observations of Williamson, who founded a new genus for it under the name of *Calamopitys*, but he afterwards let the generic distinction drop, although the type is quite distinct from the ordinary Calamitean structure already explained. The name *Calamopitys* is not admissible, as it had previously been employed by Unger in a different sense,[2] and that of *Arthrodendron* has now been substituted. The *Arthrodendron* type of stem is a rare one. The wood, in the specimens known, is of no great thickness, and the primary bundles are widely separated by the principal medullary rays. The chief peculiarity is in the structure of the rays, which are formed, for the most part, of vertically elongated prosenchymatous cells, thus differing widely from the usual parenchymatous structure of these organs; but within

---

[1] The proof that the pith tapers towards the base of the branch has enabled us to determine with certainty the upper and lower ends of specimens, a point otherwise by no means easy of decision.

[2] See Chapter XII.

these primary rays are little secondary rays of parenchyma, like those of the true wood. *Arthrodendron* has
also some other peculiarities, but the complex rays
suffice to mark it off from the ordinary Calamites.

There is another important type, not represented in
England—that of *Calamodendron*,—which is the most
complex of all (see Fig. 10). Here each of the principal
rays consists of a middle band of parenchyma, more or

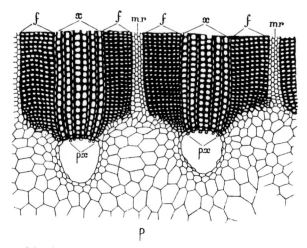

FIG. 10.—*Calamodendron intermedium.* Part of transverse section of stem, showing inner
portions of two vascular bundles, with secondary wood. *p*, pith; *px*, protoxylem in
canals of the bundles; *x*, fascicular wood, containing secondary rays; *f*, prosenchymatous parts of principal medullary rays; *m.r.*, central parenchymatous portion of
each ray. Magnified. After Renault.

less like an ordinary medullary ray, and on either side
of this, separating it from the wood, is a broad band of
fibrous prosenchyma, in which secondary rays occur.
In fact, the principal rays are here much more complex
in structure than the wood itself. The *Calamodendron*
stems are especially characteristic of the Upper Coal-
measures and Permian of Central France.

This brings us to the question of nomenclature, on
which I must say a word. Brongniart, in his earlier
works, placed all the Calamitean stems then known to

him in the one genus *Calamites*, and believed them to be related to the Equisetaceae ; subsequently he investigated specimens with the internal structure preserved, and in all clear cases of the kind he found a well-developed secondary wood. Wherever he found this, he thought he must have to do with a Dicotyledonous flowering plant of Gymnospermous affinities, for in those days Gymnosperms were usually included under Dicotyledons. Consequently, Brongniart was led to divide the Calamites into two groups : those which he supposed had no secondary growth, and which he therefore left under the old generic name of *Calamites*; and those which had such growth. The latter he transferred to Phanerogams, founding the genus *Calamodendron* for their reception.[1] *Calamodendron* was subsequently subdivided by Göppert into *Arthropitys*, with simple medullary rays, and *Calamodendron* proper, with the more complex structure which I have just described.

There is at present no evidence remaining that any Calamarian plant was without secondary growth. The Calamites supposed to be without secondary thickening have turned out to be simply medullary casts, from which the surrounding tissues have partly or wholly perished. The specimens with their structure preserved invariably possess secondary tissues, the only exceptions being excessively young twigs, and even these often show the commencement of the cambial growth (see Fig. 5). At present the evidence is that all Calamites, so far as they are known to us, formed secondary wood and bast, and consequently this distinction of Brongniart's falls to the ground. We may therefore go back to the old name *Calamites*, using it as synonymous with the *Arthro-*

---

[1] See Brongniart, *Tableau des genres de végétaux fossiles*, Paris, 1849, pp. 47-50. Brongniart was also influenced by the occurrence of seeds among the branches of *Asterophyllites*, which he regarded as the foliage of *Calamodendron*.

pitys of the French authors, and retaining the genus
Calamodendron in Göppert's restricted sense.

Another type of Calamarian stem is represented by
Protocalamites pettycurensis, already referred to (p. 21).
It is interesting that this Lower Carboniferous species
should be the only Calamite so far observed which has
centripetal wood. The protoxylem is in the usual
position, in or adjacent to the " carinal " canal, but in
this case the development of the primary xylem pro-
ceeded in both the inward and outward directions, for

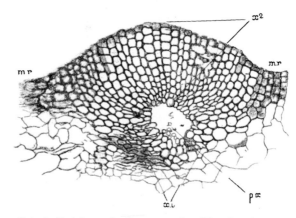

Fig. 11.—*Protocalamites pettycurensis.* Transverse section of the xylem of a vascular bundle
in the stem. *px*, protoxylem ; x^2, secondary wood ; *xi*, centripetal wood, on the inner
side of the canal ; *m.r.*, medullary rays. × about 60. S. Coll. 1104. (G. T. G.)

each bundle possesses a considerable arc of centripetal
wood on the side of the canal towards the pith (Fig. 11,
xi). The genus *Protocalamites*, Lotsy, is based on this
character. Unpublished investigations by Dr. Margaret
Benson, F.L.S., show that the vascular bundles alternate
at the nodes, proving that *Protocalamites* is quite distinct
from the contemporary genus, *Archaeocalamites*, already
mentioned (p. 22), in which the bundles pursue a straight
course, without alternation. The significance of the
centripetal xylem as a character shared with other classes
of Pteridophyta will be emphasised in later chapters.

5. *The Leaves.*—The leaves of the Calamarieae were in all cases arranged in whorls, and were usually of a simple acicular or lanceolate form, though in the genus *Archaeocalamites* they were forked (Figs. 31, 32). It is often stated that the leaves of the Palaeozoic Equisetales differed from those of their later successors in being free, and not united to form a sheath. It is no doubt true that the free laminae were much more developed in the Calamarieae than in recent Horsetails, but in several cases there is good evidence for the presence of a coherent sheath at the base. This is clearly shown in Fig. 12,

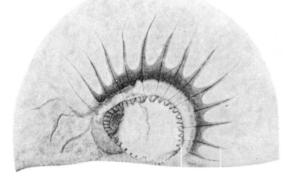

Fig. 12.—*Calamites*, sp. Transverse fracture through a node, showing leaf-sheath and free tips of leaves, each with its vein. Commissural bundles also shown. × about 2. From a specimen in the possession of Mr. Parker of Rochdale. (G. T. G.)

which represents the node of a Calamite, exposed in transverse fracture on the surface of the matrix. The greater part of the whorl of leaves is shown, and they are evidently united into a continuous sheath at the base. Each leaf is traversed by a vein, and further to the interior the commissural vascular bundles of the node are visible. It is possible that in many cases the sheath became split up as the stem increased in thickness.

Immediately below a node the cortex of the stem shows in some specimens a number of prominent ribs, corresponding to the bases of the verticillate leaves which sprang from the node.   This is well shown, in transverse section, in Fig. 13.[1]

As regards the anatomical structure of the leaves of the Calamites, our knowledge has increased of late years. In *Calamites* itself the simple acicular leaves were each traversed by a single nerve (see Fig. 12) ; in some of the other forms, as in those named *Calamocladus*[2] by Grand'Eury, they appear to have had several parallel nerves, but nothing is known as to the internal structure of these specimens.   The late Mr. Hick of Manchester[3] published an interesting paper on the structure of the

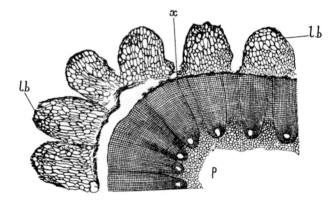

Fig. 13.—*Calamites*, sp.   Part of transverse section close to a node, showing the prominent leaf-bases, *l.b.   x*, secondary wood ; *p*, fistular pith.   Magnified.   From a section lent by the late Mr. J. Butterworth of Shaw.   (G. T. G.)

leaves of *Calamites*, and a much fuller account by Mr. Hamshaw Thomas has since appeared.[4]   Practically it is only the quite minute leaves, less than a millimetre broad, and perhaps 3 or 4 mm. long, of which the structure is known.   Such leaves are borne on the slenderest twigs,

[1] For the use of the specimens illustrated in Figs. 12 and 13 I am indebted to the late Mr. John Butterworth of Shaw.

[2] The foliage of Calamarieae will be further described, as regards its outward aspect, in the following chapter.

[3] *Mem. and Proc. Manchester Lit. and Phil. Soc.* ser. iv. vol. ix. p. 179, 1895.

[4] On the leaves of *Calamites* (*Calamocladus* section), *Phil. Trans. Royal Soc.* B, vol. 202, 1911.

which may have the ordinary Calamitean anatomy on a small scale, or may be without the carinal canals ; in some cases the xylem at the nodes, and even elsewhere, extends nearly or quite to the centre, the pith thus disappearing. In Fig. 14 a transverse section of a bud, showing a number of the leaves arranged in whorls around the axis, is represented. They have the same form in transverse section as *Pinus* leaves. In leaves referred to

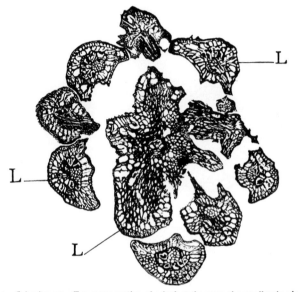

FIG. 14.—*Calamites*, sp. Transverse section of a bud at the apex of a small twig, showing axis, with parts of two whorls of leaves. L, leaves of outer verticil ; L', leaf of inner verticil, in connection with axis. × 30. S. Coll. 171. (G. T. G.)

Calamocladus (*Asterophyllites*) *charaeformis*, Mr. Thomas found the following structure (Fig. 15, A). In the centre is a small bundle, the xylem surrounded by a thin-walled tissue, possibly phloëm. Outside the bundle is a very characteristic sheath, consisting of rather large cells with black contents, and hence called by Hick the " Melasmatic layer." It is suggested that the original cell-contents may have been starch, or some other product of assimilation. Beyond the sheath is a very well-developed palisade layer, consisting of radiating columnar cells, with large intercellular spaces. This is immediately surrounded by the epidermis, which has a thicker cuticle on the abaxial (convex) surface than elsewhere. Stomata are limited to the flatter adaxial surface. Mr. Thomas made the interesting observation that the cell-walls of the guard-cells are transversely striated, just as in a modern *Equisetum*.

In this form of leaf there is very little provision of mechanical tissue. A few fibrous cells will be noticed, intercalated in the upper part of the bundle - sheath

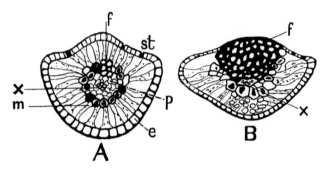

FIG. 15.—Calamite leaves in transverse section. A. Type of *Asterophyllites charaeformis*. B. Type of *Asterophyllites grandis*. *x*, xylem; *p*, phloëm (?); *m*, bundle-sheath; *f*, fibrous strand; *e*, epidermis; *st*, stomata. × about 66. After Thomas.

(Fig. 15, A). Other types of Calamite leaf differ chiefly in the greater development of mechanical elements; in the leaf figured (Fig. 15, B), probably referable to *Calamocladus* (*Asterophyllites*) *grandis*, the fibrous strand occupies a large part of the transverse section, completely displacing both bundle-sheath and palisade-tissue on the upper side. In this type the vascular bundle is much reduced.

All these minute leaves are, as might be expected, of simple structure. Nothing is known of the structure of the flat leaves of *Annularia* (see Fig. 34, p. 66), or of the comparatively large leaves found on certain Calamarian stems.

6. *The Roots.*—As regards the roots of Calamarieae, we are now in possession of a considerable stock of information. In Williamson's paper of 1871—the first of his Royal Society series—among the varieties of *Calamites* the author described some specimens which differed from the ordinary form, for they had a solid pith and no fascicular canals. In a later memoir he distinguished organs of this type under the generic name of *Astromyelon.* In the meantime Messrs. Cash and Hick had found some beautiful specimens with the cortex preserved, which they named *Myriophylloides.* These also were referred by Williamson to his genus *Astromyelon.*

The following are the chief characters of *Astromyelon* : it has often a persistent pith, though, in the larger specimens, it may have become fistular in the middle. In the specimens first described the pith is, of relatively large size. It is surrounded by a ring of bundles, and we shall find there is good evidence that the development of their primary wood was centripetal, not centrifugal as in the stem. In almost all the specimens a thick zone of secondary wood is present. Most often the wood is decorticated, but when the cortex is present it has a very lacunar structure, containing a ring of large intercellular spaces. It is only in very good specimens that the phloëm is preserved (see Fig. 16).

Now some of the smaller specimens, which used to be included in the *Myriophylloides* of Hick and Cash, have a very different structure from those just described. Some of them have no pith, and the groups of primary wood are very few in number (see Fig. 17). The structure of the cortex, however, is the same in all, and the extreme types are connected by a series of intermediate forms.

Renault, in 1885, expressed his conviction that the French specimens, which he recognised as agreeing with Williamson's genus, were the roots of *Calamites* (his *Arthropitys*) and of *Calamodendron*, and he made out a strong case for his belief.[1] His suggestion, however, was not at once accepted, because he had not obtained the evidence of actual continuity at that time. Later

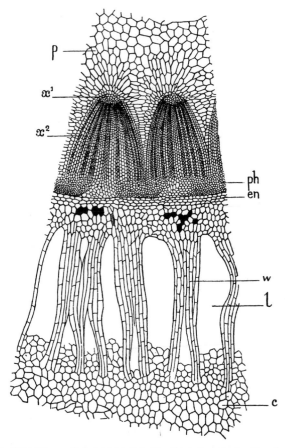

Fig. 16.—*Calamites*, sp. Part of transverse section of a large root. p, pith ; x^1, primary centripetal xylem ; x^2, secondary xylem ; ph, phloëm ; en, endodermis ; l, lacunae of cortex ; w, cellular walls separating them ; c, outer cortex. Magnified. After Renault.

on—in 1893—Renault described certain beautiful specimens of Calamites, which afforded the proof required, for

[1] Renault, " Nouvelles Recherches sur le genre *Astromyelon*," *Mém. Soc. Sci. Nat. de Saône-et-Loire*, 1885.

in them the Calamitean stem bears appendages in which the typical *Astromyelon* structure is evident.[1] This evidence proved quite conclusively that *Astromyelon* was only an appendage of the stem of *Calamites*. Since then the connection between the two organs has also been clearly demonstrated in various specimens from the English Coal-measures.

The relation between the roots and the stem has more recently been fully investigated by Mr. Maslen,[2] who finds that the roots, like the branches, were commonly inserted on the node, between two of the outgoing leaf-traces (cf. Fig. 9) ; the roots, however, arise on a level with the leaf-traces, and not above them, and pursue a somewhat downwardly directed course in passing through the wood of the main axis.

The question whether these appendages were roots or branches had to be decided from the anatomy. In the first place, as already mentioned, the primary xylem was centripetally developed. On the inner side of each woody wedge we find in transverse section a little triangular group of tracheae, and this triangular group has always the smaller elements towards the exterior (see Fig. 16, x^1). Radial sections prove that these external elements of the primary wood are spiral tracheae, and thus the position of the protoxylem is shown to be that characteristic of roots.

Another point of crucial importance is the arrangement of the primary xylem and phloëm groups ; it is not often that such a point as this can be demonstrated in a fossil. We were able, in one or two favourable cases, to trace the centripetal strands of xylem in a young root, and to find, alternating with them, groups of delicate tissue, which could only be interpreted as primary phloëm.

---

[1] *Flore fossile du bassin houiller d'Autun et d'Épinac*, Part ii. p. 106, Plate lii. etc.

[2] A. J. Maslen, " Relation of Root to Stem in Calamites," *Annals of Botany*, vol. xix. 1905, p. 61.

Hence, in this respect also, the structure proves to be that of a typical root.

We further found that the bases of branches of *Astromyelon* are surrounded by a distinct cortex of their own, as they traverse the outer tissues of the parent organ. Hence they must have been endogenous in origin, thus agreeing with rootlets. Another important point is the entire absence of anything like nodes.

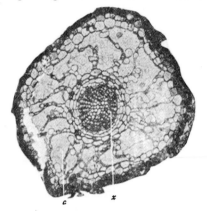

There is thus, on the whole of the evidence, no room for doubt that the old genus "*Astromyelon*" simply represents the roots and rootlets of *Calamites*.[1] Other allied forms appear to stand in a similar relation to *Archaeocalamites* and *Calamodendron.*

FIG. 17.—*Calamites*, sp. Transverse section of small tetrarch rootlet, showing wood (*x*), with slight secondary growth, double endodermis, lacunar cortex (*c*), and thickened exodermis. × 25. From a photograph. *Phil. Trans.*, W. and S. Will. Coll. 1890, A.

The endodermis was evidently double, as in the roots of recent Horsetails ; this is well shown in the small tetrarch rootlet represented in Fig. 17. The large intercellular spaces of the cortex were no doubt an adaptation for growth under water, or in wet mud. The cortex is bounded externally by a layer of cells with very thick outer walls, comparable to the exodermis of many recent roots (Fig. 17). In the older roots a periderm was formed, the external cells of which, as Dr. M. C. Stopes has shown, thickened their outer walls and replaced the primary protective layer.

[1] Williamson and Scott, "Further Observations, etc.," Part ii. The Roots of *Calamites, Phil. Trans.* vol. 186, B, 1895.

We have now obtained a fairly good idea of the whole construction of a Calamarian plant, as regards its vegetative organs. We have a thorough knowledge of the structure of the stem in various types, and much has already been learnt about the comparative anatomy of the leaves, while we now know almost the whole story of the structure of the roots and branches, and their relation to the stem.

7. *The Medullary Casts.*—One. thing remains to be said before leaving the vegetative organs, in order to complete the anatomical explanation of the markings on the casts. We have already seen, as shown in the first illustrations to this chapter, that every medullary cast shows longitudinal ridges and furrows. It is quite evident that the furrows on the cast correspond to the vascular bundles. We have to imagine the soft tissues decayed, leaving only the woody tissues behind, so that each wedge-shaped strand of wood leaves its mark on the mineral matter filling the pith-cavity. Between the furrows thus produced we find the projecting ridges, corresponding to the medullary rays which had decayed. Ultimately the wood itself became reduced to a carbonaceous film, leaving the cast within visible.

On a well-preserved Calamitean cast, a little projection is almost constantly found on each ridge, immediately below the node.[1] Various explanations have been given of these projections, but a remarkable specimen in the Williamson Collection has settled the question. This specimen is a medullary cast of the base of a branch. It owes its interest to the fact that we not only find the little projecting bumps in their usual position, but that many of them are represented by regular spokes, radiating out for a long distance from the cast. Williamson found, in the specimens with internal structure preserved, that

[1] Clearly shown in Figs. 2 and 3, pp. 15 and 16. In Fig. 3 these prints are marked *i.c.* on the right.

there was often a radial canal passing through the parenchyma of each principal medullary ray, near its upper
end, which is sometimes dilated. These "infranodal
canals," as he called them, extend through the entire
thickness of the secondary wood. In other cases, where
there is not a definite empty space, or canal, we still find
that below the node the rays are dilated, their tissue in
this part differing from that of the rest of the ray (see
Fig. 8, *i.c.*, and Fig. 9, *c*). The dilated, infranodal
portions of the rays extend far out into the wood, even
when the rest of the ray is bridged over by intercalated
tracheae.

Williamson's explanation was that these canals,
whether natural or, as is more probable, left by decay,
had, like the pith itself, become filled with mineral matter,
giving rise in ordinary cases to elevations on the cast,
which fitted into the hollow canals. In the remarkable
specimen referred to, the canals had been filled throughout
the whole thickness of the wood, and, when the wood
itself perished, the mineral casts of the canals were left
behind intact.[1] In this exceptionally beautiful case,
these radiating spokes correspond in size, shape, and
position to the dilated infranodal rays, shown in so many
of the specimens with structure. We know, from the
evidence of the medullary casts with branches, that the
prints in question occurred *below* the nodes (see Figs. 2
and 3) : it follows that the dilated rays, or "infranodal
canals," when present, were also below the node, and this
fact is often of value in determining the top and bottom
of a specimen in doubtful cases (cf. Figs. 8 and 9).

[1] This specimen is figured by Williamson in Part ix. of his memoirs
" On the Organisation of the Fossil Plants of the Coal-measures," *Phil.
Trans.* 1878, Part ii. Plate xxi. Fig. 31.

CHAPTER III

*Calamostachys ; Palaeostachya ; Cingularia ; Archaeo-
calamites ; Macrostachya ; Classification of Calamarieae ; Mesozoic Equisetales.*

1. *The Fructifications.*—We have now to consider the
important subject of the fructifications of the Calamarieae. There are four main types of cone referred
to this group, and known to us in some detail, though no
doubt there are many more not so thoroughly investigated. First we will take the type of *Calamostachys*,
representatives of which, with structure preserved, are
common in the English Coal-measures. This genus is
characterised by the fact that the cone does not merely
bear whorls of peltate sporangiferous scales, as in *Equisetum*, but that the successive fertile whorls are separated
from one another by intermediate and equidistant verticils
of sterile bracts (see Figs. 18 and 22). The peltate scales
by themselves look like those of an Equisetaceous fructification (see Figs 19 and 21). It is better to use the word
sporangiophore in this connection, rather than sporophyll,
for, as we shall see, the fossil forms considerably disturb
current morphological ideas. Secondly, there is the
Palaeostachya type, distinguished by the fact that the
sporangiophores are not inserted midway between the
whorls of sterile bracts, but immediately above each
verticil of bracts, and, as it were, in its axil (see Fig. 25,
A, p. 54). The third type is one about which we do not

know so much as we should like, because the remains are not preserved with structure, but only as impressions. This is the *Cingularia* type, which is just the reverse of that of *Palaeostachya*, for in *Cingularia* the sporangiophores are inserted immediately *below* the bracts, instead of immediately *above* them (see Figs. 29 and 30, pp. 60 and 61). Fourthly, we have a type which is essentially the

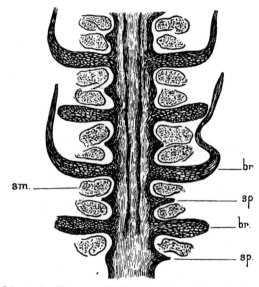

Fig. 18.—*Calamostachys Binneyana.* Radial section of part of cone, showing four whorls of bracts (*br*) with the sporangiophores (*sp*) between them, the peltate part not shown (see Fig. 21). *sm*, sporangia. × 8. Will. Coll. 1022. (G. T. G.)

same as that of *Equisetum*, e.g. *Archaeocalamites*, for here the sporangiophores are present alone, without any bracts at all, or only at long intervals (Fig. 25, B). In other cases, cones have been found which even more exactly resemble those of recent Equisetaceae.

2. *Calamostachys.*—I will now shortly describe the British species of *Calamostachys*, the genus with alternate and equidistant whorls of bracts and sporangiophores. We will first take the anatomy of the axis of the

cone, as shown in the commonest British form, *Calamo-stachys Binneyana*. The axis is traversed by a central cylinder (see Fig. 18), triangular or quadrangular as seen in transverse section, with a distinct and persistent pith (see Fig. 20). Surrounding the pith are the vascular bundles, of which there are usually either three or four according to the form of the stele. Often, at least in the triangular form, each bundle is double (Fig. 20). The number of angles and bundles is related to that of the

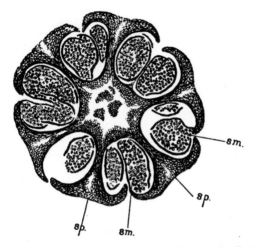

Fig. 19.—*Calamostachys Binneyana*. Transverse section of cone, passing through a whorl of six peltate sporangiophores, *sp*. *sm*, sporangia attached to the peltate laminae of the sporangiophores. × 16. Will. Coll. 1020. (G. T. G.)

sporangiophores in a whorl (six in the triangular and eight in the quadrangular form) ; these numbers and the form of the stele are often different in different parts of the same cone. Apart from these changes, it is a constant rule that the bracts of successive sterile whorls are alternate with one another, while the sporangiophores of the fertile verticils are superposed.

On the inner side of the wood of each bundle we find a more or less regular canal (*px* in Fig. 20). If we examine a radial section we see the spiral protoxylem-elements in the canals : we have thus essentially the same structure as in *Calamites,* for the vascular bundles are collateral here also, as shown by specially favourable preparations, in which the phloëm can be recognised outside the wood ; in *Calamostachys Binneyana,* however, there is a solid pith, and the bundles are comparatively few. In most of these fructifications we find distinct indications of secondary wood in the axis (Fig. 20). While the vascular bundles of the bracts are given off from regular nodes,

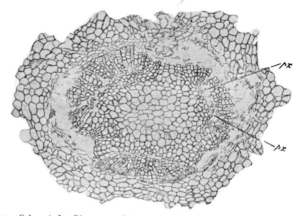

Fig. 20.—*Calamostachys Binneyana.* Transverse section of axis of cone, showing somewhat triangular stele and part of cortex. Surrounding the pith there are three double bundles with secondary wood. *px,* protoxylem groups. × about 60. *Phil. Trans.,* W. and S. Will. Coll. 1016.

like those of the vegetative axis, there is no nodal structure corresponding to the sporangiophore-bundles, which appear to belong to the next sterile node below (see p. 53).

The bundles in *Calamostachys* do not alternate at the nodes, but go straight down the axis. We see, however, that the anatomy, on the whole, is quite consistent with that of the Calamitean type of stem.

We will now pass on to the structure of the appendages, and will take the sterile bracts first. In our species (*C. Binneyana*) the bracts are coherent for a considerable distance from their insertion (see Fig. 22). In other species they are free, the whole way through. Through the coherent horizontal disc the vascular strands, springing from the node, pass out, entering the free tips of the bracts, which turn vertically upwards (Fig. 18). The structure of the bracts is much like that of the small vegetative Calamitean leaves, described above, but in the bracts there is very little assimilating tissue, and fibrous elements, especially in the apical portions, are strongly developed.

The whorls of peltate sporangiophores are midway between those of the sterile bracts, the number of the former in each whorl being about half that of the latter. Thus in *Calamostachys Binneyana* there are commonly six sporangiophores and about a dozen bracts in their respective verticils (see Fig. 19), though in other cases with eight sporangiophores the number of bracts may be thirteen or fourteen. The sporangiophores have the same peltate form which is so familiar to us in *Equisetum*, but in *Calamostachys* each peltate scale bears four sporangia only, attached in a pendent position to the corners of the lamina (Figs. 19 and 21), which has a somewhat square form when seen in superficial view. A vascular bundle runs to the base of each sporangium. In tangential sections of the cone a group of four sporangia, diagonally placed, surrounds the stalk of each peltate scale (see Fig. 22).

The sporangia are elongated sacs, stretching back from the lamina to the axis (Figs. 19 and 21). The sporangial wall, as preserved, is usually only one cell thick, and the lateral membranes of its cells are stiffened by projecting ridges (Fig. 23). When cut across, these buttresses are not easily distinguished from the cell-walls.

In *Calamostachys Binneyana* the spores are very numerous in each sporangium, and, so far as has been ascertained, they were all of one kind, the average diameter of the full-grown spores being about .09 mm. Curiously enough, we often find them united in groups of four, the tetrad being still enclosed within the membrane of its mother-cell (see Fig. 23, A, B, C). Hence we see that the fourfold division, so general in spore mother-cells, already prevailed among these Palaeozoic plants. In many cases the spores of the same tetrad are very unequally developed, some remaining quite small (Fig. 23, B and C) ; we may regard the latter as abortive spores, their suppression having allowed of the better nutrition of their surviving sister-cells. The mature spores show a

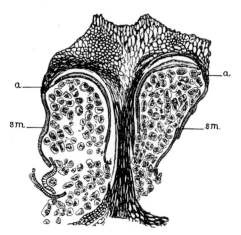

FIG. 21.—*Calamostachys Binneyana.* A single peltate sporangiophore, in longitudinal section. *sm*, sporangia, attached at *a* to the edges of the peltate lamina. They are full of spore-tetrads. × about 40. S. Coll. 174. (G. T. G.)

triradiate marking on one side, no doubt indicating the lines of junction with the sister-cells (Fig. 23, D).

Numerous specimens of *C. Binneyana*, which is a fairly common fossil, have been examined, and no traces of more than one kind of spore have been found. Except for occasional abortion all the spores are uniform. There is thus a strong presumption that this species was homosporous. In another British species, however, *Calamostachys Casheana*, heterospory, as Williamson discovered, certainly occurred (see Frontispiece, Fig. 1). In general organisation this cone is practically identical with the homosporous species *C. Binneyana*, the differences between them being of a trivial kind. In some of the sporangia, however, numerous small spores are contained—slightly smaller than those of *C. Binneyana*, while other sporangia on the same cone, and sometimes on the same sporangiophore, contain a much smaller number of large spores, the diameter of which is just three times that of the former (see Fig. 24). Here, therefore, we have a perfectly clear case of a heterosporous Calamarian cone, and some of the species from the Continent show the same phenomenon. The difference between microspores and megaspores,

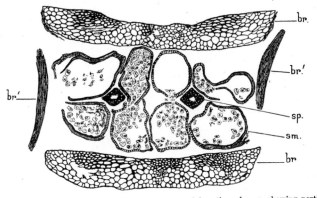

Fig. 22.—*Calamostachys Binneyana*. Part of tangential section of cone, showing portions of two whorls of bracts (*br*) with sporangiophores (*sp*) between. Around each of the latter the four sporangia (*sm*) are grouped. *br'*, free tips of other bracts. × about 25. S. Coll. 175. (G. T. G.)

though well marked, is, however, less extreme than in the heterosporous Lycopods or Rhizocarps.

We saw, in the case of *C. Binneyana*, that some of the spores were abortive, and this is a point of some importance, because we know that a similar process of abortion goes on in heterosporous, as well as in some homosporous Cryptogams, at the present day. It is an interesting fact that in the heterosporous *C. Casheana* we also find this abortion of some of the spores, but it is confined in this species to the megasporangia. It seems then that in this genus we are able to trace how heterospory originated.

The facts suggest that in the first instance a certain number of spores became abortive, and so allowed of better nutrition for the remainder ; this process, going on more freely in some sporangia than in others, may ultimately have rendered possible the excessive develop-

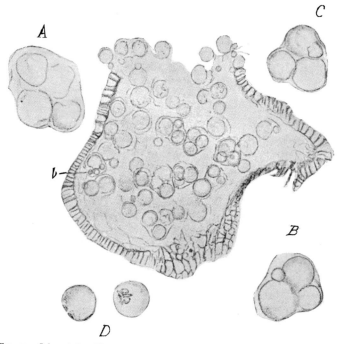

FIG. 23.—*Calamostachys Binneyana.* A single sporangium, containing spores in tetrads. Many of the spores are abortive (*b*). The structure of the sporangial wall is well shown. × 100. A. Tetrad with all four spores about equal. B, C. Tetrads, each with one abortive spore. D. Ripe spores showing the triradiate marks. A-D × 200. *Phil. Trans.*, W. and S. Will. Coll. 1011, etc.

ment of those spores that survived, at the expense of the others, and may thus have led to the development of specialised megaspores.

In the heterosporous species, *Calamostachys Casheana,* the axis of the cone formed a zone of secondary wood, precisely as in the homosporous form, *C. Binneyana,* shown in Fig. 20. This fact is of considerable significance, in view of the excessive importance which some palaeobotanists formerly attached to secondary growth, as an indication of Phanerogamic affinities.

We have next to consider the relation of *Calamostachys* to *Calamites*. A cone of *C. Binneyana* has been found by Mr. Hamshaw Thomas [1] attached to a leafy shoot ; the leaves are of the type of *Calamocladus* (*Asterophyllites*) *grandis*, illustrated above (Fig. 15, B). Very similar Continental species have also been found in

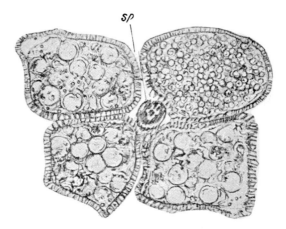

FIG. 24.—*Calamostachys Casheana*. Tangential section, showing four sporangia grouped around their sporangiophore (*sp*). Three contain megaspores and one microspores. × 30. *Phil. Trans.*, W. and S. Will. Coll. 1587.

connection with shoots. In the *Calamostachys Ludwigi* of Carruthers,[2] for example, from the German and Belgian Coal-measures, the cones are borne upon a ribbed stem with whorled leaves, agreeing exactly with the twigs known as *Calamocladus longifolius*. In this species the structure of the cone is perfectly well known ; it is that characteristic of the British forms of *Calamostachys*,

[1] On a cone of *Calamostachys Binneyana* attached to a leafy shoot. *New Phytologist*, vol. viii. p. 249, 1909.

[2] Carruthers, " On the Structure of the Fruit of *Calamites*," Seemann's *Journal of Botany*, vol. v 1867. At that time the generic name *Volkmannia* was used for Calamarian strobili.

except that in *C. Ludwigi* the bracts of the cone are free, instead of being coherent. This fossil thus also affords certain evidence that fructifications of the *Calamostachys* type were borne on Calamitean stems,[1] a fact fully recognised by Mr. Carruthers, in his memoir of 1867, just cited·

The evidence from comparative anatomy is also of considerable importance. The anatomy of the axis of the British forms of *Calamostachys*, which we have described fully above, although it agrees sufficiently well with that of *Calamites* to allow of the probability of relationship, is not exactly that of a Calamitean stem. It is very interesting to find that in some of the Continental species this difference does not exist. They combine the exactly typical anatomy of the Calamitean stem with the external morphology of a *Calamostachys*. This is the case, for example, in the fructification originally described by Renault under the name of *Bruckmannia Grand'Euryi*, which is, to all intents and purposes, a *Calamostachys*, and is placed by Count Solms-Laubach [2] in that genus.

In this case the anatomy of the axis is peculiarly well shown ; there is a fistular pith, surrounded by a ring of eighteen collateral vascular bundles, and beyond that the cortex. Each bundle has a canal, perfectly defined, at the inner margin of its wood. In fact, the anatomy of the axis is that of a young stem of *Calamites*, so that the species *Calamostachys Grand'Euryi* completely removes any anatomical difficulties we might find in

---

[1] See Weiss, *Steinkohlen-Calamarien*, ii. p. 163 ; Atlas, Plates xxii.-xxiv., in *Abhandlungen zur geologischen Specialkarte von Preussen*, Band v., 1884. In the plates cited the structure of *C. Ludwigi* is magnificently illustrated. See also A. Renier, " Observations sur des empreintes de *Calamostachys Ludwigi*," *Ann. de la Soc. Géol. de Belgique*, 1912.

[2] *Fossil Botany*, English edition, p. 329. M. Renault named this fructification *Arthropityostachys Grand'Euryi ; Bassin houiller et permien d'Autun et d'Épinac, flore fossile*, Part ii. p. 135, Plate lxii., 1896. See also his *Cours de botanique fossile*, vol. ii. p. 136, Plates xxi. and xxii., 1882. The structure of this cone is preserved with extraordinary perfection.

referring *Calamostachys* to Calamitean stems. At the
node each bundle gives off two strands to the bracts,
which are here twice as numerous as the main bundles.
According to Renault the strands supplying the sporangiophores also spring from the bract-node, pass up through
a considerable part of the internode above, and then bend
downwards and outwards to enter the sporangiophores.
(Cf. Fig. 28 from *Palaeostachya.*) Dr. Hickling [1] has
shown that this was probably also the case in *Calamostachys Binneyana.*

The morphology of the cone is in all respects that of
a *Calamostachys.* There are the usual alternate whorls
of bracts and sporangiophores, and the bracts in each
whorl are twice as numerous as the sporangiophores.
As in *C. Binneyana,* the bracts are connate in their lower
portion, forming a continuous horizontal disc. The
sporangiophores are of peltate form, and each bears four
sporangia, exactly as in the species above described.
Thirty-six bracts and eighteen sporangiophores were
counted in their respective verticils.

I must add that some of the Continental species
of *Calamostachys* (including *C. Grand'Euryi*) present a
complication not found in the English species above
described ; this peculiarity consists in the presence of
radiating vertical wings of tissue connecting each peltate
scale with the whorl of bracts just above it. There was
thus a membrane connecting the upper edges of the
sporangiophores with the lower side of the bracts ; in
some cases a similar but less complete membrane also
extended *downwards* from each sporangiophore. The
sporangia thus lay in groups of four in the compartments
formed by these radial plates of tissue. We have here
one example among many of the complexity of the
Palaeozoic Cryptogams, as compared with those of the
present day.

[1] " The Anatomy of *Calamostachys Binneyana*," *Manchester Memoirs,*
vol. 54, 1910.

3. *Palaeostachya.*—We will now go on to the second main type of Calamarian fructification, that described by Weiss under the name of *Palaeostachya.*[1] Its peculiarity consists in the fact that the sporangiophores, instead of being inserted midway between the whorls of bracts, are

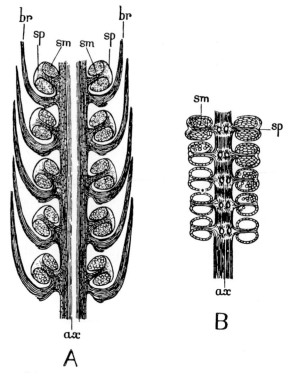

FIG. 25.—A. *Palaeostachya.* Radial section of cone, showing peltate sporangiophores (*sp*) inserted in axils of bracts (*br*). *sm*, sporangia ; *ax*, axis of cone. Magnified. Diagrammatised after Renault. B. *Archaeocalamites radiatus.* Part of cone, showing axis (*ax*) bearing sporangiophores (*sp*) only. *sm*, sporangia. Magnified. After Renault.

placed in their axils. In *Palaeostachya gracilis,* described by Renault,[2] each whorl of bracts has about twenty

[1] *Steinkohlen-Calamarien,* i. p. 103, 1876.

[2] This author uses the generic name *Volkmannia,* and refers these fructifications to the vegetative shoots known as *Asterophyllites* ; see below, p. 70 ; Renault, *Cours de bot. foss.* vol. ii. p. 114, Plates xviii. and xix. ; *Flore fossile d'Autun et d'Épinac,* p. 74, Plates xxix. and xxx.

members ; the sporangiophores, about ten in each verticil, are inserted immediately above the bracts, in the angle between the latter and the axis. In the diagrammatic Figure, 25, A, the position of the sporangiophores is well shown. In Fig. 26 another species, *Palaeostachya pedunculata*, is represented on a small scale, as in the actual specimen. In this case a large number of cones are seen attached to a Calamarian branch.

While the position of the sporangiophores in *Palaeostachya* is thus strikingly different from that in *Calamostachys*, their structure is almost identical. Each sporangiophore, as in that genus, is peltate, bearing four sporangia on its lower surface. The spores are of the same type as in the homosporous *Calamostachys*. The occurrence of heterospory is, however, proved in the case of another species perhaps referable to *Palaeostachya*.[1]

In *Palaeostachya gracilis*, according to Renault's observations, the number of sporangiophores in the whorl is about half that of the bracts, while the number of vascular bundles in

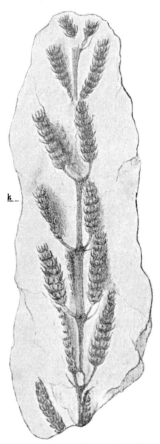

FIG. 26. — *Palaeostachya pedunculata.* Specimen from the coal-shales, showing a fertile shoot bearing about a dozen cones and a few leaves. *k*, stem. About ⅔ of nat. size. After Williamson, *Phil. Trans.* Will. Coll. 1060.

[1] Renault, *Flore fossile d'Autun et d'Épinac*, Part ii. p. 77, Plate xxix. Figs. 6 and 7.

the axis is equal to that of the sporangiophores in a whorl. In its anatomy, the axis closely resembles a young Calamitean stem.

A fructification belonging to the type of *Palaeostachya* was described by Dr. Williamson for the first time in 1869,[1] and subsequently much more fully in 1887.[2] This strobilus he called the " true fructification of *Calamites*," and, for many years, he refused to admit any other fructification as properly belonging to *Calamites*, the reason being that in this " true fructification " of his, and, as he thought, in no other, the Calamitean anatomy was manifest in all its essential points. In cases where we have both the peduncle and the axis, the former has in all respects Calamitean structure, including a secondary zone of wood, which dies out as the axis itself is approached. This form was called by Dr. Williamson in his last memoirs [3] *Calamites pedunculatus*. It was distasteful to him to give any other generic name than *Calamites* to a fructification which he felt so sure belonged to that genus. It is, however, more convenient to retain special generic names for the cones, as it is so rarely possible to refer them to particular forms of stem ; while, as we have already seen, the species of *Calamostachys* have as indubitable a claim as *Palaeostachya* to be referred to the genus *Calamites*. Williamson's specimen has therefore been re-named *Palaeostachya vera* by Prof. Seward, the specific name serving to recall Williamson's original description of the fructification.[4]

The Calamitean anatomy is shown with great perfection

---

[1] " On a New Form of Calamitean Strobilus," *Mem. Lit. and Phil. Soc. of Manchester*, 1869.

[2] " Organisation of Fossil Plants of Coal-measures," Part xiv., *Phil. Trans.* 1888, B.

[3] See Williamson and Scott, " Further Observations, etc.," Part i., *Phil. Trans.* vol. 185, B, 1894, p. 916.

[4] The specific designation *pedunculata* was inadmissible, as it had been previously given to a different species of *Palaeostachya*, namely that shown in our Fig. 26.

both in the peduncle and in the axis of the strobilus; in the canals accompanying the vascular bundles, the disorganised spiral tracheae are found, just as in the vegetative stem. In this form the number of sporangiophores is from sixteen to twenty in each whorl, the bracts, which were connate at their base, being, according to

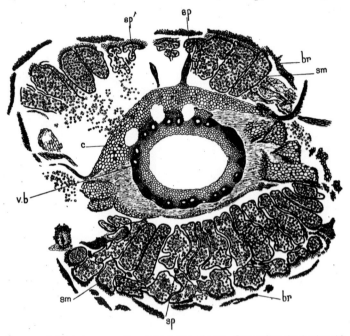

FIG. 27.—*Palaeostachya vera.* Transverse section of cone. Surrounding the fistular pith is the ring of bundles (*v.b.*) grouped in pairs. Outside them is the cortex and disc (*c*). *sp*, pedicels of the sporangiophores, some shown attached to the axis, others between the sporangia (*sm*), which are grouped in fours around the sporangiophores; *sp′*, remains of peltate lamina of a sporangiophore; *br*, bracts. × about 7. S. Coll. 474. (G. T. G.)

detailed observations by Dr. George Hickling,[1] about equal in number, as are also the vascular bundles in the axis. Fig. 27 represents a transverse section of the cone. The vascular bundles are here approximated in pairs, the pairs alternating, in the nodal region, with

[1] The anatomy of *Palaeostachya vera, Annals of Botany,* vol. xxi. July 1907.

so-called canals, which represent parenchymatous areas in the sclerotic disc which strengthened the node. The peltate part of the sporangiophores is imperfectly preserved in the English specimens, but the sporangia are well shown, and are, as usual, four in number on each sporangiophore. The structure of the sporangial wall is identical with that of *Calamostachys*. The spores, so

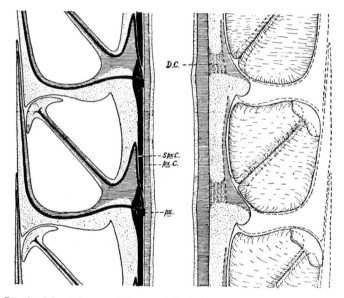

FIG. 28.—*Palaeostachya vera.* Diagrammatic longitudinal section of cone. Vascular tissue, *black*; soft parenchyma, *dotted*; sclerised, *lined*. *Left* side passes through bundle; *right*, between bundles. Sporangia omitted on left side; inserted on right in surface-view. *D.C.*, disc canal; *px.C.*, protoxylem canal of main bundle; *Spx.C.*, protoxylem canal of sporangiophore trace; *px.*, persistent protoxylem at the node. Note the sharply reflexed course of the bundles supplying the sporangiophores. From Hickling.

far as the existing specimens show, were all of one kind, and of similar dimensions to those of *Calamostachys Binneyana*.

The apparently axillary position of the sporangiophores in *Palaeostachya* evidently suggests caution in accepting the current view that these organs in Equisetineae are modified leaves. Dr. Hickling's observations have cleared up, for the first time, the course of the vascular strands which supply the sporangiophores. He finds that they start from the same node as the bundles which run to the subtending bracts, and immediately above them. The sporangiophore bundle, however, passes vertically upwards, parallel to the corresponding main bundle of the axis, until it has ascended through almost exactly half the internode. It is then sharply reflexed, descends rapidly to the upper limit of the nodal disc, and sweeps horizontally across the upper part of this to the base of the sporangiophore, which it enters [1] (Fig. 28). Thus in *Palaeostachya*, as in *Calamostachys*, the evidence of the vascular supply indicates that the sporangiophores may be regarded as the ventral append- ages of the bracts subtending them. On account of the anomalous course of the sporangiophore bundles, Dr. Hickling regards *Palaeostachya* as derived from the *Calamostachys* type.

4. *Cingularia*.—We now come to the third type of the Calamarian fructifications which I shortly described above, namely that of *Cingularia*. Our knowledge of *Cingularia*, which is chiefly due to the researches of the German palaeobotanist C. E. Weiss,[2] is less satisfactory than in the cases already considered. So far we have been dealing with fructifications with their internal structure preserved. *Cingularia* is not one of these ; it is only known from carbonaceous impressions, and not from petrified specimens, and hence only its external char- acters are open to investigation. Under these circum- stances we cannot feel the same certainty in the inter- pretation of the facts as in specimens with the whole structure preserved. We may, however, accept Weiss's description of the type-species, *C. typica*, as essentially correct. The plant itself had the usual Calamarian habit,

---

[1] Hickling, *l.c.* p. 375.

[2] *Steinkohlen-Calamarien*, i. p. 99, Plates vi.-ix. 1876.

with a jointed stem and whorled leaves. It appears that the successive whorls were superposed, not alternating as in most Calamarieae. The fructifications were long, very lax cones, with the whorled appendages rather remote from each other (see Fig. 29).

The conclusion at which Weiss arrived was that each whorl was a double one, and that it consisted of a verticil of coherent bracts running out into sharp teeth at the

FIG. 29.—*Cingularia typica.* Part of branch, bearing whorled leaves and a lax cone, with whorled bracts. Nat. size. After C. E. Weiss.

edges, and of another coherent verticil immediately below the first, consisting of the sporangiophores (see Fig. 30). Thus the relative position of bracts and sporangiophores is just the reverse of that in *Palaeostachya.* According to Fischer's observations the bracts and sporangiophores were not free whorls, but were partly united to each other, an important point of analogy with the Sphenophyllales. (See next chapter, p. 88).[1] The strap-shaped

[1] See Ed. Fischer, " Einige Bemerkungen über die Calamarieen-gattung *Cingularia,*" *Mitt. d. Naturf. Gesellsch. in Bern,* 1893.

sporangiophores separate from one another as they approach the exterior, and further to the outside each divides into two lobes, as shown in Fig. 30. Looking at the under surface of a fertile whorl, we notice on each of the flattened sporangiophores four prints, which are known to have been the points of attachment of the sporangia, as the latter are occasionally found *in situ*. Each of the sporangiophores thus bore four sporangia on its lower surface (Fig. 30). The sporangia were of

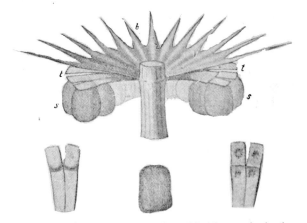

Fig. 30.—*Cingularia typica.* Enlarged diagram of a verticil of the cone, showing the connate bracts (*b*) above, and the strap-shaped sporangiophores (*t*) below, bearing the sporangia (*s*). The small figures show two sporangiophores, that on the left seen from above, and that on the right from below. In the middle a sporangium. After C. E. Weiss.

approximately spherical form, and remarkably large, averaging 5 mm. in diameter, which is five times the size of the sporangia of *Calamostachys Binneyana*. The number of bracts in a whorl seems to have been about double that of the sporangiophores. The great peculiarity of *Cingularia typica* consists in the fact that the sporangiophores lie immediately below the sterile bracts of each whorl, instead of immediately above them, as in the last type. This is different from anything we are accustomed to find among other Pteridophyta. In the absence of better evidence than we at present possess, it is impossible to draw any decisive conclusions as to the morphology or affinities of *Cingularia*. We cannot even be absolutely certain whether we have to do with a Calamarian or a Sphenophyllaceous plant. The question can only be cleared up if specimens with the structure preserved should be discovered. *C. typica*, hitherto known from Coal-fields in Germany, France, and Belgium, has recently been discovered by Dr. Kidston in the Middle Coal-measures of Shropshire. From the same locality, he has also described a second species of the genus, *C. Cantrilli*, Kidston, remarkable for the entire absence of any sterile whorls. Each verticil consists of ten sporangiophores, surrounding the axis in a cup-like manner, the successive whorls somewhat overlapping each other. The detailed organisation of the fertile whorls is otherwise similar to that in the type-species.[1]

5. *Archaeocalamites.*—A fourth type of Calamarian fructification remains to be noticed. This is a simple one to describe, because it has much in common with that of the only surviving genus of Equisetales, the recent *Equisetum*. The remarkable genus *Archaeocalamites*, characteristic of the oldest Carboniferous strata, appears, according to M. Renault's observations, to have borne the fructification of which a fragment is represented in Fig. 25, B. The cones occur associated with the stems and dichotomous leaves of that genus, though the evidence from actual continuity is wanting. The cone bears whorls of sporangiophores, from eight to ten in each whorl ; they have the usual peltate form, with the expanded portion little developed, and each appears to have borne four sporangia. Sterile bracts are not shown, but it is quite probable that they may have occurred in scattered whorls, at long intervals, as was clearly the

[1] Kidston, Cantrill, and Dixon, " The Forest of Wyre and the Titterstone Clee Hill Coal-fields," *Trans. Royal Soc. Edinburgh*, vol. li. pp. 1042-1047, 1917.

case in the genus *Pothocites*, associated with *Archaeo-calamites* in the Lower Carboniferous of Scotland. *Pothocites* consists of large cylindrical strobili, constricted at intervals, the constrictions marking the position of whorls of small leaves or bracts.[1] The fructifications of *Archaeocalamites* are not yet known in the petrified condition.

Archaeocalamites is a very ancient type of Calamarian tree, characterised by the non-alternation in succes-

FIG. 31. — *Archaeocalamites radiatus.* Branch bearing whorled leaves, which are dichotomously subdivided. Half nat. size. After Stur.

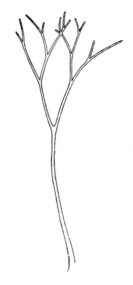

FIG. 32.—Single leaf of the same. Half nat. size. After Stur.

sive internodes of the furrows on the casts corresponding to the vascular bundles, and also by the remarkable foliage,

[1] See Kidston, " Affinities of the Genus *Pothocites*," *Trans. Bot. Soc. Edinburgh*, 1883.

for the leaves were forked, instead of being simple.[1]
Fig. 31, from a work by the Austrian palaeontologist, Stur,
gives a good idea of the habit of a leafy branch, and in
Fig. 32 a single, repeatedly forked leaf is shown. M.
Grand'Eury has discovered fructifications resembling the
cones of living Equisetaceae, from the French Coal-
measures, and Mr. Kidston has described, under the
name of *Equisetum Hemingwayi*, a large cone, which
presents the external characters of a fructification of the
recent genus. There is altogether a considerable amount
of evidence to show that fructifications of the *Equisetum*
type already existed in the Coal-period, but unfortunately
none of the specimens in question have their internal
structure preserved. The Permian plant known as
Phyllotheca deliquescens has a fructification presenting
some analogies with *Pothocites*, the long fertile spikes
being interrupted at intervals by whorls of sterile leaves.
A similar condition occurs as an abnormality in recent
species of *Equisetum*.

6. *Macrostachya.*—In addition to these well-characterised types, we have various fructifications which
have been referred to Calamarieae, but as to which our
information is contradictory and scanty. Among these
it is only necessary to mention the genus called *Macrostachya*, the cones of which are of great size, attaining
8 inches in length by an inch or more in diameter (see
Fig. 33). They were often borne in whorls, on stout
stems with typical Calamitean structure, and these cones
are among the most striking fossils of the Coal-period.
There is great doubt as to the internal structure of the

[1] The anatomy of the stem of some species of *Archaeocalamites* has
been worked out by M. Renault and Count Solms-Laubach, and is
described as exactly that of an ordinary Calamite, of the kind in which
the medullary rays become bridged over by interfascicular wood.
The roots were of the " *Astromyelon* " type. See Renault, *Flore fossile
d'Autun et d'Épinac*, Part ii. p. 80, Plates xlii. and xliii. ; and Solms-
Laubach, *Botanische Zeitung*, 1897, p. 219.

cones. M. Renault examined the carbonised cones of a *Macrostachya*, found in connection with the stem, which was of the *Calamitina* type (see footnote below), and showed the usual Calamitean structure. The fructification proved to be heterosporous, the microsporangia and megasporangia occurring on the same strobilus, as is the case in *Calamostachys Casheana*.[1]

Fig. 33.—*Macrostachya infundibuliformis.* Cone borne laterally on a branch. Half nat. size. After C. E. Weiss.

7. *Classification.* — Before leaving the Calamarieae I must say a few words as to their classification. This is a most difficult, and indeed, in the present state of our knowledge, insoluble question, because we only have the plants as preserved in the form of fragments. Consequently, we shall not be surprised to find that the classification of Calamarieae has been based on totally different principles, according to the parts of the plants selected. For example, Weiss classified Calamarieae by means of the characters presented by their medullary casts, and more especially according to the form and distribution of the scars marking the position of the branches. For the purposes of geologists his is a useful arrangement.[2] Again, we

---

[1] *Notice sur les Calamariées*, Part iii., Autun, 1898.

[2] Weiss's subgenera may be shortly characterised as follows :— *Stylocalamites* : branches few, and irregularly scattered (see Figs. 2 and 3). *Calamitina* : internodes usually short ; branches in whorls, limited to certain nodes, often surmounting internodes shorter than the rest. *Eucalamites* : branches on every node, in some cases one, in others many, on each. *Archaeocalamites* : ribs continuous, not alternating as in the three former ; branches limited to certain regions of the stem, where they are present on every node. See *Steinkohlen-Calamarien*, Part ii. 1884.

may classify these plants with reference to the structure of their wood. We have ourselves distinguished the simple structure of *Arthropitys* or *Calamites* proper from the more complex organisation of *Calamodendron*, between which the *Arthrodendron* form is intermediate. Then again it might be possible to arrange them according to their foliage, and as we shall see, considerable use has actually been made of characters drawn from the leaves. For example, the simple leaves of most Calamarieae contrast sharply with the dichotomous leaves of the *Archaeocalamites* type. A far better plan would be to classify the specimens according to the fructification, the character on which we should chiefly rely in the case of recent plants. But we have not yet any scheme which combines all these characters into a natural classification of the plants themselves, and, from the nature of the material, such a scheme is chimerical, though a slow approach towards it may be made, as new evidence accumulates.

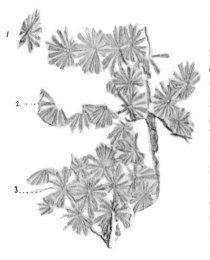

Fig. 34.—*Annularia brevifolia.* Twigs, bearing whorled leaves. Nat. size. After Stur.

Two main types of foliage referred to *Calamites* (omitting *Archaeocalamites*) have been distinguished, under the names *Annularia* and *Asterophyllites* ; for the latter *Calamocladus* has often been used as a synonym. These names are applied to the smaller, leafy twigs, which are but rarely found in connection with the main stems ;

such connection, indeed, is only possible in the exceptional cases in which the external surface of the stem is preserved. The twigs, however, are shown to belong to *Calamites* by their whorled leaves and alternating ribs.

In *Annularia* the leaves are linear, lanceolate or spatulate, and more or less united into a sheath at the base of each whorl, though this feature is often scarcely noticeable. As found in the form of flat impressions, the whorls are usually spread out in the same plane as the axis (Fig. 34). Two opposite branches are borne on a node.

In *Asterophyllites* the leaves are always linear and narrower than those of *Annularia* ; they are not spread out in one plane, and are not united at the base (Fig. 35). Though there is usually a considerable difference in habit between the two genera, the distinction is not always clear. It is only in the case of certain species of *Asterophyllites* that the anatomy of the leaf is known (see above, p. 34).

In all cases where fructifications have been referred with certainty either to *Annularia* or *Asterophyllites*, they have so far proved to be of the *Calamostachys* type ; it is therefore evident that no constant correlation between reproductive and vegetative characters can be traced. There is, in fact, indirect evidence that *Palaeostachya* cones were also borne on stems with *Asterophyllites* foliage.[1]

The only Calamite in which all the organs, stem, foliage and cones, as well as roots, have actually been found in connection, is the species *Calamites ramosus*, Artis, a member of the Eucalamitean group. The leafy twigs of this plant are known as *Annularia radiata*, Brongniart, and the fructifications as *Calamostachys ramosa*, Weiss. This is an unusually favourable case, for both the medullary casts and the external surface of

[1] See Jongmans, " Anleitung zur Bestimmung der Karbonpflanzen West-Europas," Band i. p. 199, 1911.

the stem are known, though we have no information as to the anatomical structure. At present, in fact, we have no means of correlating the anatomy of Calamites with

Fig. 35.—*Asterophyllites densifolius.* Branch bearing distichously arranged twigs ; both branch and twigs with verticillate leaves. Somewhat restored. After Grand'Eury.

their external characters. The late Prof. Grand'Eury made some attempts in this direction, but his results were inconclusive ; he found, for example, that the casts corresponding to the structural genus *Calamo-dendron* were of the type of Weiss's *Stylocalamites*, but casts of this kind are also common at the lower horizons of the Coal-measures, where *Calamodendron* is unknown. The foliage which Grand'Eury referred to *Calamodendron* does not seem to be really distinct from *Asterophyllites*, while the associated cones are indeterminable. No one has ever had a greater knowledge of fossil plants as they actually occur *in situ* than Grand'Eury, but even his able efforts at correlation, on which some stress was laid in former editions of this book, seem to have led to little definite result, as regards the Calamites.

The most distinct group is undoubtedly that of the ancient *Archaeocalamites*, in which the continuous ribs of the stem, the forked leaves, and the somewhat *Equise-tum*-like cones are all characteristic, though even here the anatomy presents no really distinctive characters.

The presence of a creeping rhizome, from which the upright aerial stems took their rise, seems to have been general in the various forms of Calamites.

The natural classification of the Calamarieae is a question for the future. Recent work, such as the investigation of the external morphology of the stem, by the late Dr. Arber and Mr. Lawfield,[1] and the elaborate systematic " Monograph of the Calamites of Western Europe " by Kidston and Jongmans,[2] may, it is hoped, ultimately afford the data for a scientific arrangement.

It is important to point out how nearly some of the Calamarieae of the Carboniferous period approached our living *Equisetum*. In some, as we have seen, the fructification was of a very similar type, and there is no longer any doubt that many members of the family had leaves coherent at the base, so as to form a regular sheath (see Fig. 12). It is probable, as already mentioned,

[1] *Journal of the Linnean Society, Botany*, vol. xliv. p. 507, 1920.
[2] In course of publication by the Government of the Netherlands, at the Hague. Atlas, 1915; Text, Part i. 1917.

that the sheath may often have become split, as the stem within grew in thickness, and that this may account in certain cases for the apparently distinct leaves.

So far, I have treated the Calamarieae generally as being Cryptogamic plants with manifest Equisetaceous affinities, and I do not think that at the present day any difference of opinion now remains on that point, though for many years their position was warmly disputed. I mentioned in the last chapter the views of Brongniart. His distinguished disciple, the late M. Renault, took the same side in the controversy, but, as time went on, considerably modified the original Brongniartian view. Brongniart would not have allowed that all the plants now grouped as Calamarieae were nearly allied to one another. He separated them sharply, at least in his later works, into two wholly different families, the one Cryptogamic, the other Phanerogamic.[1] M. Renault, on the other hand, recognised the family of Calamarieae as including all fossil plants, *whether Cryptogamic or Phanerogamic*, which possess a " Calamitoid " stem.[2] Within this main group, however, he separated the Equisetineae (with Cryptogamic, homosporous or heterosporous cones) from the Calamodendreae ; the latter he still inclined to regard as Gymnospermous Seed-plants. In his latest works he gave up the distinction based on the presence or absence of secondary wood, and recognised the existence of Cryptogamic Calamarieae with cambium, as in the case of the *Calamites* which bore *Macrostachya* as its fructification. Thus, in the end, there came to be substantial agreement between the great French palaeo-botanist and the English school, of which Williamson was the leader.

If M. Renault's view that a certain part of the Cala-marieae bore seeds were tenable, we should have the remarkable case of a transition from Cryptogamic to

---

[1] *Tableau des genres de végétaux fossiles*, p. 49, 1849.
[2] *Flore fossile d'Autun et d'Épinac*, Part ii. 1896, p. 60.

Phanerogamic plants within the limits of a single family. For this conclusion, though not without analogy,[1] there is no satisfactory evidence in the present case.

M. Renault was led, by his belief in the existence of Phanerogamic Calamarieae, to regard some of the fructifications of the *Calamostachys* type as male cones, others as Cryptogamic strobili, a distinction which the identity of structure renders improbable, in the absence of more positive evidence. He also attributed certain highly developed seeds (*e.g. Gnetopsis* and *Stephanospermum*) to the Calamarieae, but this was never more than a conjecture, and on present evidence it appears that the affinities of the seeds in question lay in a totally different direction, *i.e.* with the Pteridospermeae (see Chapter XI.). A specimen, named by M. Renault *Arthropityostachys Williamsonis*,[2] was interpreted by him, though with some doubt, as a Calamarian cone bearing at the same time both seeds of the *Gnetopsis* type and pollen-sacs, but this interpretation has not stood the test of further investigation.[3]

There is, in fact, no evidence, in the present state of our knowledge, that the Calamarieae were anything more than a varied and highly organised family of Vascular Cryptogams, closely allied to the recent Horsetails. But, although none but Cryptogamic Calamarieae are known to us, the question remains whether they show marked affinities to any of the groups of Seed-bearing Plants, or are likely to have lain on or near any of the lines of Phanerogamic descent.

If there were any such affinity, it might be supposed to lie in the direction of Coniferae, or possibly, as M. Renault suggested, of Gnetaceae. The anatomy of the stem somewhat approaches that of the former family,

---

[1] See below, Chapter VI. p. 173.

[2] *Flore fossile d'Autun et d'Épinac*, Part ii. p. 137, Plate lxiii.

[3] Cf. Zeiller, " Revue des travaux de paléontologie végétale," 1893–1896, in *Revue Générale de Botanique*, 1897, p. 371.

while the usually simple form and structure of the leaves might be regarded as pointing the same way. Even the fructifications are not without analogy in the two groups. The relative position of the sporangiophore and bract in *Palaeostachya* has been compared with that of the ovuliferous and carpellary scale in Abietineae. It is almost certain, however, that these points of resemblance between Calamarians and Conifers are nothing more than analogies —interesting examples of parallel development, but not marks of relationship. There is an entire absence of transitional forms between Equisetineae and either Coniferae or Gnetaceae, whereas, as we shall see later on, there is strong evidence for the derivation of the Gymnosperms generally (or at least of the Cycads and Conifers) from a different stock, namely, that represented by the Pteridosperms.

8. *Mesozoic Equisetales.* — The Calamarieae hitherto considered are strictly Palaeozoic plants ; the last survivors of the true Calamites appear to have died out in the Permian at the close of the Primary period. The Equisetineae, however, were well represented during the Secondary epoch,[1] by forms in some respects intermediate between the Palaeozoic Calamites and the recent Horsetails. In the Trias very large Horsetails are found, the stem of one of them, *Equisetites arenaceus*, even attaining a diameter of 20 cm. (8 inches). All parts of this plant —rhizome, aerial stem, leaf-sheaths, and cones—are preserved, and though all the organs are not in connection, there seems no reason to doubt that they really belonged to the same species. In all respects there is a close agreement with our recent Horsetails, but the Triassic plant was on an immensely greater scale ; it had, for example, as many as 120 leaves in a whorl. It is possible that these

---

[1] For a fuller account of the Mesozoic Equisetales, see Seward's *Fossil Plants*, vol. i.

great stems, like those of the still larger Palaeozoic forms, possessed secondary tissues, but at present this is only a conjecture. In the Rhaetic and Liassic *Equisetites* of Sweden M. Halle finds that the internodal bundles are twice or three times as numerous as the leaf-teeth of a whorl ; the bundles must therefore have traversed two or three internodes. In *Neocalamites*, a genus separated by M. Halle from *Schizoneura* (see below), each bundle passed through at least two internodes, from the leaf downwards. The leaves were completely separate and closely resembled those of such Palaeozoic forms as the species shown in Fig. 35. These facts show a close relation with the Palaeozoic Calamites (see above, p. 23). Numerous Mesozoic species are known ; on the whole their dimensions diminish as the higher horizons are approached. Some of the later forms, as, for example, *Equisetites Burchardti* from the Wealden, had tubers just like those of some recent species.

The genus *Phyllotheca*, very similar to *Annularia*, but with the leaves more united, appears to represent a Palaeozoic type which extended into the Mesozoic period as far as the Lower Jurassic. *Schizoneura*, a characteristic Triassic genus, is remarkable for the splitting of the leaf-sheath into leaf-like segments of variable width. The Secondary Equisetales appear to offer a promising field for research. M. Halle, who has investigated the Stockholm collections of Rhaetic and Liassic Equisetaceae from Scania in Sweden, succeeded in finding the sporangia on the lower surface of the peltate sporangiferous scales ; this is the first time they have been observed in Mesozoic specimens. The sporangiophores, which appear to have been of an almost ligneous texture, have on their lower surface the prints of about twenty-four sporangia — a larger number than in the recent genus. The sporangia and spores closely resemble those of the recent *Equisetum* ; the elaters, however, are not preserved. An interesting point is that the spores show a triradiate marking almost identical with that on the spores of *Calamostachys Binney-ana* (cf. Fig. 23, D).[1]

From the rapid sketch of the fossil Equisetales which has now been given, it is evident how greatly our whole idea of the family is widened by the study of the extinct forms. It is from these alone that we can form any conception of the variety of which this type of organisa-tion is capable, and of the high differentiation to which it once attained. In fact, it is no exaggeration to say that, as regards this important Cryptogamic stock, the study of the fossil forms far outweighs in scientific interest that of the few humble species which have survived to our own day.

[1] Halle, " Zur Kenntnis der mesozoischen Equisetales Schwedens," *K. Svenska Vetenskapsakademiens Handlingar*, Band 43, 1908.

CHAPTER IV

SPHENOPHYLLALES

Sphenophylleae ; Cheirostrobeae ; Pseudoborniales

So far, we have been endeavouring to extend our knowledge of a class already familiar to us, by the study of its extinct representatives. We now go on to fill in a gap in the natural system in a different way, by the description of a group which appears so remote from any recent plants, that it is only quite within the last few years that a possible affinity with an isolated existing family (the Psilotaceae) has been suggested. The class in question —that of the Sphenophyllales—was not, so far as our present knowledge shows, an extensive one, but it is of great phylogenetic interest.

I. SPHENOPHYLLEAE

1. *Sphenophyllum—Vegetative Organs.*—The external aspect of the various species of *Sphenophyllum* has long been familiar to palaeobotanists ; the specimens, when preserved in the form of impressions, are often among the prettiest of the Carboniferous remains (Fig. 37). The genus, which is nearly co-extensive with the family Sphenophylleae, while already represented in the Upper Devonian Flora, is characteristic of the Carboniferous formation, and occurs throughout its whole extent, appearing also in the Permian immediately above it, but scarcely reaching the Triassic. The slender stems of

Sphenophyllum were ribbed ; the ribs did not alternate in successive internodes, but ran straight on through the nodes ; in like manner, the leaves of successive whorls were not alternate, but superposed, a point of great importance among the distinctive characters of *Sphenophyllum*. In the typical species, on which the genus was founded, the leaves, usually six in a whorl, were wedge-shaped, with an entire or toothed margin (Figs. 36, 37). It was soon found, however, that the wedge-shaped form of leaf was not universally present. In very many cases the leaves were dichotomously divided into narrow lobes, and in some we find a whorl of perfectly simple narrow leaves, which may be regarded as corresponding to the segments of a smaller number of deeply-cut palmate leaves. In some members of the genus, both forms of leaf, the simple and the compound, are found on the same stem (see Fig. 36) ; and as, in certain cases, the finely-cut leaves are found below, and the broader wedge-shaped leaves above, a comparison has been suggested with the dimorphic foliage of many aquatic *Ranunculi*, and other water-plants of the present day. It is a familiar fact that in the Water Crowfoot, for

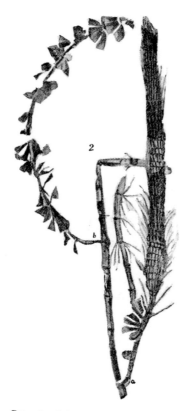

FIG. 36. — *Sphenophyllum*, sp. Branched stem, bearing linear and cuneate whorled leaves on different parts. The branch *a* terminates in a long and slender cone. Half nat. size. After Stur.

example, the lower submerged leaves are finely divided into capillary segments, while the upper floating leaves are entire or but slightly lobed. Hence it was inferred that *Sphenophyllum* itself was an aquatic genus. But this comparison will not really hold good, for in *S. cuneifolium*, for example, the upper cone-bearing branches

FIG. 37.—*Sphenophyllum saxifragaefolium*, showing the whorled, deeply-cut leaves. Note the ribbed stems on the left. Nat. size. Middle Coal-measures, Barnsley, Yorks. From a photograph by Mr. W. Hemingway.

show the finely-cut foliage, while the leaves of the main stem are often cuneate.

Apart from this difference in the form of the foliage, there is considerable uniformity in the external characters of *Sphenophyllum*.[1] The stem was branched, the lateral

[1] In *S. speciosum*, sometimes separated under the generic name *Trizygia*, derived from the Gondwana formation (probably Permo-Carboniferous) of India, the six leaves of each whorl are grouped in three pairs, one pair being constantly smaller than the other two. The

branches springing from the nodes ; their exact relation to the leaves has not yet been cleared up. The
fructification consisted of fairly large cones (Fig. 36),
which from their external appearance might in some
cases very well be taken for those of the Calamarieae.
We shall see, however, that their organisation was
different.

We will now go on to describe the internal structure.
The anatomy of the stem is exceedingly remarkable,
and quite unlike that of the stem in any other group of
plants. It was made known, in the first instance, by
the investigations of M. Renault [1] on the French specimens. This observer was so fortunate as to find the
internal organisation preserved, in specimens which at
the same time showed the external characters of definite
species, and this is one reason why *Sphenophyllum* has
become one of the best - known fossil genera. One
anatomical feature is constant in all the forms examined.
We always find, in the middle of the stem, a solid strand
of primary wood without pith, and this strand is either
triarch or hexarch in structure, and was always centripetally developed, as shown by the position of the spiral
elements at the prominent angles (see Figs. 38-40, 42
and 44, B).

First of all, we will confine ourselves to the primary
structure, as shown, for example, in the species from the
Lower Coal - measures of Lancashire and Yorkshire,
named *Sphenophyllum plurifoliatum* [2] (Figs. 39 and 40).
The primary wood, as seen in transverse section, is triangular ; it consists entirely of tracheae, without pith or

---

leaves are accurately superposed, and the small pair is always on the
same side of the stem. A similar differentiation has been observed in
some European species of *Sphenophyllum*.

[1] See his *Cours de botanique fossile*, vols. ii. and iv., and the earlier
papers there cited.

[2] See Williamson and Scott, " Further Observations on the Fossil
Plants of the Coal-measures," Part i., and the earlier memoirs of
Williamson, there cited.

conjunctive parenchyma. At the angles, narrow spiral or reticulate elements are found, marking, no doubt, the starting-points of the development. The more internal part of the wood consists of large, pitted tracheae. In

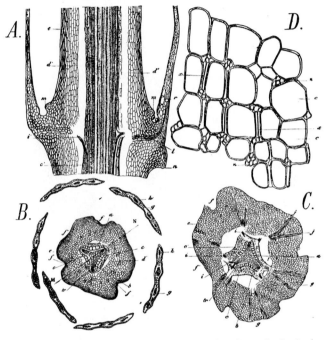

FIG. 38.—*Sphenophyllum quadrifidum*. A. Radial section through a node, showing leaves, cut in the plane MN of Fig. B. In the middle is the stele, showing primary and secondary wood. *c'*, phloëm ; *d'*, inner, *e*, outer cortex ; *i'*, leaf-trace ; *l*, base of leaf ; *m*, axillary bud (?) ; *n*, cortical emergence below node. B. Transverse section of same stem, a little above node, showing six leaves surrounding stem. *a, b*, primary wood ; *tr*, proto-xylem ; *c*, secondary wood ; *c'*, phloëm ; *d, e*, cortex ; *f*, furrows ; *g, h*, leaves, each with four vascular bundles. C. Transverse section through a node, showing the forking leaf-trace bundles, *j, j*. Other lettering as before. A, B, C×9. D. Transverse section of a portion of secondary wood. *c*, tracheides ; *x*, parenchyma between them. The radial direction is vertical in this figure. × about 60. All after Renault.

this case the structure is clearly triarch, like that of so many roots ; such a structure is very rare in stems, though we find an example in the smaller branches of *Psilotum*. In some French species of *Sphenophyllum*, described by M. Renault, the protoxylem-groups are double,[1] so that here the wood may be described as hexarch, though the triangular sectional form is retained. In the young specimens but little remains of phloëm have been found ; the inner layers of the cortex are of delicate tissue, but towards the outside is a fibrous zone (Fig. 39). The external outline of the cortex, as seen in transverse section, is characteristic, for there are

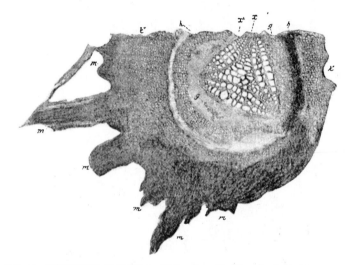

FIG. 39.—*Sphenophyllum plurifoliatum*. Transverse section through whorl of leaves. *m*, *x*, primary wood ; *x²*, secondary wood ; *g*, phloëm (?) ; *h*, periderm ; *k*, outer cortex × about 20. After Williamson, *Phil. Trans.* Will. Coll. 874.

usually three well-marked furrows, lying opposite the three flat sides of the triangular stele (see Fig. 38, B).

It is only in the most minute specimens that the primary structure just described is found unaltered.[2] At a very early stage the formation of secondary wood and bast, by means of a normal cambium, began (Fig. 39). The secondary wood possesses some very remarkable

---

[1] The scale of Fig. 38, B and C, is too small to show this point. Cf., however, Fig. 44, B.

[2] See Fig. 38, B and C, where only one layer of secondary wood is shown. Cf. Fig. 44, B.

characteristics. It consists of radial series of tracheae, of large size, with numerous bordered pits, chiefly on the radial cell-walls (Fig. 41). Between these tracheae, which, as seen in transverse section, appear square with truncated angles, we find little groups of thin-walled cells, fitting into the spaces at the corners (see Fig. 38, D).

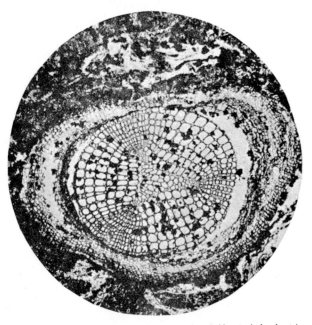

FIG. 40.—*Sphenophyllum plurifoliatum.* Transverse section of older stem, showing triangular primary wood, broad zone of secondary wood, remains of phloëm, and thick periderm ; primary cortex cast off.   ×18. From a photograph.   *Phil. Trans.*, W. and S. Will. Coll. 899.

These represent vertical strands of parenchyma, which are not isolated, but are connected with one another, in the radial direction, by horizontal cells or strands of cells, which are usually quite short, not forming continuous medullary rays (Figs. 38, D, and 41). This peculiar structure of the wood is found both in the English (Figs. 40 and 41) and in the French forms (Fig. 38, D), but is not common to the whole genus, as we shall see presently.

The elements of the wood are arranged with the greatest regularity (Fig. 40). There is a marked difference in size between the secondary elements found opposite the sides of the primary wood, and those corresponding to its angles ; the former are much the larger (see Fig. 40). In the small-celled wood opposite the angles there is an approach to the formation of continuous rays.

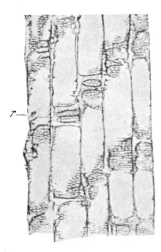

FIG. 41.—*Sphenophyllum plurifoliatum.* Radial section through part of secondary wood, showing pitted tracheides and parenchyma (*r*). × 50. *Phil. Trans.*, W. and S. Will. Coll. 884.

In the best-preserved specimens we find, immediately beyond the wood, the delicate tabular cells of the cambium itself, sometimes most distinctly shown, and beyond this we come to a zone of thin-walled radially-arranged tissue, which can only be interpreted as the phloëm (see Fig. 40).[1] Beyond this again, in older stems, lies a wide band of firmer tissue, also radially arranged, which we must regard as internal periderm (Fig. 40). If we examine a comparatively young stem of *Sphenophyllum*, we find, in many cases, a very distinct beginning of periderm-formation in the inner cortex (Fig. 39, *h*). In older stems, the primary cortex had been cast off altogether. Sometimes traces of its disorganised tissues remain, but ultimately the primary cortex was replaced by a regular scale-bark, formed by successive layers of periderm (Fig. 40). This formation cut deeper and deeper into the cortex, until it reached the phloëm itself, just as in an oak-tree, for example, at the present day. So it appears

---

[1] For more complete illustrations of the various tissues, see Williamson and Scott, *l.c.*

that the secondary tissue lying outside the wood consists in its inner part of the phloëm, and in its outer part of the periderm, which was formed by a phellogen, arising first in the cortex and afterwards in the phloëm itself.

The species *Sphenophyllum plurifoliatum* is based on petrified specimens ; it appears that in habit the plant must have closely resembled the contemporary *S. myriophyllum*, Crépin, known in the form of impressions. The species agree in the large number of linear leaves or leaf-segments in a verticil, and in the large diameter (about I cm.) attained by the main stems.[1]

I must now say something as to another form of *Sphenophyllum*, known by the name of *Sphenophyllum insigne*. This species was described by Dr. Williamson as long ago as 1874. It is a very interesting form, because it comes from some of the oldest Carboniferous strata, namely, from the Burntisland beds, belonging to the Calciferous Sandstone series, at a horizon far below the Coal-measures. In this species, the stem attains a diameter of almost a centimetre—a rather large size for a *Sphenophyllum*. In its general anatomy, the stem, which has been found at all stages of growth, is like that of the former species, but there are some not unimportant differences of detail. At each of the three angles of the primary wood is a canal, formed, no doubt, in consequence of the disorganisation of the protoxylem (Fig. 42). The tracheae generally have a scalariform sculpturing, instead of the numerous rows of bordered pits characteristic of other species. A still more important difference is the constant presence, in *S. insigne*, of continuous medullary rays, which replace the complicated system of vertical and radial parenchymatous strands in the species above described. In these latter points the Burntisland species differs, not only from *S. plurifoliatum*, but from all other species of *Sphenophyllum* of which the

[1] See Zeiller, *Bassin houiller de Valenciennes, flore fossile*, p. 422, Pl. lxii. Figs. 2-4.

structure is known. For these reasons, and because the older specimens, which have lost their primary cortex, present a very root-like appearance, several palaeobotanists disputed the identification of the fossil as a *Sphenophyllum*,

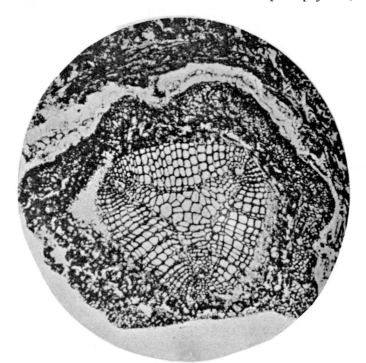

Fig. 42.—*Sphenophyllum insigne.* Transverse section of rather young stem, showing triangular primary wood, with a canal at each angle, marking the protoxylem, then secondary wood, remains of phloëm, and the primary cortex, showing two of the furrows. × about 30. From a photograph. *Phil. Trans.*, W. and S. Will. Coll. 919.

imagining that it might be a root of a Cycad or of some unknown plant. The discovery of younger plants, still retaining their cortex (Fig. 42) and nodes, and even portions of the leaves, has completely removed these doubts, and justified Williamson's original opinion.[1] The

[1] Williamson and Scott, *l.c.* p. 926. Williamson's original description is in Part v. of his " Organisation of the Fossil Plants of the Coal-measures," *Phil. Trans.* 1874.

same species has now been found in the Lower Carboniferous of Silesia, of an age comparable to that of the Scotch specimens. In some specimens of *Sphenophyllum insigne*, the phloëm is remarkably well preserved, and large elements, much resembling the sieve-tubes of some recent Cryptogams, are present.

It is a fact of interest that this, the oldest known *Sphenophyllum* with structure, presents a less peculiar organisation than the forms from later deposits. This fact would seem to indicate that the remarkable arrangement of the wood-parenchyma in the latter species is a later modification, and not a primitive character of the group. Although the near affinities of *S. insigne* with *Sphenophyllum* are now clearly established, it is possible that its anatomical characteristics may ultimately justify its *generic* separation.

Now that we have dealt sufficiently with the morphology and anatomy of the stem, the organisation of the leaves and roots remains to be considered, before going on to the organs of fructification. I have already mentioned that the leaves of *Sphenophyllum* are whorled, and that they vary very much in form, some being broad and wedge-shaped (the type of leaf from which the genus derives its name), while others are deeply divided, or even assume a very simple linear form. It appears to be the rule, that the number of leaves in a whorl was always some multiple of three, a fact which is no doubt correlated with the triarch or hexarch structure of the vascular cylinder. Six was perhaps the most usual number (see Fig. 38, B) ; but where the leaves were linear this number was considerably increased. In the Coal-measure species, *Sphenophyllum plurifoliatum*, the leaves in each verticil seem to have been eighteen, at least, on the larger stems (Fig. 39). The nodes from which the leaves spring are somewhat enlarged, and the vascular strands pass out almost horizontally (Fig. 38, A). As regards the course of the leaf-trace bundles, our information is chiefly due to M. Renault, who succeeded in working out this question in some of the French forms. In these species, as we have seen above, there are two distinct groups of spiral elements at each angle of the stele—six such groups in all. At the node, one bundle starts from each of these groups, dividing, as it passes through the cortex, into two, three, or four branches, which supplied the various veins of the leaf (Fig. 38, C). Further division of the bundles took place within the leaf itself, as it widened out, or divided into segments. Where the leaves were linear, the course of the bundles was the same, but in this case each leaf received a single strand only, as in the British species, *S. plurifoliatum.* Numerous vascular bundles, apparently equal in number to the leaves in a whorl, have been found in this species in the outer cortex of the node. They no doubt arose, here also, from the subdivision of a smaller number of strands, given off from the angles of the stele. The branching of the leaf-traces within the cortex is very characteristic of *Sphenophyllum.*

The anatomical structure of the leaf was fully worked out by Renault. The vascular bundles are small and simple, apparently of the concentric type. The tissue of the leaf was strengthened by bands of sclerenchyma, lying next the epidermis of the upper and lower surfaces The parenchyma is uniform throughout. There is thus nothing remarkable in the anatomy of the leaf, unless it be the strong mechanical construction, a point of some interest, for it seems to show that these leaves could not have been floating, as some botanists have assumed, though with but little reason. The narrow, unifascicular leaves or segments of *S. plurifoliatum* had a rather simpler structure.

The roots have also been investigated by Renault. The specimens which he examined were of diarch structure, with secondary wood, resembling that of the stem. Somewhat similar structures are occasionally found in association with the Burntisland *Sphenophyllum* (*S. insigne*), and with the Coal-measure species, *S. plurifoliatum*, and *S. fertile* (see p. 100), and were probably the roots of those species. As regards the insertion of the roots, we do not yet know the details, but they were no doubt borne on the nodes.

The Coal-measure specimens regarded as roots, are

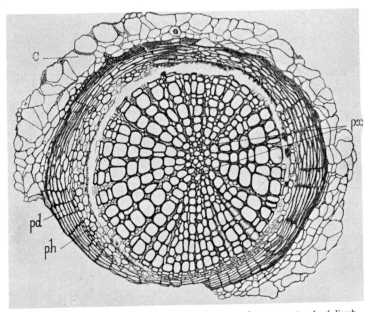

FIG. 43.—*Sphenophyllum*, sp.   Root, transverse.   *px*, protoxylem-groups at ends of diarch primary xylem ; *ph*, phloëm ; *pd*, periderm ; *C*, large cells of outer cortex.   × about 30.   S. Coll. 2533.   (G. T. G.)

distinguished from the stems by the simple structure or the cortex, and by the small size of the primary xylem, which is rarely triarch, and often diarch, or in some cases apparently tetrarch, with the protoxylem-groups in pairs at the ends of the short plate. A good example of an unusually fine root (about 3 mm. in diameter) is shown, in transverse section, in Fig. 43. The small xylem-plate is here diarch ; the secondary wood is well developed, and shows the usual structure, except that, as compared with the stem, the regions opposite the protoxylem-groups are little differentiated from the rest of the wood. The phloëm is well. preserved. A broad zone of internal periderm is present ; the surrounding cortex is remarkable for the layer of large peripheral cells, quite different from any tissue present in the stem. It is probable, however, that this conspicuous layer does not represent the original outer surface. It cannot be determined whether the specimens of this type belonged to *S. plurifoliatum* or *S. fertile*, as stems of both species occur in the same coal-balls. The roots associated with the Lower Carboniferous species, *S. insigne*, are of similar structure. In one case Dr. Gordon has found a root in direct connection with a node of the stem of this species, so that all doubt as to the attribution is removed.

2. *Fructifications of Sphenophyllum—S. Dawsoni Type.*
—We now come to the question of the fructification of *Sphenophyllum*, which shows considerable variety in different species. Our first accurate information, with regard to the fructification of the genus, depended on the observations of Williamson, who described in the greatest detail a fructification which has since been proved to be that of a species of *Sphenophyllum*, named provisionally *S. Dawsoni*. We are now, however, acquainted with five distinct types of fructification in *Sphenophyllum*, on which a subdivision of the genus has been proposed, though not adopted here.

We will begin with the description of the type of cone investigated by Williamson, with which, as Zeiller has shown, the fructifications of the well-known species *Sphenophyllum cuneifolium* agree in all essential respects.[1]

[1] Zeiller, " Étude sur la constitution de l'appareil fructificateur des Sphénophyllum," *Mém. de la Soc. géol. de France*. " Paléontologie," Mém. II, 1893.

The British specimens, which come from the calcareous nodules of the Lower Coal-measures, show the internal organisation in great perfection,[1] while those of the French observer, which are preserved in the form of impressions, give an excellent idea of the external characters, and afford the proof that these cones were really borne on *Sphenophyllum* stems. It appears that under the type-name *Sphenophyllum Dawsoni* two forms are included, the larger of which is probably identical, as M. Zeiller believed, with *S. cuneifolium*, while the smaller may represent the fructification of *S. plurifoliatum* (cf. *S. myriophyllum*). The following description applies, except when otherwise stated, to the larger species, which may be distinguished provisionally as the α form.

In external aspect, the cones, which reach a length of several inches, with a diameter of half an inch or more, are not unlike some of the Calamarian fructifications (see Fig. 36). The free surface of the cone is formed by the upturned tips of the whorled bracts. The arrangement of the organs, as shown in *Sphenophyllum Dawsoni*, and illustrated by the diagram, Fig. 44, A, is as follows : the cone has an axis 2-3 mm. in diameter, bearing at intervals numerous whorls of bracts ; the bracts of each verticil are coherent for a considerable distance from the axis, forming a kind of cup ; at the edge of the cup, the individual bracts become free from one another and turn vertically upwards, extending for a distance equal to several internodes, so that the tips of several successive

[1] Williamson first described his specimens under the name of *Volkmannia Dawsoni*, using a generic name of very indefinite signification, and subsequently called them *Bowmanites Dawsoni*. The name *Bowmanites* (a genus founded in 1871 by Binney) is still retained for fructifications of Sphenophylleae, but, as we have some evidence in this case as to the vegetative structure, it is simpler to call Williamson's specimens *Sphenophyllum Dawsoni*—a name which may turn out to be synonymous in part with *S. cuneifolium*. See Williamson, " On the Organisation of an undescribed Verticillate Strobilus, etc.," *Manchester Lit. and Phil. Soc.* 1871 ; " Organisation of Fossil Plants of the Coal-measures," Parts v. (1874) and xviii. (1891) ; Williamson and Scott, *l.c.*

verticils overlap each other (cf. Figs. 44, A, and 45).
The number of bracts in each whorl varies, ranging from
fourteen to about twenty in the cases where it was
possible to count them. It has not yet been decided

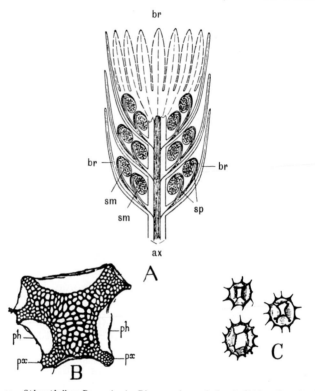

FIG. 44.—*Sphenophyllum Dawsoni.* A. Diagram of cone in longitudinal section, showing
three whorls. *ax*, axis; *br*, bracts; *sp*, sporangiophores; *sm*, sporangia; *br*, whorl
of bracts seen from the inside in surface view. (G. T. G.) B. Stele of axis, in transverse section. Wood only preserved. *px*, protoxylem-groups, of which there are six
in all; *ph*, remains of phloëm. × about 20. Will. Coll. 1049. C. Spores, in superficial
aspect. × about 100. B and C after Williamson, *Phil. Trans.*

for certain whether the bracts of successive whorls were
alternate or superposed; though the analogy of the
vegetative leaves would lead one to expect superposition,
the direct evidence is in favour of an alternate arrangement. The sporangia were borne singly on long pedicels

or sporangiophores, which sprang from the upper surface of each verticil of bracts in its united part, near the axis (Fig. 44, A, *sp*, Fig. 45, B and C). The pedicels are generally twice as numerous as the bracts; they are ranged in a single whorl, but are of unequal lengths, so that the sporangia of the same whorl overlap each other (Fig. 45). This gives the impression that more than one verticil of sporangiophores may spring from a single whorl of bracts, but this is not the case, though the point at which the sporangiophore becomes free from the bract is variable.

The pedicel is a slender stalk, becoming rather thicker near the top, where it bends over towards the axis of the cone, and bears a single pendulous sporangium. The position of the sporangium on its pedicel is much like that of an anatropous ovule in relation to its funiculus (cf. Figs. 44, A, 45, E, 46, and 47).

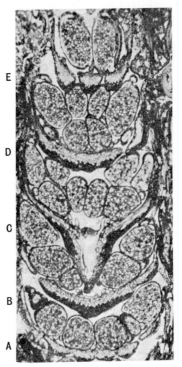

Fig. 45.—*Sphenophyllum Dawsoni, β.* Somewhat oblique longitudinal section of cone, mostly tangential, but passing through axis below C, where the bracts are connected with the axis. Five verticils (A-E) are shown. At B and D the bracts are connate; at A and E they have separated; at B and C the attachment of sporangiophores to bracts is shown; at E, especially to the right, the relation of sporangiophore to sporangium is very clear. × 9. From a photograph by Mr. Lomax. University College Collection, EE, i, c.

We have now gained some idea of the general morphology of the cone, the chief points in which are the gamophyllous verticils of sterile bracts, and the sporangiophores, twice as numerous as the bracts, springing from their upper surface, and bearing each a single pendulous sporangium at the end. The complex structure of the whole strobilus is well shown in the transverse section, Fig. 46, from one of Williamson's drawings, and in the longitudinal section, Fig. 45.

We will now go on to describe the structure more in detail. In some specimens of *S. Dawsoni* the axis is well preserved ; it is traversed by a triquetrous strand of solid wood, without pith (Fig. 44, B), like that of the vegetative stem in other species of the genus. It was this anatomical similarity which first led Williamson to regard his specimens as akin to *Sphenophyllum,* long before Zeiller's observations proved their identity. In *S. Dawsoni,* form *a,* the corners of the wood are truncated, or even widely forked, and there are two strands of primitive tracheae to each (Fig. 44, B, *px*), so that the whole stele is hexarch,[1] as in some French species. Associated with the cones of *S. Dawsoni,* a single fragment of a vegetative stem has been found, showing a primary structure just like that of the axis of the strobilus, but with the addition of a broad zone of secondary wood and bast. There can be little doubt that this specimen represents the vegetative stem of *Sphenophyllum Dawsoni,* form *a,* and if so, that species was evidently distinct from any other *Sphenophyllum* of which the structure is known, though probably identical with *S. cuneifolium.* In the smaller form (*β*) there is a slender, triarch xylem.

In the axis of the cone we find that the cortex, so far as it is preserved, resembles that of a young vegetative stem. The course of the vascular strands supplying the bracts and sporangiophores has been, to some extent, traced ; the bundles given off from the central cylinder underwent much subdivision in passing through the cortex, until they were equal in number to the bracts

---

[1] Owing to irregularities in the forking, the stele sometimes appears pentarch.

in a verticil. It is commonly the case that each of these strands, immediately on entering the verticil, divides

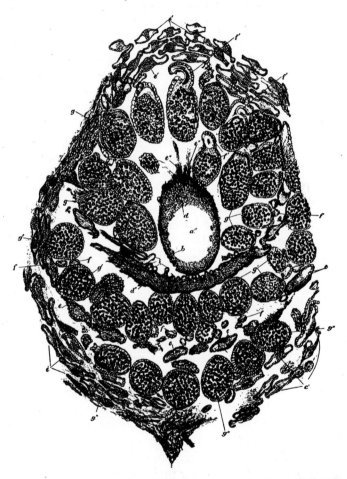

FIG. 46.—*Sphenophyllum Dawsoni,* a. Obliquely transverse section of cone, showing pιtιs of three whorls of bracts. *a″*, hollow axis (stele missing) ; *b, d,* cortex of axis ; *e, e′,* bracts cut at different levels ; *f,* sporangiophores, the innermost just springing from a whorl of bracts (*d″*) which are here coherent ; *f′,* sporangiophores in connection with their sporangia ; *g, g′, g″,* sporangia of the three whorls. × 7. After Williamson, *Phil. Trans.,* Will. Coll. 1049 B.

into three branches, one of which lies below the other two. The lower branch passes through the coherent whorl and out into the free tip of the bract to which it belongs ; the two upper branches of the strand pass out into the pedicels of the two sporangiophores corresponding to the bract in question (see Fig. 44, A, sp) ; where, however, the number of sporangiophores is less than double that of the bracts, as has been observed in the β form, the division of the bundles is less regular. In any case we see that by anatomy, as well as position, the sporangiophores are shown to be appendages of the bract from which they arise.

The bracts themselves are of simple structure (Figs. 45, 46) ; the epidermis contains stomata, similar to those of some Ferns. The slender vascular bundle extends right through the bract.

The sporangiophores either separated from the whorl of bracts as soon as the latter became free from the axis, or remained adherent for some distance to their upper surface ; the vascular strand in each sporangiophore traversed the whole length of the pedicel, increasing in thickness towards the top, and eventually ending suddenly at the base of the sporangium (see Fig. 46, f' ; Fig. 47). In the upper part of the pedicel, and especially where it bends over towards the axis, the epidermal cells are much enlarged, and these large cells of the pedicel are continuous with those that form the wall of the sporangium itself (Figs. 46 and 47). Towards the free end of the sporangium, the cells of the wall become much smaller, and it was probably at this end that dehiscence took place, the large cells perhaps performing the functions of an annulus. These cells were strengthened by buttresses projecting from their lateral cell-walls, much as in the sporangium of *Calamostachys*. The sporangium is seated, with a broad base, on the recurved end of the pedicel ; the sporangial wall in this region is lined by a delicate tissue (Fig. 47).

The spores were numerous in each sporangium, and so far as at present observed, were all of one kind, though rather variable in size. Their average diameter is about .09 mm. The spore-membrane shows a characteristic sculpturing, consisting essentially of prominent spines, connected together by a network of elevated ridges or wings (see Fig. 44, C).

The above description, based on the *Sphenophyllum Dawsoni* of Williamson, is now known to hold good, in all essential points, for *Sphenophyllum cuneifolium*, with which, indeed, the late M. Zeiller, to whom we are indebted for a minute comparison of the two cones, thought it identical ; this conclusion is probably correct as regards the larger form of *S. Dawsoni*. Several species, in addition to *S. cuneifolium*, were examined by M. Zeiller, and in these also he was able to show that the sporangia were borne on pedicels, arising from the upper surface of the bracts.

This also seems to have been the case in *S. charaeforme*, Jongmans, in which no distinct cones are differentiated.

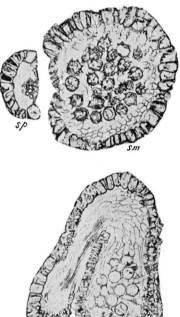

FIG. 47.—*Sphenophyllum Dawsoni.* Sporangiophore and its sporangium, shown in transverse section above, and in longitudinal section (somewhat oblique) below. *sp*, sporangiophore ; *sm*, sporangium, containing spores. × 45. *Phil. Trans.*, W. and S. Will. Coll. 1898, H. and E.

So many specimens of *S. Dawsoni*, all showing spores of the same kind, have now been investigated that there is little doubt that these cones were homosporous. A specimen described many years ago by M. Renault, and supposed to show heterospory, is now admitted to have been wrongly interpreted; the structure which was formerly regarded as a megaspore is in reality nothing but a fragment of tissue, probably forming part of the wall of a sporangium.

The occurrence of spores of somewhat different dimensions in adjacent sporangia (averaging .083 mm. in one sporangium, and .106 mm. in another), those of the larger size being accompanied by minute, presumably abortive spores, has been interpreted as a possible indication of incipient heterospory.[1]

Zobel has described a condition in *S. verticillatum* which he interprets as indicating heterospory. He finds, in different cones, sporangia of two kinds. In the one case the sporangia are only about 0.5 mm. in diameter, and numerous (about 20) in each verticil; in the other, they are 1 mm. in diameter, and apparently seated singly on each of the six sporophylls of a whorl. This is an interesting observation, but at present only one kind of spore has been detected, so the evidence for heterospory is unconvincing.[2] The specimens are preserved as carbonised impressions.

3. *Bowmanites Römeri, Sphenophyllum fertile, S. majus, and S. trichomatosum.*—Shortly after Zeiller's discovery the investigations of Solms-Laubach made us acquainted with a fructification, of the *Sphenophyllum* type, which differs in important respects from those already described The author named his specimen *Bowmanites Römeri*,[3] using the generic name *Bowmanites* to include all fructifications referable to the family Sphenophylleae.[4] This

---

[1] Thoday, *New Phytologist*, vol. v., April 1906.

[2] Zobel, in Potonié's "*Abbildungen u. Beschreibungen foss. Pflanzen*," Lief. vii. (1916), No. 138.

[3] "*Bowmanites Römeri*, eine neue Sphenophylleen-Fruktifikation," *Jahrbuch der k. geolog. Reichsanstalt*, Vienna, 1895.

[4] The appropriate but, as the author allows, sesquipedalian name, *Sphenophyllostachys*, has been introduced by Prof. Seward in the same sense.

nomenclature is the most suitable in this case, for, in the absence of any vegetative organs, we cannot be certain that the specimen belonged to a member of the genus *Sphenophyllum*, though most probably this was the case. *Bowmanites Römeri* is at present only known from a single fragment, happily very well preserved, from the Coal-measures of Cracow. The axis is not present, but the arrangement and structure of the bracts and sporangia have been made clear by the researches of the discoverer. The bracts are in whorls, and those

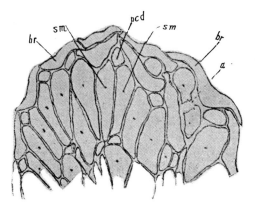

FIG. 48.—*Bowmanites Römeri.* Part of transverse section of cone. *br,* bracts ; *pcd,* pedicel of sporangiophore ; *sm,* the two sporangia belonging to it. At *a* the lamina of a sporangiophore is shown. × 10. After Solms-Laubach.

of each whorl are united towards the base, though not for so long a distance as in *Sphenophyllum Dawsoni* ; the bracts are directed steeply upwards, and several successive verticils overlap each other. In this case it seems to be proved that the members of successive whorls were superposed, like the foliage-leaves of *Sphenophyllum*. The structure of the bracts is similar to that in *S. Dawsoni* ; each is traversed by a single vascular bundle. (See Fig. 48, for an outline transverse section of half the strobilus.)

The point of chief interest is the position of the

sporangia, two of which were borne on each sporangiophore. The pedicel expanded at the top into a scale
of considerable size (Fig. 49, A), from which the two
sporangia hung down side by side, towards the axis of

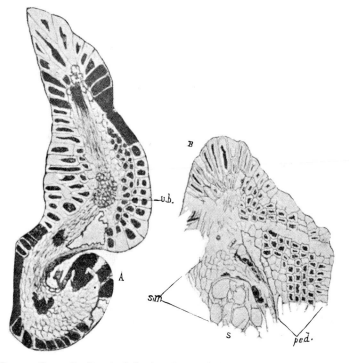

FIG. 49.—*Bowmanites Römeri.* A. Lamina of sporangiophore, cut nearly parallel to its
upper surface, and above the insertion of the sporangia. *v.b.,* vascular bundle. B.
Longitudinal section through upper part of sporangiophore, showing insertion of sporangium. *ped,* pedicel; *sm,* part of sporangium; *s,* spores. × about 60. After Solms-
Laubach.

the cone.[1] It appears that the pedicels in this species
were short, and that they were arranged in three concentric verticils, on each whorl of bracts — another
apparent difference from *Sphenophyllum Dawsoni.* The

---

[1] In the transverse section (Fig. 48) the pairs of sporangia (*sm*) are'
shown, with the pedicel (*ped*) between the two sporangia, and on their
outer side.

pedicel, which much resembles a sterile bract in structure, is traversed by a vascular bundle, which, where it enters the scale at the top, divides into two branches to supply the two sporangia (Fig. 49, A). The anatomical structure of the sporangiophore, allowing for the greater size and complication associated with the presence of two sporangia instead of one, closely resembles that of *Sphenophyllum Dawsoni* (Fig. 49). The sporangium has a wall several cells in thickness ; in *S. Dawsoni* this is only the case at the base, but the difference may be merely a matter of preservation. The spores in each sporangium are numerous, and closely resemble those of *Sphenophyllum Dawsoni*, the resemblance extending to the most minute details of structure of the spore-membrane.

There can be no doubt that this discovery of Count Solms-Laubach's threw a great light on the morphology of *Sphenophyllum*. In particular, the structure of the complex sporangiophores, each bearing two sporangia, showed that these organs cannot be regarded as mere sporangial stalks, but that they are rather comparable to the peltate scales of the Equisetales. At the same time, their structure and position go far to confirm Zeiller's opinion that the sporangiophores of Sphenophylleae may be interpreted as ventral lobes of the leaf, the bract itself representing the dorsal lobe. On all these points much further light has been thrown by the more recent discovery of other new types of fructification, now to be described.

A well-preserved fructification (*Sphenophyllum fertile*, Scott [1]) from the Lower Coal-measures of Shore Little-borough, in Lancashire, resembles *Bowmanites Römeri* in having peltate, bisporangiate sporangiophores, but is peculiar in the fact that both the dorsal and ventral lobes of the sporophyll are fertile ; the sterile bracts,

---

[1] Scott, " On a New Type of Sphenophyllaceous Cone (*S. fertile*) from the Lower Coal-measures," *Phil. Trans. Roy. Soc.* B, vol. 198, 1905.

which in other Sphenophyllaceous strobili represent the dorsal lobes, are here replaced by additional sporangiophores. The sporophyll is also more complex than in other species, its lobes, both dorsal and ventral, dividing in a palmate manner into several branches, each of which constitutes a sporangiophore (Fig. 50). The anatomy of the axis of the cone is in all respects that of a typical *Sphenophyllum*, so that in this case there can be no doubt as to the attribution of the fructification. The vegetative stem has also been identified; it differs from

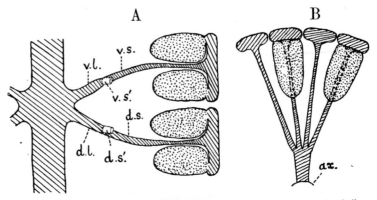

FIG. 50.—*Sphenophyllum fertile*. Diagram A. Node in radial section, showing one sporophyll. *v.l.*, ventral lobe; *v.s.*, a ventral sporangiophore bearing two sporangia; *v.s.'*, stump of another sporangiophore; *d.l.*, *d.s.*, *d.s.'*, corresponding dorsal parts. B. One lobe of sporophyll, as seen in a transverse section of the cone. *ax*, axis. On two of the sporangiophores a sporangium is shown. From Scott, *Phil. Trans*.

that of *S. plurifoliatum*, chiefly in the absence of any marked cortical furrows.

It is only in a few cases, of which the three types already described are the chief, that the preservation of structure enables us to clearly understand the organisation of Sphenophyllaceous strobili. Specimens preserved only as carbonaceous impressions may, however, afford suggestive indications, and suffice to show that, within the limits of what we call the genus *Sphenophyllum*, there must have been great variety in the fructification. In *S. majus*, for example, and probably in *S. tenuissimum*,

Kidston, there are no distant cones, but the fertile parts of the stem are both preceded and followed by regions bearing the ordinary foliage. The doubly forked bracts resemble certain forms of the sterile leaves. The sporangia are usually grouped in fours, each group resting on the upper surface of the bract, below the first bifurcation (Fig. 51). In *S. trichomatosum*,[1] on the other hand, the arrangement seems to have been a very simple one, the sporangia appearing to be sessile and solitary on each bract a little beyond the axil. It is quite possible,

Fig. 51.—*Sphenophyllum majus*. Forked sporophyll bearing four sporangia. After Kidston.

however, that a short pedicel was present. We thus know of five types of fructification; namely, those of *S. Dawsoni, Bowmanites Römeri, S. fertile, S. majus*, and *S. trichomatosum*.

It follows sufficiently, from what has already been said, that *Sphenophyllum* represents a perfectly distinct group of plants, of which all the parts—stem, leaves, roots, and fructification—are known in one species or another. There is no longer any room for the idea, once sanctioned by good palaeobotanical authorities, that

[1] I am indebted to my friend Dr. R. Kidston, F.R.S., for information as to these species. On *Sphenophyllum trichomatosum*, see Dr. Kidston's paper in *Proc. Royal Phys. Soc. of Edinburgh*, vol. ii. 1891, and on *S. majus* and other species, his Carboniferous Lycopods and Sphenophylls, *Trans. Nat. Hist. Soc. Glasgow*, vol. vi. Part i. 1899-1900; also " Végétaux houillers dans le Hainaut Belge," p. 222, Brussels, 1911; and " Fossil Flora of Staffordshire Coal Fields," Part iii. *Trans. Royal Soc. Edinburgh*, vol. l. Part i. p. 129 ; 1914.

Sphenophyllum might represent the foliage of some of the Calamites. This mistake arose from the fact that the finely-divided or linear form of foliage, often occurring in species of *Sphenophyllum*, sometimes bears a great external resemblance to the foliage of the branches known as *Asterophyllites*, which really belonged to Calamitean stems. This resemblance may easily lead to confusion, in cases where we have to deal with imperfect specimens without structure, but of course it proves nothing as to any connection between the two groups of plants. External characters of the foliage are as unsafe a guide among fossil as among recent plants. If the genus *Galium* had existed in Carboniferous times, we should no doubt have often been puzzled to distinguish its remains from those of *Sphenophyllum* or of *Calamites*. It is the specimens with their structure preserved which give the only safe clue to the interpretation of the rest. The discussion of the affinities of *Sphenophyllum* will best be postponed until the next family has been considered.

II. CHEIROSTROBEAE

4. *Cheirostrobus.*—This very distinct type of strobilus was originally described from a single specimen of the actual cone, and another fragment containing the peduncle. The specimens, of which a few more have since come to light, were derived from the famous deposit at Pettycur, on the Firth of Forth, belonging to the Calciferous Sandstone series, at the base of the Carboniferous formation. The fossil is therefore of great antiquity, and is, in fact, older than any of the *Sphenophyllum* fructifications already described. It occurs side by side with the stems of *Sphenophyllum insigne*, from which, however, it differs so much in structure as to preclude all idea of any connection between them.

The structure is admirably preserved, so that the whole organisation of the strobilus could be worked out, though unfortunately nothing is known for certain as to the vegetative organs on which it was borne. The cone was a large one—from 3.5 cm. to 4 cm. in diameter,

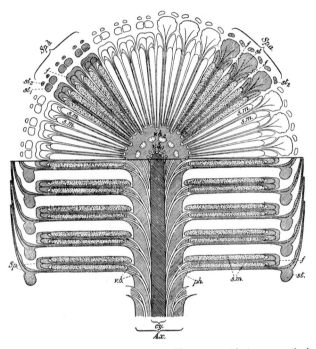

Fig. 52.—*Cheirostrobus pettycurensis*. Diagram. The upper part in transverse, the lower in radial section ; the position of the organs corresponds in the two sections.

1. Transverse section. Six complete sporophylls, each with three segments, are shown. *Sp.a.*, section passing through *sterile* segments ; *Sp.b.*, do. through *fertile* segments or sporangiophores ; *st*, lamina of sterile segment ; st_1, downward outgrowths of sterile laminae, cut transversely ; st_2, their apices, transverse ; *f*, peltate sporangiophores ; *sm*, sporangia. Note that in *Sp.a.* each peltate lamina, *f*, is seen in two distinct lobes, with the sterile lamina between. $v.b._1$, $v.b._2$, vascular bundles of two whorls.

2. Radial section. The sporophylls are separated from one another for clearness' sake ; in nature they are in close contact. *Ax.*, axis of cone ; *cy*, its stele ; *ph*, base of sporophyll. Other lettering as in transverse section. The diagram is true to nature as regards proportions of parts, as well as their relative position. × about 2. *Phil. Trans.*, S.

and certainly exceeding 10 cm. in length. Its whole organisation is exhibited in the diagrammatic sections in Fig. 52. The axis, about 7 mm. thick, bore numerous crowded verticils of modified leaves or sporophylls, of which there were about twelve in each whorl, the number diminishing towards the apex ; the members of successive whorls were accurately superposed in vertical series, as in *Sphenophyllum*. The sporophylls were compound, and indeed remarkably elaborate in form and structure, so much so as to differ widely from any other organs to which the name is applied. The important point is, that in *Cheirostrobus* each sporophyll was subdivided in two planes ; immediately above its base it branched into an inferior and a superior lobe, while at the same time both lobes subdivided, in a palmate manner, into segments. The total number of segments was usually six, of which three belonged to the lower lobe and three to the upper, the latter lying directly above the former (see diagram, Fig. 52). The sporophyll attained a length of 1.4 cm. or more, almost the whole of which was occupied by the free segments, for the common basal portion was quite short. The general direction of the whole organ was horizontal (see diagram, Fig. 52). The segments of each sporophyll were of two kinds, the one set fertile, bearing the sporangia, the other sterile ; the three superior segments were the fertile sporangiophores, while the three inferior members were sterile bracts.[1] The two kinds of segments resemble each other in their stalks, which are long and slender in both, but differ in the form of the laminae in which they terminate at their distal extremities.

The fertile segments or sporangiophores had each a thick peltate lamina, much like that of an *Equisetum* or *Calamostachys*, bearing four sporangia on its inner side (see Fig. 52, *f*, and Fig. 53, *s*). The sporangia were of great length, extending inwards as far as the axis, parallel to the stalks of the segments, between which they were closely packed (Fig. 52). The sterile segments or bracts were slightly longer than the sporangiophores,

[1] This latter point was not determined without difficulty, as the same segment can rarely be traced from end to end, but is now settled beyond doubt.

so that their laminae overlapped those of the latter. The packing was so close that the fertile laminae were grooved above and below to allow the sterile pedicels to pass through (Fig. 52, *Sp.a, f*). The sterile lamina was itself a complex structure, for it divided into two apical prongs, directed almost vertically upwards, while it was prolonged below into two shorter and stouter outgrowths

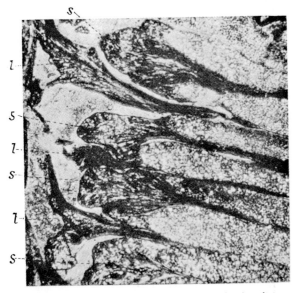

FIG. 53.—*Cheirostrobus pettycurensis.* Part of radial section, showing the peltate sporangiophores, *s*, with the foliaceous sterile segments, *l*, between them. The lowest sterile segment shows the form of the lamina well. The sporangia are seen to the right. × about 10. *Phil. Trans.*, S. Kidston Coll. 87.

(Fig. 53, *l*, and Fig. 52, *st*). The whole external surface of the cone was thus effectually protected by this complex system of overlapping laminae. We see then that the complete sporophyll consisted of three lower sterile segments and three sporangiophores above them, each of which bore four sporangia, so that the sporophyll as a whole produced no less than twelve sporangia. As there were eleven or twelve such sporophylls in a verticil, and the verticils were very numerous, the total production of

sporangia by a cone of *Cheirostrobus* must have been
on a great scale. In each sporangium a vast number
of spores were produced, which were all of one kind, so
far as the few known specimens show.

It remains for us to describe the anatomical structure
of the strobilus. Its axis was traversed by a central

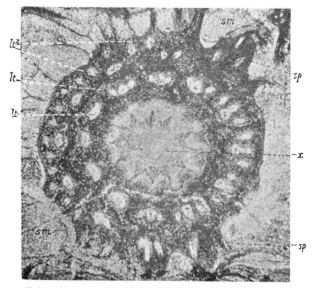

Fig. 54.—*Cheirostrobus pettycurensis.* Transverse section of axis of cone. *x,* xylem with
twelve prominent angles ; *l.t.,* leaf-traces, one undivided, the other divided into three ;
l.t.², leaf-trace, already divided into four bundles, and the inner one subdividing ; *sp,*
bases of sporophylls ; *sm,* inner part of sporangia. × about 8. *Phil. Trans.,* S. Kidston
Coll. 84 A.

cylinder ; the wood, which is alone preserved, had a
stellate transverse section, with about twelve prominent
angles, corresponding in number and position to the
vertical series of sporophylls (Fig. 54, *x*). At these
angles the spiral elements are placed, so the development
of the wood ·was evidently centripetal,[1] as in *Sphenophyllum* or in the Lycopodiaceae. The rest of the
tracheae bear multiseriate bordered pits, as is commonly

---

[1] There is some evidence that a minute amount of primary xylem
was developed centrifugally.

the case in *Sphenophyllum*. There was no pith, the wood extending to the centre of the stele, though intermixed with conjunctive parenchyma.

The cortex presents no points worth special notice, except that it contained long sacs, perhaps of a secretory nature. The course of the leaf-trace bundles, however, is highly characteristic. They start from the angles of the stele, as simple vascular strands, each of which ultimately supplies one sporophyll. When about one-third of the way through the cortex the trace divides into three bundles, a median and two smaller lateral strands (see *triple* bundle *lt* in Fig. 54). A little further out the median bundle branches again, but this time in a plane at right angles to the first division, so that one of its branches lies above and inside the other (see Fig. 54, on right ;[1] also diagram, . Fig. 52, *v.b.*). The upper median bundle next divides into three, just as the main strand had previously done, so that now there are six bundles altogether, constituting each leaf-trace, three above and three below ; all six enter the base of the sporophyll, and pass out into its segments, the three upper strands supplying the three sporangiophores, while the lower three enter the sterile leaflets (Fig. 52).

The bundle of the sporangiophore, on reaching its peltate lamina, divides into four branches, which run out to the bases of the four sporangia (Fig. 52, *f*). In the sterile lamina the vascular strand divides into two, which enter the two apical points.

The vascular system was thus a highly complex one, corresponding to the great elaboration of the external organisation. Each of the four sporangia of a fertile segment is connected with the peltate lamina by a neck of tissue (Fig. 53, *s*), into which the vascular bundle enters, ending at the base of the sporangium itself. The wall of the latter, which in its actual state of preservation

---

[1] The reference-line to *x* crosses the median bundles of the trace referred to.

is only one cell thick, consists of long cells, with their lateral membranes stiffened by buttresses, precisely as in a *Calamostachys*. A similar structure occurs, as we have seen, in *Sphenophyllum Dawsoni*. The spores have an average diameter of .065 mm. ; their outer membrane is ridged, the ridges apparently corresponding to the lines of junction of the four sister-cells. The specimens known are too few to afford decisive evidence as to whether the plant was homosporous or heterosporous ; it is worth noting, however, that the sporangia at the base of the cone show no difference from those borne near the apex, as regards the dimensions of their spores. The peduncle much resembles the axis of the cone itself, but in the peduncle well-marked secondary tissues are present, which in places are well preserved, so as to show the phloëm, and even remains of the cambium, as well as the secondary wood, in which medullary rays can be recognised, separating the rows of tracheae. In one specimen of the cone slight secondary growth had also taken place in the axis.

The cone of *Cheirostrobus pettycurensis* is perhaps the most complex Cryptogamic fructification at present known to us, and it is a striking fact that it should occur at so ancient an horizon as the base of the Carboniferous formation. But, highly modified as it is, *Cheirostrobus* bears the impress of great antiquity in the fact that it is a synthetic type, combining the characters of different groups of plants. In its peltate sporangiophores, and in the insertion and details of structure of its sporangia, *Cheirostrobus* agrees closely with the Calamarieae. In the anatomy of the stele it presents some analogies with a Lycopod, of the type of *Lepidodendron*, as we shall see in the next chapter. Whatever the value of these resemblances may be, there is no doubt that *Cheirostrobus* shows the most marked affinities with the Sphenophylleae, as indicated by the following characters : the arrangement of the appendages in superposed verticils, the palmatifid segmentation of the leaves (sporophylls), the repeated branching of the leaf-traces within the cortex, and the relation of the sporangiophores to the sterile segments or bracts. In *Cheirostrobus* it is evident that the sporangiophores are ventral or superior segments of the same leaf of which the sterile bracts are the dorsal or inferior segments. The same relation holds good for *Sphenophyllum Dawsoni*, and still more clearly for *Bowmanites Römeri*, where the homology between sporangiophores and bracts is patent. In fact, this latter species occupies, in this respect, exactly an intermediate position between *Sphenophyllum Dawsoni* and *Cheirostrobus*. *Sphenophyllum fertile*, in which both dorsal and ventral segments are fertile, resembles *Cheirostrobus* in their palmatifid branching. The course of the vascular bundles supplying the sporangiophores and bracts is essentially the same in *Sphenophyllum* and *Cheirostrobus*, though necessarily more complex in the latter. The stelar structure of *Cheirostrobus* may be regarded as an elaboration of the *Sphenophyllum* type.

The general conclusion, to which the various characters point, is that *Cheirostrobus* has more in common with *Sphenophyllum* than with any other group of plants at present known, and that, though the former genus must constitute the type of a distinct family, it is most naturally placed in the same main division of Cryptogams, which we may call the Sphenophyllales. At the same time, *Cheirostrobus* [1] undoubtedly approaches the Equisetales, especially *Calamostachys*, in certain characters, and thus confirms the hypothesis of an affinity between that class and the Sphenophyllales. The anatomical analogies with the Lycopods appear to be of much less significance. The general question of the relationships of these groups will be considered in the concluding chapter of the book.

[1] A fuller account of the organisation of *Cheirostrobus* is given in my " Structure and Affinities of Fossil Plants from the Palaeozoic Rocks," Part i. On *Cheirostrobus*, *Phil. Trans.* vol. 189, B, 1897.

III. Pseudoborniales

5. *Pseudobornia.*—Professor Nathorst has described a remarkable type of plant, from the Upper Devonian of Bear Island in the Arctic Ocean, which may belong to the same stock with the Sphenophyllales. *Pseudobornia ursina* [1] is only known at present in the form of impressions, but the external characters are shown in great perfection. The main stems, believed to have been creeping, attain a diameter of about 10 cm. in their present flattened condition. The stem was articulated and branched ; the smaller branches still bear the whorled leaves, of which there appear to have been four in a verticil. The leaves are compound, dividing by repeated dichotomy into several leaflets, each of which is deeply pinnatifid, with numerous fine segments. The isolated leaves were formerly supposed to belong to some unknown group of Ferns. The fructification is in the form of long, lax spikes, bearing whorled sporophylls which resemble reduced vegetative leaves. In the sporangia, borne on the lower part of each sporophyll, indications of probable megaspores have been traced.

Professor Nathorst makes this striking plant the type of a distinct class, the Pseudoborniales, showing affinity with the Sphenophyllales, as well as with *Archaeocalamites* among the Equisetales. The complexity of the leaves suggests a comparison with the compound sporophylls of *Cheirostrobus*, of which the vegetative organs are still unknown, though the fructification of *Pseudobornia* does not favour any near affinity. In *Pseudobornia* we appear to have a new and impressive representative of that ancient synthetic race of plants of which the Sphenophyllales have, until now, formed the only known examples.

---

[1] A. G. Nathorst, " Zur oberdevonischen Flora der Bären-Insel," *Svenska Vetenskaps-Akademiens Handlingar*, Bd. 36, No. 3, Stockholm, 1902.

CHAPTER V

LYCOPODIALES

Lepidodendron and Lepidophloios

WE now come to another of the great divisions of Vascular Cryptogams, that of the Lycopods, or Clubmosses. Here, just as in the case of the Equisetales with which we began, our object, as students of fossil botany, is to extend and deepen our knowledge of a group already more or less familiar to us from our experience of recent plants. We shall find that, as regards the Lycopodiales also, our idea of the Class will become a much more adequate one, when we have made ourselves acquainted with its ancient representatives.

The recent Lycopods are all, in one direction or another, highly specialised forms, with the possible exception of *Phylloglossum*, and even with respect to *Phylloglossum* we are left in much doubt whether its simple organisation may not be due to reduction, rather than to the persistence of primitive characters.

In *Lycopodium* itself, while the external characters are simple enough, we find a singularly complex anatomy of the stem, very different from that of any other plants,[1] and evidently much modified along peculiar lines of its ow .

Selaginella, in a few species (*e.g. S. spinosa*), has a simple and probably primitive anatomical structure, but in a great majority of the forms this has become much elaborated ; in a large part of the genus the dimorphic foliage is another mark of specialisation.

[1] See, however, *Asteroxylon*, Chap. X. pp. 397, 412.

The genus *Isoëtes* is clearly a reduced form, and differs in so many points from the rest of the Lycopods, that some doubt has even been cast on its affinity with them, and it is largely by a comparison with fossil types that its position has been re-established.

The Psiloteae, as we shall see in the concluding chapter, appear, in the light of our present knowledge, to be remote from the true Lycopods, and possibly to show affinity with the Sphenophyllales, or, as some authorities hold, to be far more primitive than either.

Broadly speaking, then, we may say that the representatives of the Class now living consist of a number of specialised forms, from which it is not easy to form an idea of the primitive characters of the common stock. The Palaeozoic Lycopods throw a new and welcome light on the problem.   They were not, it is true, simple forms ; like so many other Cryptogams of early periods, they attained in some respects a much higher grade of organisation than their living representatives.   Yet, in the ground plan of their structure, the fossil forms probably give us a better idea of the essential characters of the group than any of their recent allies.

1. *Habit.*—We will begin with the great genus *Lepidodendron*, of which more than a hundred so-called species have been described, according to their external characters. The genus has a wide geological range, first recorded from the Devonian, attaining its maximum in the Carboniferous period, and dying out, according to our present knowledge, in the Permian. These plants somewhat resembled in habit the *Lycopodia* of the present day, but enormously exceeded them in dimensions, growing into large trees, of which trunks a hundred feet long have been found.[1]   The main stem was vertical, rising to a

---

[1] Mr. Lomax, in 1910, discovered a gigantic stem of a *Lepidodendron* in the Arley Seam at Chequerbent, near Bolton.   The trunk, up to the first branching, was 114 feet in length, and from this point the remains of the leafy branches extended for about another 20 feet.

great height before the crown of branches was reached (see restoration, Fig. 55). The ramification was con-

Fig. 55.—*Lepidodendron elegans.* Restoration of tree, bearing cones. After Grand'Eury, modified.

stantly dichotomous; the two limbs of the dichotomy were sometimes equal, as in the forking of the main branches, but were often very unequal; in the latter case the relatively main shoots formed a sympodium, the smaller members of the successive dichotomies simulating lateral branches (Fig. 55).   The whole system of ramification was thus an exceedingly complex one, built up of

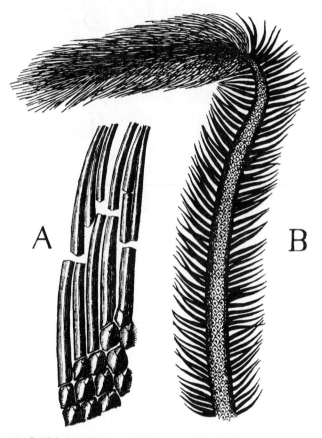

Fig. 56.—*Lepidodendron Ophiurus*.   A. Fragment of stem-surface, showing leaf-bases and leaves.   B. Leafy branch, bearing a cone at its extremity.   Nat. size.   After Zeiller.

branches of many degrees, and differing much from each other, not only in size, but in structure—a fact which is of great importance in dealing with the comparative anatomy of trunks and twigs.

The young stems and branches were densely clothed with numerous simple leaves of acicular or linear form (Fig. 56), and sometimes of great length, amounting in certain cases to as much as 6 or 7 inches. The phyllotaxis was either a close spiral with some very complex divergence, such as $\frac{8\,9}{2\,3\,3}$, or consisted of a system of whorls, the members of successive whorls having themselves a complicated spiral arrangement.

When the leaves were shed, their bases remained

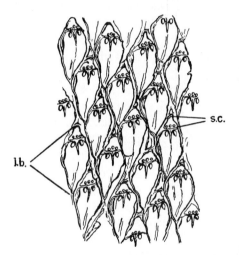

FIG. 57.—*Lepidodendron Veltheimianum.* Portion of surface of stem, showing the leaf-bases (*l.b.*), with the leaf-scar (*s.c.*) at the upper end of each. ¾ nat. size.

attached to the surface of the stem, forming the leaf-cushions (Fig. 56, A), which were persistent even on the larger trunks. It is chiefly on the superficial characters presented by this armature of leaf-cushions (Fig. 57) that the distinction of species has been founded. It will be well to describe in some detail the essential features of the persistent leaf-base.

The leaf-cushions are either packed together quite closely and separated only by narrow grooves (Fig. 57), or more scattered, with wider flat bands of the stem-surface exposed between them. The whole cushion is rhombic in outline, and somewhat prominent, having a flatly pyramidal form. The apex of the pyramid is truncated, forming a flat surface, which' represents the scar left by the fall of the leaf (see Fig. 58, *s.c.*). Thus the actual scar only occupies a small part of the whole rhombic area, most of which is formed by the persistent leaf-cushion. The whole is not symmetrical, for the leaf-scar always lies near the upper end of the cushion. On the flat surface of the scar itself, three marks or prints are seen, all of which lie in a horizontal line, towards the

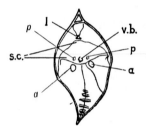

FIG. 58.—*Lepidodendron.* Leaf-base. *s.c.*, leaf-scar ; *v.b.*, print of bundle ; *p*, double parichnos ; *a*, superficial prints on either side of cushion ; *l*, ligule. Figs. 54 and 55 after Stur.

lower edge of the scar. The anatomy of specimens with their structure preserved has shown that, of these three marks, the median one alone represents the vascular bundle, which originally passed out into the leaf. The two lateral scars, as we shall see presently, represent parenchymatous strands ; together they bear the name of the *parichnos.*

Besides the marks on the actual scar, there are others on the surface of the leaf-cushion. The most conspicuous of these are two large round prints or depressions below the scar, lying one on each side of the prominent angle of the pyramidal cushion (see Fig. 58, *a*). These, as is shown by anatomical investigation, were connected internally with the parichnos.

Immediately above the scar, and in the median line of the cushion, is a small triangular print (Fig. 58, *l*), which has been proved to mark the position of the *ligule* ; in *Lepidodendron* this organ was constantly present on the upper side of the leaf-base, as in the genera *Selaginella* and *Isoëtes* at the present day.

Other marks are sometimes found on the leaf-cushions, but those already described are the most constant and important.

The above description is based on the most perfect specimens preserved as *casts, i.e.* with the surface showing its natural form. Where, as is often the case, the specimen represents a " mould " of the exterior, the depressions and elevations are, of course, reversed.

We have a curious illustration of the difficulties of nomenclature in fossil botany, in the fact that distinct genera have been founded on specimens which are now known to represent merely imperfect states of preservation of various *Lepidodendra.* Thus, when the epidermis had been lost before fossilisation, some of the characteristic markings disappear, or change their form, and we get the so-called genus *Bergeria.* If the destruction had gone a little deeper, removing the outer layers of cortex, the leaf-trace is the only print that remains, and that now lies in the middle of each rhombic area, giving rise to the form called *Aspidiaria.* Lastly, where the whole bark of an old stem had been stripped off, a totally different appearance is produced, resembling an irregularly fluted column. The inclined, overlapping ridges here correspond to the course of the leaf-trace bundles through the middle cortex, and on this state of preservation the genus *Knorria* has, in part at least, been founded.[1]

Leaving these false genera, which are only of botanical interest in so far as they illustrate the difficulties of the subject, we pass on to a group of fossils which are really distinct from, though closely allied to, *Lepidodendron.* This is the genus *Lepidophloios,* typically characterised by the form of the scale-like, overlapping leaf-cushions, which are in most cases transversely elongated, the hori-

[1] Illustrations of these forms of preservation will be found in Solms-Laubach's *Fossil Botany,* English edition, Figs. 19 and 20.

zontal diameter exceeding the vertical[1] (Fig. 65, p. 139). The leaf-scar, which bears the usual three prints, is also, as a rule, elongated in the horizontal direction, and of rhomboidal or oval form. Another peculiarity is, that in *Lepidophloios* the leaf-cushions are very prominent, with the pyramidal form much more marked than in *Lepidodendron* (see Fig. 71, B, p. 151). It appears that the leaf-scar was placed towards the upper side of the cushion in the younger specimens, but that the leaf-bases bent downwards in the older stems, bringing the scar to a lower level (cf. Fig. 66, p. 141). *Lepidophloios* is of interest, though differing so slightly from *Lepido-dendron*, because some of the specimens with structure certainly belonged to it, as did also some of the forms to be described further on, in which the probable position of the fructifications or of deciduous branches on the stems has been determined. So far as is known, however, there is no constant difference in internal structure between *Lepidophloios* and *Lepidodendron*, and in dealing with the anatomy, the latter name will usually be employed, treating *Lepidophloios*, for our present purpose, as a subgenus.

2. *Stem.*—We have now a very considerable mass of material for the study of the internal structure of Lepidodendreae, and of this material the greater part has been derived from the British Carboniferous rocks. Our knowledge of the anatomy of the group is chiefly due to the researches of Williamson, who worked out and described the anatomy of no less than nine distinct forms of the group, though some of these are better known than others. The Continental strata have so far yielded comparatively few specimens of *Lepidodendron*, with structure preserved, so our description will be chiefly based on the British fossils.

[1] See Kidston, "On the British Species of the Genus *Lepidophloios*," *Trans. Roy. Soc. Edinburgh*, vol. xxxvii. 1893.

The great anatomical feature, which is common to all known stems of *Lepidodendron*, is the presence of a single stele, with centripetally developed primary wood. The occurrence of a pith is inconstant, not only among different species, but even in different parts of one and the same individual ; sometimes (as in the larger stems of most species) the interior of the vascular cylinder is occupied by a medulla, around which the wood forms a continuous ring (Figs. 59 and 61) ; sometimes the wood constitutes a solid mass extending to the middle of the stele ; this is the case, for example, in *L. rhodumnense*, Renault, and *L. pettycurense*, Kidston, and, in a modified form, in *L. selaginoides* (Figs. 62 and 63). In all cases, the wood of the stem, whether solid or hollow, forms a perfectly continuous cylinder or ring, and is not broken up, as in the higher plants, into distinct vascular bundles. The xylem-cylinder is surrounded by a ring of phloëm (Figs. 60 and 63). From the outer border of the stele, numerous leaf-trace bundles arise, passing out obliquely through the cortex to the leaves, each of which receives a single bundle (Figs. 59 and 62). The cortex is of great thickness relatively to the vascular cylinder. Its structure varies much according to the species, and to the dimensions and age of the branch.

The majority of the British species, in which the anatomy is preserved, are known to have formed a zone of secondary wood and bast, often of considerable thickness, around the primary cylinder. In addition to this growth of the stele, a still more extensive development of secondary tissues went on in the outer cortex, leading to the formation of a thick periderm (Figs. 61 and 62), which seems to have been produced in all the species, even in cases where no secondary vascular tissues have so far been found. The following is a list of the British forms, hitherto described, of which the structure is known :—

I. Secondary Wood not observed

1. *Lepidodendron* (*Lepidophloios* ?) *Harcourtii*, Witham ; Lower Carboniferous.
2. *L.* (*Lepidophloios*) *Scottii*,[1] Gordon (probably = *Lepidophloios scoticus*, Kidston) ; Lower Carboniferous.
3. *L. Hickii*, Watson ; Coal-measures.
4. *L. parvulum*, Williamson ; Coal-measures.
5. *L. macrophyllum*, Williamson ; Coal-measures.
6. *L. aculeatum*, Sternberg ; Coal-measures.

II. With Secondary Wood

7. *L. brevifolium*, Williamson (= *L. Veltheimianum*, Sternberg) ; Lower Carboniferous.
8. *L.* (*Lepidophloios*) *Wunschianum*, Williamson ; Lower Carboniferous.
9. *L. pettycurense*, Kidston ; Lower Carboniferous.
10. *L. selaginoides*, Carruthers ; Coal-measures.
11. *L.* (*Lepidophloios*) *fuliginosum*, Williamson ; Coal-measures.
12. *L. intermedium*, Williamson ; Coal-measures.
13. *L. obovatum*, Sternberg ; Coal-measures.

L. mundum, Will., formerly included in this list, has now been shown by Mr. Lomax to be the stem of a *Bothrodendron* (see p. 180).

Now, of all these forms, there are only two which are known to have constantly attained any considerable size without showing secondary growth of the vascular tissues ; these species are *L. Harcourtii*, the first *Lepidodendron* discovered with its structure well preserved, and *L. Hickii*, since recognised as a distinct species by Mr. D. M. S. Watson. The original specimen of *L. Harcourtii* was found in 1832, in the Hesley Heath Colliery, Northumberland (Calciferous Sandstone Series, Lower Carboniferous), and was first described by Witham of Lartington,[2]

---

[1] For a full account of the anatomy of this typical *Lepidophloios*, see W. T. Gordon, " On *Lepidophloios Scottii* (a new species from the Calciferous Sandstone Series at Pettycur, Fife)," *Trans. Roy. Soc. Edinburgh*, vol. xlvi. Part iii. 1908.

[2] *Internal Structure of Fossil Vegetables*, Edinburgh, 1833.

who named it *Harcourtii* after its discoverer. Our first minute knowledge of the structure of this fossil was due to the great French palaeobotanist, Adolphe Brongniart, who gave an admirable account of the anatomy.[1] Subsequent investigations, especially those of Williamson and Bertrand, aided by the discovery of a few additional specimens, have rendered *Lepidodendron Harcourtii* one of the best known among fossil stems. Mr. Watson regards this species as a *Lepidophloios*. The largest specimen hitherto found has a diameter of over 8 cm. (not counting the leaf-bases), while its stele, or rather the wood, which is alone perfect, is rather more than a centimetre in diameter. The wood forms a broad continuous ring, enclosing a parenchymatous pith (see Fig. 59). The outer edge of the wood is crenulated, having a large number of prominent angles, with furrows between them. It is at the prominent angles that the narrow spiral tracheides are placed ; all the interior of the wood is made up of uniform, scalariform elements. Hence it is evident that the whole ring of xylem was centripetally formed, the development having started at the external angles. It appeared from M. Bertrand's researches that these angles formed a prominent network on the surface of the woody cylinder. Prof. Seward, however, finds that the protoxylem-angles ran in vertical lines, not constituting a network.[2] The attachment of the strands was at the sides of the tracheal prominences, and not at their extreme points. The phloëm, of which the preservation is very imperfect, appears to have formed a narrow continuous band round the wood (see Fig. 59, B).

The leaf-traces passed very gradually outwards through the cortex to the leaves, one bundle entering each leaf. Hence a large number of the outgoing strands are met with in every transverse section of the stem, forming a very characteristic feature (see Fig. 59, A).

---

[1] *Histoire des végétaux fossiles*, vol. ii. 1837.
[2] Seward, *Fossil Plants*, vol. ii. 1910, p. 163 ; Fig. 179, D.

They have a complex spiral arrangement, related to that of the leaves to which they ran.[1]

The structure of the individual leaf-trace bundles in *L. Harcourtii* has been described as characteristic of the species ; its peculiarity consists in the presence of a conspicuous strand of dark-coloured, apparently fibrous cells, on the outside of the bundle (see Fig. 59, B, *l.t.'*). Other Lepidodendreae, however, show the same structure, as Prof. Seward found in the case of *Lepidophloios fuliginosus*, and Mr. Watson in his Coal-measure species, *Lepidodendron Hickii*. That the elements in question were really of the nature of hard bast in very improbable. Prof. Bertrand regards them as organs of secretion, comparable to laticiferous cells, and Prof. Seward's observations led him to a similar conclusion,[2] which may be provisionally accepted.

The vascular bundles appear, judging from the best-preserved specimens, to have been of the collateral type, the phloëm lying between the xylem and the strand of secretory elements, and perhaps including the latter. The spiral tracheae are placed near the middle of the xylem, a position which they often occupy in the foliar bundles of Lycopods. Outside the phloëm of each bundle, where it traverses the outer cortex, is a large strand of delicate parenchyma, seldom perfectly preserved, which was continuous with the parichnos of the leaf-base.

The inner zone of cortex consisted of soft parenchyma, usually badly preserved, while the more external region, where the whole tissue was thick-walled, is perfect (Fig. 59, A). The cortex was covered on the exterior by the

---

[1] For a detailed account of the anatomy of *L. Harcourtii*, see Bertrand, *Remarques sur le Lepidodendron Harcourtii de Witham*, Lille, 1891. For *L. Hickii*, see Watson, " On a Confusion of two Species under *Lepidodendron Harcourtii*," *Mem. and Proc. Manchester Lit. and Phil. Soc.* vol. li. Part iii. 1907.

[2] A. C. Seward, " Notes on the Binney Collection of Coal-measure Plants," i. *Lepidophloios, Proc. Cambridge Phil. Soc.* vol. x. 1899.

crowded bases of the leaves, but the latter have often been
lost.   In the outer cortex, a little below the leaf-bases,

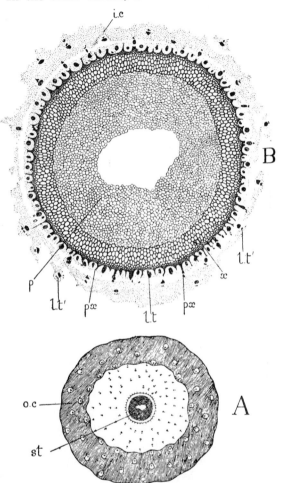

FIG. 59.—*Lepidodendron Harcourtii.*   A. Transverse section of stem.   *st*, stele ; *o.c.*, outer
cortex ; both here and in the inner cortex the leaf-traces are shown.   About nat. size.
B. Stele of same.   *p*, pith, hollow in middle ; *x*, xylem-ring ; *px*, protoxylem-points ;
the leaf-traces join the stele between them ; *l.t.*, the leaf-trace bundles, of which the
outer, *l.t.'*, show xylem and phloëm ; *i.c.*, inner cortex. × 7. Will. Coll. 1594. (G. T. G.)

periderm was formed at a rather early stage, by the
tangential division of the cortical cells.   The develop-

ment of the periderm took place on both sides of the initial layer, and was therefore partly centripetal and partly centrifugal in direction. The leaf-bases were thus separated by a zone of secondary cortex from the inner tissues of the stem, but remained attached to the outer surface of the back, even on old trunks.

Very definite groups or strands of cells, no doubt of the nature of internal glands, occur in the outer cortex, just within the periderm. These secretory organs are also present in various other Lepidodendreae, as in *Lepidophloios fuliginosus* and in *Lepidodendron Wunschianum*, where they are ranged in concentric bands in the periderm.

Except for the periderm, *Lepidodendron Harcourtii*, as known to us at present, shows no sign of secondary formations. It is, however, perfectly possible that cambial activity may have started at the periphery of the stele, in specimens still larger than any we possess. That this may have been so, is rendered highly probable by the analogy of another species, *L. Wunschianum*, from the Lower Carboniferous strata in the Isle of Arran. In this case secondary wood was formed in great quantity, but it is never found except in stems of still greater dimensions than the largest known specimens of *L. Harcourtii*.

Williamson sometimes said that it was an unfortunate chance for fossil botany that the first Lepidodendron stem, of which the structure was investigated, happened to be that of *L. Harcourtii*. The absence of secondary wood in this species, which we now know to have been quite exceptional, led Brongniart to believe that the *Lepidodendra* generally were without exogenous growth. On this ground, he removed *Sigillaria*, in which the secondary tissues were discovered early, both from the Lycopodiaceae and from the Cryptogams, and classed the genus among Gymnospermous Phanerogams. Even when *Lepidodendra* with secondary wood began to be discovered, there was for a long time a strong tendency, on the part of the French school of palaeobotanists, to regard all such specimens as really *Sigillariae*, and so to keep up the supposed distinction. We now know, chiefly as the result of Williamson's researches, that most of the Carboniferous *Lepidodendra* agreed essentially with *Sigillaria* in their anatomy, and that the two genera were closely allied members of the Lycopodiales. The controversy, however, proved valuable as a stimulus to research.

Lepidodendron Wunschianum,[1] a species which is abundant in the volcanic beds of Arran, belonging to the oldest part of the Carboniferous formation, essentially resembles *L. Harcourtii* in its primary structure, and needs no detailed description here.[2] Secondary wood has only been found in stems with a primary xylem-cylinder 2 cm. or more in diameter. Cambial growth here went on vigorously, producing a zone of wood nearly 3 cm. thick in the larger trees, some of which were a couple of feet in diameter. In one particular specimen the state of preservation was very remarkable. To quote Williamson's words :—" At Laggan Bay [Arran] the bases of thirteen large stems stood erect and closely aggregated. Further investigation showed that twelve of these were merely cylinders of outer cortex, all their more internal tissues having disappeared and been replaced by volcanic ash, with which the trees had been destroyed and buried. The decay of the softer portions of the bark had loosened all the harder vascular structures compassing their several steles, and allowed them to float out when the area became submerged. But the exceptional stem had met with different treatment. In the first instance, it also had lost all its vegetable contents, which had evidently floated out upon the neighbouring waters. Directed by some fortunate current, a quantity

---

[1] Possibly referable to the genus *Lepidophloios*.

[2] Seward and Hill are inclined to identify these two types, but I do not find sufficient evidence to justify us in uniting them.

of the floating débris had been washed back into and filled the vacant cavity of the thirteenth stem. Further examination of this débris showed that it consisted of fragments of bark and of Stigmarian rootlets, including a fragment of a vascular axis of a *Stigmaria* ; [1] but what was still more important, we found in it the entire and fully developed steles of no less than five of the remaining trees, which had been tumbled into this single one." [2]

The base of this curious stem, showing all the steles thus accidentally enclosed in it, is now preserved in the Museum of the University at Manchester.

A magnificent specimen from Dalmeny (see Fig. 60), referable to the *L. Wunschianum* type, has the interesting peculiarity that the leaf-traces, after leaving the stele, are accompanied by a broad arc or zone of secondary wood and phloëm, the only case of the kind hitherto found in a Lepidodendroid, as distinguished from a Sigillarian, stem. The specimen is fully described in the *Transactions of the Royal Society of Edinburgh*, by Prof. A. C. Seward and Mr. A. W. Hill.[3]

Another form, which in its primary condition somewhat resembles *Lepidodendron Harcourtii*, is the Burntisland species named by Williamson *L. brevifolium*, but no doubt identical with Sternberg's species, *L. Veltheimianum*. This, like *L. Wunschianum*, comes from the Calciferous Sandstones, at the base of the Carboniferous formation. Twigs and branches of all sizes have been found in abundance, and the first beginnings of secondary growth have thus been traced. The species differs strikingly from *L. Wunschianum*, in the dimensions of the branches with secondary tissues. In *L. brevifolium*, even comparatively small twigs have a zone of radially seriated

[1] We shall see further on that these *Stigmariae* were the rhizomes or roots of the *Lepidodendra* themselves, and of the allied *Sigillariae*.

[2] Williamson " Growth and Development of the Carboniferous Arborescent *Lepidodendra*," *Mem. and Proc. Manchester Lit. and Phil. Soc.* ser. iv. vol. ix. p. 45, 1895.

[3] *l.c.* vol. xxxix. Part iv. 1900.

wood of cambial origin, surrounding a primary cylinder, sometimes only about 3 mm. in diameter. In the larger branches, the secondary zone of wood attained a thickness enormously greater than that of the primary ring.

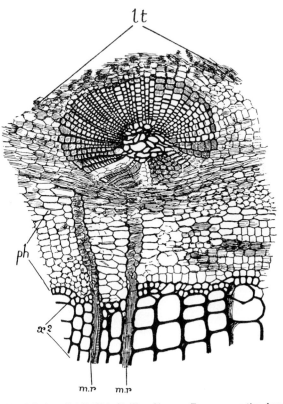

FIG. 60.—*Lepidodendron* (*Lepidophloios* ?) *Wunschianum*. Transverse section from outer part of stele, showing leaf-trace. x^2, secondary wood; *m.r.*, medullary rays, one of which contains tracheides; *ph*, phloëm (meristematic zone of Seward) : *l.t.*, leaf-trace, with a small mesarch strand of primary xylem, and a broad zone of secondary wood (with short tracheides) and phloëm. × about 55. From a section presented by Mr. Kidston. S. Coll. 1183. (G. T. G.)

An example of this stem, at a fairly advanced stage, is shown, in transverse section, in Fig. 61.

For the more detailed study of the structure and development of the stem in a *Lepidodendron* with secondary growth, we will choose, however, another example, namely, *L. selaginoides*, which, from the abundance of specimens and their extraordinarily good preservation, has proved exceptionally favourable for investigation.

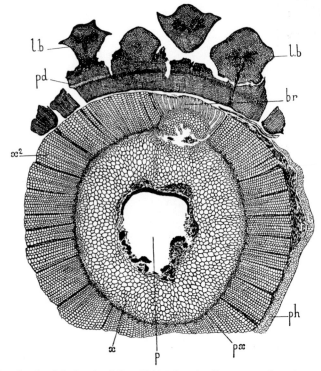

Fig. 61.—*Lepidodendron brevifolium (Veltheimianum)*. Transverse section of stem. *p*, pith, almost wholly destroyed ; *x*, broad zone of primary wood ; *px*, protoxylem at periphery of primary wood ; *x²*, secondary wood ; *ph*, phloëm ; *br*, small stele becoming detached to supply a branch ; *pd*, periderm ; *l.b.*, leaf-bases, showing bundle and parichnos. All the more internal cortex, which once intervened between stele and periderm, has perished. ×4½. S. Coll. 54. (G. T. G.)

In this form, which is abundant in the Lower Coal-measures, the specimens showing structure have been identified, at least with great probability, with those preserved as impressions or casts, in which the external characters are visible.[1]

[1] See Carruthers, " Structure of the Stems of the Arborescent Lycopodiaceae of the Coal-measures," *Monthly Microscopical Journal*, vol.

Lepidodendron selaginoides is at once distinguished anatomically from the other species by the peculiar structure of the central cylinder. No definite pith is present; the tracheae of the primary wood extend to the centre of the stele (Figs. 62 and 63). The outer

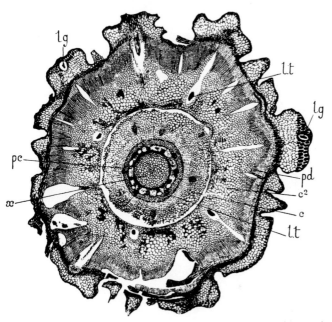

FIG. 62.—*Lepidodendron selaginoides.* Transverse section of young branch, before secondary wood has formed. *x*, primary xylem-cylinder; *pc*, zone of phloëm and pericycle; *c*, inner cortex, differentiated into three layers : *c²*, outer cortex; *pd*, periderm; beyond this are the leaf-bases; *lg*, ligule; *l.t.*, leaf-traces, at various points on their outward course. × about 7. S. Coll. 1376. (G. T. G.)

part of the primary xylem has the structure usual in the genus; at the extreme periphery there are a number of slightly prominent points, at and near which the spiral elements are placed. Here then, as in other forms, the development of the xylem must have been centripetal. Immediately within the protoxylem the elements become

ii. 1869. As, however, the identification is not absolutely certain, some authors prefer to use Binney's name, *L. vasculare*, rather than *L. selaginoides.*

much larger, forming a broad continuous zone, which consists exclusively of long scalariform tracheides, without any admixture of parenchyma (Figs. 63 and 64). As we advance further inwards, however, parenchyma begins to make its appearance, and at the same time the tracheides change their character, becoming much shorter,

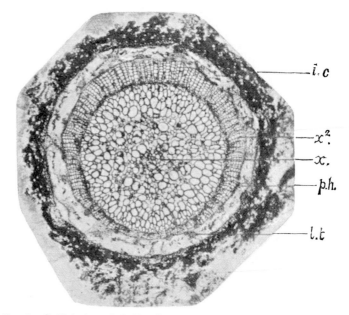

FIG. 63.—*Lepidodendron selaginoides.* Transverse section of stele after commencement of secondary thickening. x, primary xylem-cylinder, with reticulate tracheides in central part, and small protoxylem-elements at periphery; x^2, secondary wood, unequally developed; ph, phloëm-zone; $i.c.$, part of inner cortex; $l.t.$, leaf-traces. × 17. From a photograph by Dr. Bousfield. S. Coll. 17.

with horizontal transverse walls (Fig. 63, x). Thus the whole central part of the stele is occupied by mixed tracheides and parenchyma. The former are often no longer than the cells which accompany them. The transverse walls of the short tracheides are reticulately thickened, and form a conspicuous feature in the transverse sections, by which the species can be easily recognised.

The phloëm, which is fairly preserved in some of the best specimens, forms a zone of thin-walled tissue, including strands of elongated elements, surrounding the wood, and itself surrounded by a somewhat broader band of larger-celled parenchyma, which may be regarded as the pericycle. The leaf-trace bundles, where they cross this zone, are each enclosed in a special sheath, sometimes forming a kind of bridge or trabecula across the more delicate tissues of the phloëm and pericycle (Fig. 63).

The endodermis is simply a layer of tangentially elongated cells. Then we come to the broad zone of inner cortex, which consists of delicate short-celled parenchyma, only preserved in the best specimens, as in that shown in Fig. 62. The more internal layers, however, are of firmer structure, and often persist when the rest has perished. In the middle part of this zone the cells show some trace of radial arrangement. Through this region the leaf-trace bundles pass, still taking a steep upward course (Fig. 62). Beyond the inner cortex is another broad belt, the outer cortex, the tissue of which is formed of elongated cells with, for the most part, rather thick cell-walls ; this zone, owing to its solid construction, is always well preserved. The leaf-traces, which in this region gradually assume a more horizontal course, often pass through gaps, due to the disappearance of delicate tissue (Fig. 62). The outer cortex ends at the exterior of the stem in the zone of the leaf-bases, which collectively cover almost the whole surface. The tissue immediately within the leaf-bases remained thin-walled, for it was here that the phellogen arose.

The leaf-trace bundles start, so far as their xylem is concerned, directly from the angles of the primary wood, and not between them, as in *L. Harcourtii*. The leaf-traces are normally collateral, with xylem directed inwards and phloëm, consisting of elongated narrow elements, outwards. The spiral elements, where their position can be determined with certainty, lie on the inner edge of the xylem, which was thus, as a rule, *endarch*, another point of difference from *L. Harcourtii*, where the structure in the corresponding region was regularly *mesarch*.[1] The soft bast is bounded on the exterior by some elements with thicker cell-walls, which may be most probably interpreted as secretory sacs. The whole bundle is surrounded by a well-marked sheath.

Where the leaf-trace enters the denser outer cortex, a large strand of delicate parenchyma—much larger than the bundle itself—accompanies the latter on its lower side,[2] and passes out with it into the leaf-base ; here the parenchymatous strand forks into two, the two branches diverging to the right and left of the bundle. It is these strands of tissue which give rise to the two lateral prints on the leaf-scar, called the parichnos (cf. Fig. 65). This structure is common to the Lepidodendreae in general.

We have so far considered the anatomy of the stem in its primary condition ; in most of the specimens the structure is modified by the appearance of secondary tissues, namely, of periderm in the outer cortex, and of new wood and bast around the stele. In *L. selaginoides* even the smallest twigs found (which, however, are not usually less than 1 cm. in diameter) may show both these new formations, while in some of the other species, as we have seen, the secondary wood and bast appear to have been limited to the main stem and its principal branches.

The periderm began to appear early ; in some of the younger specimens its first origin can be traced. It was developed from a zone of cells of the outer cortex,

[1] These are convenient terms for shortly characterising the development of the wood of a vascular bundle. If the protoxylem lies on the inner side the strand is *endarch*; if in the middle of the xylem, *mesarch*; if on its outer side, *exarch*.

[2] Indicated by the gaps accompanying the leaf-trace bundles in Fig. 59, A, from *L. Harcourtii*.

lying immediately within the leaf-bases, between which it was only separated by a few cells from the outer surface of the stem. This zone of tissue became meristematic; its elements divided tangentially, and acted as a phellogen, producing a very large quantity of secondary cortical tissue (see Fig. 62, *pd*, and compare Fig. 61). There has been some difference of opinion as to the position of the phellogen in the older specimens, but there is now little doubt that it lay in the outer part of the secondary zone, so that the larger portion of the new tissue was produced on its inner side, and a smaller portion towards the exterior. Thus the greater part of the secondary cortical zone, as it was produced on the inside of the generative layer, is to be regarded as phelloderm. Whether the smaller outer portion was really of the nature of cork is doubtful—the more so, as the bases of the leaves outside it certainly persisted for a very long time.

The periderm (as we may call the whole of the secondary cortical tissue) consisted of elongated, rather thick-walled cells, and must have contributed very materially to the mechanical strength of the stem. It doubtless had other functions as well, serving as a tissue for the storing of reserve food-material, and was certainly much more than a mere bark.[1] The late M. Hovelacque, to whom we owe the most detailed study of the anatomy of this species,[2] was mistaken in supposing that the periderm was formed entirely from within; on its inner margin the tissue is, as a rule, thick-walled, and quite unlike a meristem, while a delicate zone of cells is constantly to be found in its outer part (see Fig. 62). It appears probable, however, that additions may sometimes have been made to the periderm from the interior also, new layers of primary cortical cells taking up the divisions.

[1] In *L. Wunschianum* it contained strands of cells probably with a secretory function.

[2] Hovelacque, "Recherches sur le *Lepidodendron selaginoides*," *Mém. Soc. Linnéenne de Normandie*, 1892. This fine memoir is magnificently illustrated.

In old specimens, the periderm attained a thickness of as much as 3 inches. The course of the leaf-trace bundles through it is marked by radial strands of tissue more delicate than the rest. The periderm also shows concentric markings, due to the alternation of zones of wider and narrower elements. What has been said of the periderm of *Lepidodendron selaginoides* may be taken as holding good for the genus as a whole (cf. Figs. 61 and 62.).[1]

The secondary vascular tissues began to develop rather later than the periderm. Very often the new growth began on one side of the central cylinder, so that for a time the secondary wood formed a crescent, and not a complete ring (cf. Fig. 63) ; in other cases it was fairly equal all round from the first. The cambial divisions started in the conjunctive tissue between the primary wood and phloëm ; the very first beginning of the new formation can be traced in some of the specimens (see Fig. 63, on lower side of figure). The secondary wood usually abuts directly on the small external tracheides of the primary ring (see longitudinal section, Fig. 64) ; sometimes a layer of parenchyma intervenes. The secondary wood consists of regular radial series of tracheides, with medullary rays between them ; the tracheal rows are more numerous than the rays. The secondary tracheides, like the primary, are scalariform (Fig. 64), with the bars on their tangential as well as their radial walls. The rays vary much in height and width ; sometimes a ray consists of a single row of cells ; sometimes it is one cell thick, but many cells high ; while in other cases the middle part of the ray is several cells in thickness. We must remember that these rays are only called " medullary " from analogy with those of other plants ; in *Lepidodendron* they do not really reach

---

[1] For a full investigation of this subject, see Mabel H. Kisch, "The Physiological Anatomy of the Periderm of Fossil Lycopodiales," *Ann. of Bot.* vol. xxvii. 1913, p. 281.

the pith, even where one is present, because the ring of primary wood is quite continuous, so as to shut off the rays completely at their inner ends. The muriform character of the rays, as seen in radial section, is shown in Fig. 64.

The leaf-traces, or rather their woody portions, extend through the secondary wood, traversing enlarged medullary rays. Quite apart from the leaf-traces, how-

FIG. 64.—*Lepidodendron selaginoides.* Part of radial section, showing primary wood on left, and secondary wood, with medullary rays, on right; the narrow elements between the two are the protoxylem. × about 25. From a photograph by Dr. Bousfield. S. Coll. 24.

ever, the rays generally contain numerous reticulated or spirally thickened elements, which probably served to keep up water-communication in the radial direction throughout the wood ; they would thus be analogous to the tracheides occurring in the medullary rays of many of the Coniferae.

The phloëm underwent comparatively little increase, at least during the earlier stages of cambial activity. In the older stems, where the secondary wood reaches

a thickness of half an inch, the phloëm is seldom preserved. The actual amount of new vascular tissue was
small compared with the much greater development of
periderm.

Although the details of the cambial growth have not
yet been satisfactorily cleared up, there is no doubt that
it was normal, in the sense that the cambium produced
wood internally, and phloëm, though probably to no
great extent, on its external side.

The cells of the cambium in Lepidodendreae, where
preserved, are not usually found to correspond exactly
to the radial series of xylem-elements on their inner side
(cf. Fig. 60). It appears probable that the same initial
layer was not active throughout the duration of secondary
growth, but that new zones of cells may have taken up
the cambial divisions periodically. In this respect there
would be a certain similarity to the secondary increase
in *Isoëtes*, among living plants.

The phloëm of the Lepidodendreae also presents considerable difficulties. Typical phloëm, consisting of
delicate elongated elements, has not always been recognised, even in the best-preserved specimens, such as that
illustrated in Fig. 60. In other cases, however, as in
the leaf-traces of *L. selaginoides* and in the vascular
bundles of the cones, the phloëm appears to have been
quite of the normal type,[1] so we are not justified in
supposing that there was any fundamental difference in
this respect between the Lepidodendreae and their recent
allies.[2]

Before leaving the subject of the anatomy of the
Lepidodendroid stem, it is of some interest to note that

[1] See Maslen, " Structure of *Lepidostrobus*," *Trans. Linn. Soc.* vol.
v. 1899, Plates xxxvi.-xxxviii. Figs. 11, 13, 14, and 33.

[2] On the controversy as to phloëm in Lepidodendreae, see F. E.
Weiss, " On the Phloëm of *Lepidophloios* and *Lepidodendron*," *Mem.
and Proc. Manchester Lit. and Phil. Soc.* vol. xlv. Part iii. 1901 ; and
Seward, " The So-called Phloëm of *Lepidodendron*," *New Phytologist*,
vol. i. 1902, also " Fossil Plants," vol. ii. 1910, chap. xv. §§ iv. and vii·

in *Lepidophloios fuliginosus* (Williamson), a species which resembles *Lepidodendron Harcourtii* so closely that for many years they were not distinguished, a certain amount of secondary xylem was formed. It was, however, much less regular than in the other species which show it, such as *Lepidodendron selaginoides* or *L. brevifolium*. In *L. fuliginosus* the cambium was an anomalous one, arising irregularly in various parts of the phloëm-zone and pericycle. It produced a good deal of secondary parenchyma, among which there are usually scattered groups of wood ; the secondary tracheides have a very sinuous and irregular course. In some cases tracheides appear to be altogether absent from the secondary zone. We may regard this species (which, from the form of its leaf-bases, must certainly be referred to *Lepidophloios*, as first pointed out by Cash and Lomax in 1890) as exhibiting either a primitive and rudimentary or a reduced form of secondary growth. In a rather doubtful species, *Lepidodendron intermedium*, there is a similar mode of secondary thickening ; this form derives its specific name from combining to some extent the characters of *Lepidophloios fuliginosus* and *Lepidodendron selaginoides*.

Certain cases have been described, in which the external features of a petrified specimen are preserved, so as to allow of its reference to a definite species, based on the superficial characters, while at the same time the internal structure could be investigated. In a stem referable to the type of *Lepidodendron obovatum*, Sternb., various details of the anatomy, and especially the presence of a parenchymatous secondary zone, show a close agreement with *Lepidophloios fuliginosus*.[1] Curiously enough, the other specimen in question, referred by Prof. Seward to *Lepidodendron aculeatum*, Sternb., likewise " exhibits an exceedingly close agreement with that type of structure which it has been customary to

[1] Scott, " Structure of *Lepidodendron obovatum*," *Ann. of Bot.* vol. xx. 1906, p. 317.

describe as *Lepidophloios fuliginosus.*"[1] It is thus evident that no anatomical distinction can be drawn between the two so-called genera *Lepidodendron* and *Lepidophloios.*

The Lower Carboniferous species, *L. pettycurense,* discovered by Dr. Kidston, is of interest as having a perfectly solid primary xylem cylinder, surrounded by a well-developed zone of secondary wood. One may therefore infer that in this plant, at any rate, the solid xylem, without pith or parenchyma, was present in the main stem. This character is an early and probably a primitive one in the Lepidodendreae.[2]

3. *Leaves.*—We next come to the structure of the leaves of the Lepidodendreae. It is, of course, necessary to distinguish between the leaf-bases or cushions, which remained in connection with the stem, and the leaves themselves, which were thrown off. The great majority of the specimens with structure preserved bear the leaf-bases only ; in the literature it has sometimes happened that the latter have been confused with the actual leaves.

The external form of the leaf-base has already been described. We have also seen that on the scar, left by the fall of the leaf itself, there are three prints (cf. Fig. 58, p. 116). The middle one is caused by the vascular bundle, which remained simple throughout the leaf. The two lateral prints, called the parichnos, are, as stated above, of quite a different nature ; a strand of large-celled parenchyma accompanies the leaf-trace through the outer cortex on its lower side, and divides, in the base of the leaf, into two strands, which take up their position to the right and left of the vascular bundle. When the leaf fell off, the broken ends of these two parenchymatous strands appeared on the scar, with the print

---

[1] Seward, "Anatomy of *Lepidodendron aculeatum,*" *Ann. of Bot.* vol. xx. 1906, p. 378.

[2] Kidston, Note on a new species of *Lepidodendron* from Pettycur. *Proc. Royal Soc. Edinburgh,* vol. xxvii. Part iii. 1907.

marking the bundle between them (see Fig. 65, showing the leaf-bases of a *Lepidophloios* in tangential section).

The two external prints on the surface of the leaf-cushion below the scar (see Fig. 58, *a, a*) were in connection with the parichnos, as was first shown by Potonié in a *Lepidophloios*. Prof. F. E. Weiss has further investigated the structure, and finds that in *Lepidophloios* the parich-

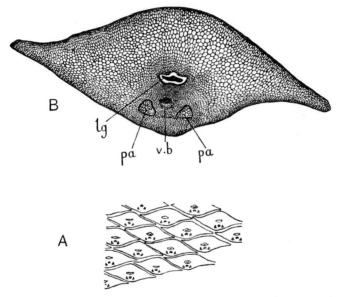

FIG. 65.—*Lepidophloios*, sp. A. Tangential section from the outside of a stem, passing through the leaf-bases, and showing their characteristic form. Slightly enlarged. B. A single leaf-base, to show details. *v.b.*, collateral vascular bundle ; *pa*, the two parichnos-strands ; *lg*, ligule in its pit. × 10. Cf. Fig. 66. Will. Coll. 1974 A. (G. T. G.)

nos-strands run very close to the surface and communicate with a delicate sub-epidermal tissue containing well-developed intercellular spaces. In a *Lepidodendron*, probably *L. Hickii*, Watson, this lacunar tissue lies at the base of the depressions which constitute the external prints. There appear to have been numerous stomata in the overlying epidermis.

The parichnos-strands die out in the leaf itself, losing themselves in the mesophyll. Thus the parichnos-tissue kept up communication between the delicate parenchyma of the inner cortex and the assimilating mesophyll of the leaves, as well as with the patches of aërenchyma in the persistent leaf-bases. The function may probably have been to facilitate respiration.[1] Major T. G. Hill has shown that strands comparable to the parichnos occur in the leaves of *Isoëtes Hystrix* and various species of *Lycopodium*; in these plants the function of the strands is secretory, as may sometimes have been the case in fossil Lycopods.[2]

The little triangular print on the upper part of the cushion, immediately above the leaf-scar, is of special interest, for we now know that this represents the *ligule*, an organ which is characteristic of *Selaginella* and *Isoëtes*, though absent from the other recent genera of Lycopods. Stur was the first to identify the ligule in *Lepidodendron*, but until it was demonstrated in specimens with structure preserved, there was no proof of the correctness of his interpretation. The presence of a ligule was proved almost simultaneously by Count Solms-Laubach[3] in specimens from the Lower Carboniferous of Silesia, probably referable to *L. brevifolium*, Will. (*L. Velt-heimianum*, Sternb.), and by M. Hovelacque[4] in *L. selaginoides*. It has since been demonstrated in several other species, and was probably common to the whole family.

In all the species in which the ligule has been found, it presents much the same features. Its position is always on the upper surface of the cushion, immediately above the leaf-scar.

The ligule is seated at the base of a deep flask-shaped

---

[1] F. E. Weiss, " The Parichnos in the Lepidodendraceae," *Mem. and Proc. Manchester Lit. and Phil. Soc.* vol. li. 1907.

[2] T. G. Hill, " On the Presence of a Parichnos in Recent Plants," *Ann. of Bot.* vol. xx. 1906.

[3] *Bot. Zeitung*, 1892, p. 110, Plate ii. Figs. 2 and 4.

[4] " Recherches sur le *Lepidodendron selaginoides*," *Mém. de la Soc. Linnéenne de Normandie*, Caen, 1892.

cavity, and is very rarely found projecting beyond it (see Figs. 65, B, and 66, *lg*). The ligule was, of course, a delicate organ, and is often imperfectly preserved ; often the ligular cavity is shown, when the ligule itself has perished altogether. In some cases, however, the cellular structure of the ligule is perfectly shown, and is found to agree, on the whole, with that in recent Ligulatae. The deep ligular cavity is very characteristic of Lepidodendreae, but is not without parallel among recent plants,

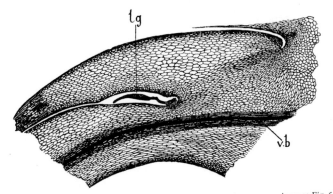

FIG. 66.—*Lepidophloios*, sp. Radial section of a leaf-base from the same specimen as Fig. 65. *v.b.*, vascular bundle of leaf ; *lg*, ligule, seated in a deep pit, communicating by a canal with the upper surface. × 10. Will. Coll. 1960. (G. T. G.)

for Professor Harvey Gibson has shown that in *Selaginella oregana* and *rupestris* " the free margin of the ligule scarcely appears above the edge of the very deep pit in the leaf in which it is seated." [1]

The base of the ligular cavity lies above the vascular bundle, and is in some cases (*e.g.* *L. Hickii*) surrounded by a sheath of short tracheides, forming a connection with the wood of the bundle, just as in *Isoëtes* and in some *Selaginellae* among recent plants. In other species, a strand of delicate cells, not tracheides, runs from the base of the ligule towards the bundle. The cavity slopes

[1] " Anatomy of the Genus *Selaginella*." Part ii. The Ligule, *Annals of Botany*, vol. x. p. 83, Plate viii. Fig. 19, 1896.

from its base, upwards and outwards, opening just above the scar, where the leaf itself was inserted (see Fig. 66). The print on the casts corresponds to the mouth of the ligular cavity.

The presence of a ligule in Lepidodendreae is an interesting discovery, indicating affinity with *Selaginella* or *Isoëtes*, rather than with *Lycopodium*, among recent members of the order. There are a few other facts which point in the same direction, but it is not likely that the relation to any recent genus was at all a close one.

The structure of the free part of the leaf was thoroughly worked out by M. Renault[1] in a species (*L. esnostense*) from the Lower Carboniferous rocks (Culm) of France ; certain leaves, associated with and probably belonging to the British form *L. Hickii*, Watson, agree in several respects with the French specimens, while leaves of other British Lepidodendreae are also similar. In *L. esnostense* the leaves were acicular, and not very different in form from those of some species of *Pinus*. Along the under surface, on either side of the midrib, are two furrows, which are very deep near the base of the lamina, but become less marked towards the apex. It is on the epidermis lining these furrows that the stomata are found. They are very numerous, and of the usual bicellular structure. The rest of the leaf is covered by a small-celled epidermis with a thick-walled hypoderma below it. The mesophyll consists of a spongy tissue, like that of many recent leaves. This was no doubt the green, assimilating part of the leaf when alive. The middle of the leaf is traversed by a central strand of tissue, enclosing the vascular bundle. The bundle itself is small, but it is surrounded by a wide zone of spiral or reticulated tracheides, much larger and more numerous than those of the xylem itself. This peculiar formation appears to have been analogous to the transfusion-tissue in the

---

[1] *Flore fossile d'Autun et d'Épinac*, Part ii. p. 178, Plate xxxiv. Figs. 4-8.

leaves of Coniferae. In the leaf of *Lepidodendron*, as in that of the Coniferae, there is some ordinary parenchyma surrounding the bundle, in addition to the tracheides.

In the leaves referred to *L. Hickii*, the structure is much like that just described, except that their form

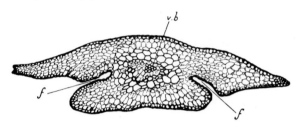

FIG. 67.—*Lepidodendron Hickii.* Transverse section of leaf. *v.b.*, vascular bundle ; some of the large elements round it constitute the transfusion-tissue ; *f,* furrows in which the stomata are placed. × 60. S. Coll. 51. (G. T. G.)

was not acicular, but linear, or narrowly lanceolate, the leaf having a lamina of some width (see Fig. 67). The stomata are extremely well shown (see Fig. 68), and appear to have occupied the same position as in the French species.

In the structure of the leaves, as in so many other points, we see that the Palaeozoic Lycopods were more

FIG. 68.—*Lepidodendron Hickii.* Epidermis of leaf, with stomata. × about 300. S. Coll. 51. (G. T. G.)

highly organised than their representatives in our own period.

4. *Branching.*—We now come to the question of the branching of the stem. So far as the external and anatomical characters enable us to judge, the branching was dichotomous throughout, and it is usual to assume that this was the case, though, in the absence of any

knowledge of the growing point, it is impossible to say whether the strict definition of dichotomy applies here.

We must distinguish, with Williamson, between equal and unequal dichotomy. The former prevailed

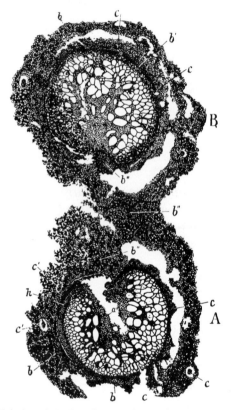

FIG. 69.—*Lepidodendron selaginoides.* Transverse section showing the two steles (A and B) of a bifurcating stem. *a*, pith ; *b*, inner cortex ; *c*, leaf-traces ; *h*, secondary wood. The pith in this species only exists near a bifurcation, where the steles are still incomplete on the inner side. × about 9. After Williamson, *Phil. Trans.* Will. Coll. 340.

in the forking of the main stem and its principal branches, where the two limbs into which the parent axis divided were similar (Fig. 69). Immediately below the dichotomy the stele separates into two parts, which for some distance have the form of horse-shoes, with the pith of each stele open towards the other. Where there was secondary growth, the cambium in this region sometimes extended into the medulla, forming an inverted band of secondary tissues within the primary wood. This occurred even in *L. selaginoides*, where the pith was replaced by scattered parenchyma. Although limited to the place of bifurcation, this condition is of some interest, because analogous anomalies occur among the higher plants at the present day. The cambium, in fact, shows similar eccentricities in its behaviour wherever it occurs, quite irrespective of taxonomic relationship. As we trace the two branches higher up, we find that the stele in each gradually regains its normal circular form. (Fig. 69, from a forking branch of *L. selaginoides*, shows the steles in an intermediate state.)

Unequal dichotomy simply means that one branch of the fork is much smaller than, and sometimes differently organised from, the other. This no doubt often occurred in the vegetative region, in cases where a main axis bore a comparatively small twig, as an apparently lateral branch. Unequal dichotomy was probably also of common occurrence in connection with the fructification, when one branch of a dichotomy was fertile, while the other remained vegetative. Some special cases will be considered in the next chapter.

Anatomically, unequal dichotomy is characterised by the behaviour of the stele. It is frequently the case that the smaller of the two branches has no medulla. Then, instead of the two equal horse-shoes described above, we find only a small part of the main stele diverging to the minor branch. Sometimes a segment of the wood was cut out, as it were, from the stele, leaving a small opening, which soon closed up. The segment destined for the branch was thus solid from the first (*e.g. Lepidophloios fuliginosus*, Fig. 72, *b'*). In other cases the strand of wood passing out to the smaller member was so insignificant that the continuity of the main ring was never interrupted, a group of its more external tracheae sufficing to supply the wood for the branch (see Fig. 61, *br.* from *L. brevifolium*).

To complete the description of the vegetative organs of the Lepidodendreae, we ought now to describe the root. As, however, we cannot as yet distinguish with certainty between the underground organs of *Lepido-dendron* and those of *Sigillaria*, it will be necessary to postpone their consideration until the latter genus has also been described.[1]

---

[1] The anatomy of Lepidodendroid stems was dealt with by William-son in Parts ii., iii., ix., x., xi., xii., xvi., and xix. of his series of memoirs in the *Philosophical Transactions*, 1872-93. Some of his final con-clusions are summed up in his last work, " Growth and Development of the Carboniferous Arborescent *Lepidodendra*," *Mem. and Proc. Manchester Lit. and Phil. Soc.* ser. iv. vol. ix. 1895. A later general account will be found in Seward, *Fossil Plants*, vol. ii. chap. xv. 1910.

CHAPTER VI

LYCOPODIALES—*continued*

Ulodendron and Halonia ; Fructifications of Lepido-dendreae ; Bothrodendron ; Pinakodcndron

1. *Ulodendron and Halonia.*—In the last chapter we described the morphology of the stem and leaf of the Lepidodendreae ; we have now to consider their organs of reproduction. Before going on to the cones, something must be said as to two forms of Lepidodendroid stem (often regarded as bearing the fructifications) which differ so conspicuously from the ordinary type that they were long described as belonging to distinct genera, to which the names *Ulodendron* and *Halonia* were given. The genus *Ulodendron* was still kept up for certain species by the late Prof. Zeiller.

The Ulodendroid forms of stem is often of large size, attaining in some cases a diameter of about a foot, and is sometimes dichotomously branched. The general surface bears the ordinary markings of the Lepidodendreae ; where the leaf-bases are perfect they present, however, in some cases, according to Dr. Kidston, the characters of a *Sigillaria*, and so do not come under our immediate subject, but in other specimens the superficial characters are clearly those of a *Lepidodendron* (see Fig. 70). The characteristic feature of the *Ulodendron* stem consists in the presence of roundish scars, often of very large size, usually arranged alternately in two vertical rows, one row on each side of the stem. On the larger *Ulodendron* these scars may have a diameter of from 4 to 6 inches. Within the scar, usually somewhat

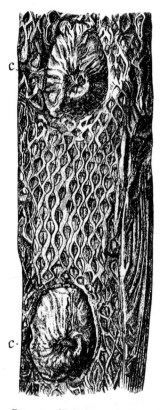

below the centre, is a print or stump, representing either the stalk or the woody cylinder of some lateral appendage. The scar as a whole is depressed, having the form of a shallow cup, with the print or *umbilicus* at the bottom (see Fig. 70). The surface of the cup is usually marked with radiating ridges on the part above the umbilicus, while the lower part bears spirally arranged prominent points.

The nature of these curious objects was long in dispute, and is still by no means cleared up, though specimens have been described with "cones" still attached to the scars,[1] thus appearing to confirm by direct evidence an idea which had long previously been suggested. The *Ulodendra*, then, were supposed to represent the fertile branches of various species of *Lepidodendron* (*e.g.* L. *Velt-heimianum*), *Bothrodendron*, and perhaps *Sigillaria* also, which thus bore their fructifications on thick stems, and not on terminal twigs. The peduncle, represented by the print within the scar, was

FIG. 70. — *Ulodendron.* Surface of branch, showing two large scars, with the central print *c*, and numerous Lepidodendroid leaf-bases. On the right the leaves are seen. Reduced. After Schimper. The large scars are really depressions, but, owing to the shading, appear in the figure as elevations. They can be seen as depressions if the figure is reversed.

[1] D'Arcy Thompson, "Notes on *Ulodendron* and *Halonia*," *Trans. Edinburgh Geol. Soc.* vol. iii. 1880. Cf. Solms-Laubach, *Fossil Botany,*

assumed to be quite short, so that the base of the almost sessile strobilus was in contact with the leafy surface of the main axis ; the large cup-shaped scar appeared to have owed its origin to the mutual pressure between the two organs. The great size of the scars, in some cases far exceeding the diameter of any known Lepidodendroid cones, was still, however, unaccounted for, their shape being inconsistent with dilatation by secondary growth. Further, in *L. Veltheimianum* the slender cones are known to have been borne at the ends of small twigs, though this species has *Ulodendron* scars.

Mr. D. M. S. Watson [1] has pointed out the great difficulties involved in the current interpretation of the Ulodendroid scar, and the inadequacy of the evidence in its support. He maintains that the scars are those of caducous branches, which were attached to the whole area of the scar, the umbilicus corresponding to the central cylinder and the dots and radial marks on the scar representing the leaf-traces of the branch. For certain cases, at all events, his interpretation appears to correspond best with the observed facts, though various difficulties remain.

Another modern writer, M. A. Renier, who has investigated the question very fully, comes to the conclusion that the Ulodendroid scars were those of branches, not cones. He finds, however, that the branch was attached to the umbilicus only, and accepts the pressure theory as accounting for the features of the outer zone of the scar.[2] Mr. Watson in a later paper has dealt critically with the

---

English edition, p. 208. Kidston, " On the Relationship of *Ulodendron* to *Lepidodendron*, etc.," *Ann. and Mag. Nat. Hist.* vol. xvi. 1885. Zeiller, " Sur les *Ulodendron* et *Bothrodendron*," *Bull. Soc. Géol. de France*, sér. iii. t. xiv. 1885.

[1] " On the Ulodendroid Scar," *Mem. and Proc. Manchester Lit. and Phil. Soc.* vol. lii. Part i. 1908.

[2] A. Renier, " L'origine raméale des Cicatrices Ulodendroïdes," *Ann. de la Soc. Géol. de Belgique*, t. xi. 1910.

question at issue, bringing forward new evidence in support of his view.[1]

The other form of stem to be considered—that known as *Halonia*—has certain points in common with the Ulodendroid branches, but presents a different appearance. The Halonial branch, which, though on the whole smaller than *Ulodendron*, is often several inches in diameter, is characterised by bearing a number of prominent knobs or tubercles, most often spirally arranged (see Fig. 71, A). The general surface is usually badly preserved, the specimens having evidently been partially decorticated before fossilisation, a fact which accounts for the prominence of the tubercles. Where, however, the external characters are well exhibited, so as to show the leaf-bases clearly, they prove that the specimens belonged to *Lepidophloios*, though it is quite possible that the Halonial condition may have also occurred in the true *Lepidodendra*. Halonial branches have been found in connection with the ordinary vegetative stems of Lepidodendreae, though whether of *Lepidodendron* or of *Lepidophloios* could not in all cases be determined—a point, however, which is of secondary importance. The fact that the *Haloniae* occurred as ultimate branches of the dichotomous stem,[2] quite disposes of the idea, once maintained by some French writers, that they were of the nature of roots or rhizomes.

As regards the anatomy, the main Halonial axis may either have in all respects the structure of an ordinary vegetative stem, or may differ from it in the absence of a medulla. The latter was the case in a Halonial branch of the Arran species, *Lepidodendron Wunschianum*, probably a *Lepidophloios*.[3] The branch is not quite an

---

[1] D. M. S. Watson, " On the Structure and Origin of the Ulodendroid Scar," *Ann. of Bot.* vol. xxviii. 1914. See also Marjorie Lindsey, " The Branching and Branch Shedding of *Bothrodendron*," *ibid.* vol. xxix. 1915.

[2] See Williamson, " Organisation, etc.," Part xii. Plates iii. iv. 1883.

[3] Williamson, " Organisation, etc.," Part xii. 1883.

inch thick, and contains a stele about 3·5 mm. in diameter. The wood is perfectly solid, consisting entirely of tracheae, without any indication of a medulla. This is not, however, a peculiarity of the Halonial form of branch, for in

FIG. 71.—*Lepidophloios scoticus*, Kidston. A. Bifurcating Halonial branch, showing numerous tubercles, and the characteristic leaf-bases. About ¼ nat. size. B. Leaf-cushions enlarged, showing the scar with the usual three prints. From the Calciferous Sandstone Series. After Kidston.

this species, *L. Wunschianum*, the ordinary vegetative branches of the same size also have a solid woody axis, and it is only in the larger stems that a pith is present. As regards the leaf-traces and cortical structures, the

Halonia shows no peculiarities ; a thick layer of periderm forms its outer boundary. From the central cylinder small cylindrical steles are given off, which pass obliquely outwards to supply the tubercles (see Fig. 72, *b'*, from *Lepidophloios fuliginosus*). The tubercular steles are surrounded by their own leaf-traces, which no doubt supplied the leaves, borne on the lateral shoots of which the tubercles are the persistent bases.

In *Lepidodendron Hickii* similar tubercles have been observed on some of the smaller branches. In this case the branch itself has the ordinary structure of the species, with a medullate stele, while the small strands running out to the tubercles are without any pith. A similar condition has been found in *Lepidodendron obovatum* and in *Lepidophloios fuliginosus* (Fig. 72). All these cases afford striking examples of the so-called unequal dichotomy described in the last chapter (p. 145).

What then was the nature of these Halonial branches, which evidently did not constitute a separate genus, but occurred as terminal ramifications on certain Lepidodendroid stems ? Their position and structure alike prove that they were neither roots nor root-bearing rhizomes. Evidently they bore some kind of lateral appendages of the nature of branches, but different from the ordinary vegetative twigs.

The distinction between *Halonia* and *Ulodendron* is not always an obvious one. As a rule the appendages of *Ulodendron* were distichously arranged, while those of *Halonia* were multiseriate, and quincuncially disposed. Williamson, however, described a specimen with multiseriate, quincuncially arranged scars apparently of the *Ulodendron* character, and also a *Halonia* with the tubercles in two series, so this distinction loses its value.[1]

A magnificent specimen of the latter kind was discovered some years back by Mr. J. Lomax, and described

[1] Williamson, xix. Plate vi. Figs. 22 and 25, A.

by Prof. F. E. Weiss. The stem, which has a mean diameter of about 8 cm., bears, on opposite sides, two series of large tubercles, with all the characteristics of *Halonia*. The main stem, the structure of which is

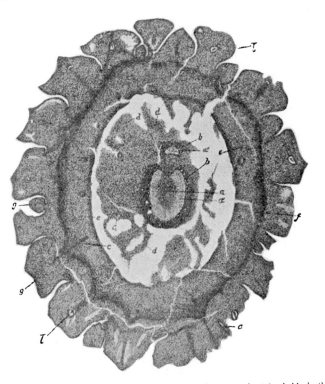

FIG. 72.—*Lepidophloios fuliginosus*. Transverse section of a young shoot (probably in the Halonial condition). *a*, pith, *a'*, xylem, of main stele; *a''*, xylem of branch; *b, b'*, phloëm of main and branch steles; *c*, leaf-traces; *d*, inner cortex; *e*, middle cortex; *f*, periderm; *g*, leaf-bases; *l*, ligule. × about 2. After Williamson, *Phil. Trans.* Will. Coll. 379.

perfectly preserved, agrees very closely with that of *Lepidophloios fuliginosus.*[1] Fig. 72 is from the latter species, and shows a younger branch, also with the Halonial mode of branching and apparently biseriate.

[1] F. E. Weiss, " A Biseriate Halonial Branch of *Lepidophloios fuliginosus*," *Trans. Linn. Soc. Bot.* ser. ii. vol. vi. 1903.

These specimens, together with others, in which the leaf-bases are preserved, have been regarded as showing that the Halonial shoots of *Lepidophloios* in some cases bore their tubercles in two rows, though this conclusion is disputed by Dr. Kidston,[1] who considers the attribution of these specimens to *Lepidophloios* as unproved.

In the Halonial branches of *Lepidophloios Scottii*, described by Dr. Gordon,[2] the pith contains scattered tracheides ; the tubercle-steles, as usual, have no pith.

The tubercles of *Halonia* appear in most specimens more prominent than they were in nature, owing to the axis which bears them having lost its outer cortex. In specimens with the natural surface preserved, the tubercles appear rather as scars, but are quite distinct from those of *Ulodendron*, owing to the absence in *Halonia* of the cup-shaped area characteristic of the former. The conclusion to which the facts appear to point is that the so-called *Halonia* consisted of branches of *Lepidophloios* (and possibly other Lepidodendreae) bearing either deciduous stalked cones, or twigs.

A specimen figured by Grand'Eury[3] appeared to strongly support the former hypothesis. He represented a portion of a thick stem of *Lepidophloios laricinus*, bearing four slender branches, on which were scales differing entirely from the vegetative leaves. These branches he regarded, with apparent probability, as the peduncles of cones. The specimen seemed to be of the same nature as the Halonial branches which are known to occur in this species. It is fair, however, to mention that Grand'Eury, in the same work, still inclined to regard *Halonia* as a rhizome.

From the whole of the facts, as known up to a few years ago, the view generally accepted as probable was that *Halonia* consisted of the cone-bearing branches of

---

[1] Kidston, " On the Internal Structure of *Sigillaria elegans*," *Trans. Roy. Soc. Edinburgh*, vol. xli. Part iii. 1905.

[2] " On *Lepidophloios Scottii* (a new species from the Calciferous Sandstone Series at Pettycur, Fife "), *ibid.* vol. xlvi. Part iii. 1908.

[3] Grand'Eury, *Bassin houiller du Gard*, Plate vi. Fig. 17, 1890.

certain Lepidodendroid plants (especially *Lepidophloios*), the tubercles representing the places where the cones themselves were inserted. In these forms, then, the cones would have been borne on relatively thick branches, but this was not the usual case in Lepidodendreae, for there is no doubt that in many species the cones occurred at the ends of slender twigs, the ultimate ramifications of a much-branched stem (see Fig. 56, B, p. 114). More recently Dr. Zalessky has found that the cones of *Lepidophloios*, like those of *Lepidodendron*, terminated the extremities of branchlets, and had no relation to the Halonial branches. It thus appears that the old interpretation of *Halonia*, like that of *Ulodendron*, must be given up.

2. *Lepidostrobus.*—We now come to the consideration of the actual fructifications. In a few instances the strobili have been found in connection with the branches of *Lepidodendron*, as, for example, was the case in *L. Ophiurus* (see Fig. 56, B). As a rule the specimens are isolated, but their nature has been determined by comparison with the cones still in position. In cases where the structure is preserved, additional and convincing evidence is afforded by the anatomy of the axis of the cone, which is quite similar to that of a young vegetative twig of *Lepidodendron*.

As it is very rarely possible to refer the fructifications to the particular species of stem to which they belonged, it is convenient to retain a distinct generic name for them. Most Lepidodendroid cones are described under the name of *Lepidostrobus*, but, as we shall see below, all the fructifications of the group cannot be included under a single genus. For the present we will confine ourselves to the characters of the true *Lepidostrobi*.

The cones of different species vary greatly in their dimensions, the length ranging approximately from about an inch to about a foot, and the diameter from less than half an inch to 3 inches. The form is usually cylindrical (Fig. 73), but in some of the shorter cones is more ovoid. The strobilus was either sessile or stalked ; the former may have been the case if the fruiting stem was ever of the Ulodendroid form, while the stalked cones were borne on the twigs of the young growth, or, as was once supposed, on the tubercles of Halonial branches.

The general characters of the cones of *Lepidostrobus* are those of Lycopodiaceous fructifications. In habit the agreement is closest with *Lycopodium,* while in some important details there is a nearer approach to *Selaginella*, but of course the Lepidodendreae have no near affinity with any of the modern genera. The axis of the strobilus bore a very large number of crowded sporophylls (or bracts, as they are often called), usually arranged spirally, but occasionally verticillate. Each sporophyll bore a single sporangium on its upper surface. The sporangia were of large size, enormously exceeding the dimensions of those in existing Lycopods. Thus, in the magnificent specimen known as *Lepidostrobus Brownii,* Schimper, the radial length of the sporangia reaches 16-17 mm., with a maximum breadth of about 5 mm.[1]

Fig.   73. — *Lepidostrobus Hibbertianus,* Binney.   Compressed specimen of an almost perfect cone, with the matrix.   The exterior surface is shown, except at the base, where the axis, with some of the megasporangia, is exposed.   ⅔ nat. size.   After Binney.

[1] For a full account of this Lower Carboniferous species see Zeiller, "Étude sur le *Lepidostrobus Brownii,*" *Mém. de l'Acad. des Sci.* Paris, 1911.

The great radial elongation of the sporangia is characteristic of the genus, and is correlated with the peculiar form of the sporophylls, which consist of a long, slender stalk or pedicel, usually more or less horizontal, terminating in a large lamina, which turns vertically upwards, several sporophylls overlapping each other. There is also usually a shorter downward prolongation of the lamina, so that the form of the whole is somewhat peltate (see diagram, Fig. 74). The sporangium is attached all along its lower side to the upper surface of the horizontal pedicel, but is free from the lamina. In its form, and mode of attachment to the sporophyll, the sporangium resembles that of *Isoëtes*.

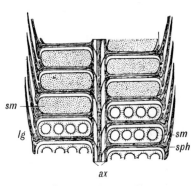

Fig. 74.—*Lepidostrobus*. Diagram of heterosporous cone in radial section. *ax*, axis; *sph*, sporophylls; *sm*, sporangia, seated singly on the upper surface of each sporophyll; *lg*, ligules; the microsporangia, in upper part of cone, contain numerous microspores, while the megasporangia below are shown containing four megaspores each. (G. T. G.) Sporophylls shown as if superposed.

The cones are often preserved as casts or impressions; where the external surface is perfect, it is completely invested by the overlapping laminae of the sporophylls, which are closely packed together (Fig. 73). When the preservation is less complete, the free tips of the laminae have perished, leaving only their more solid basal portions, which often assume a hexagonal form from mutual pressure. The fractures of the casts often show something of the internal organisation, the tissues being preserved to some extent, though in a carbonised condition (Fig. 73). It is only, however, in the petrified specimens that the structure is completely revealed.

Our more detailed description will be based on a form

named by Williamson *Lepidostrobus oldhamius*,[1] of which several examples in a calcified state have been yielded by the calcareous nodules of the English Coal-measures.

The largest specimens of this strobilus reach a diameter of about 4 cm. ; the axis is slender, about 4 or 5 mm. in thickness. The anatomical structure is of the usual Lepidodendroid type (cf. Fig. 75). The centre of the axis is occupied by a small stele, in which a ring of primary wood surrounds the pith. In the wood the larger elements, which have a scalariform thickening, are towards the interior ; the outer margin is produced into a number of somewhat prominent points, and here the narrow spiral elements of the protoxylem are found ; thus the development of the wood was evidently centripetal, as in the vegetative stem. In exceptionally well preserved specimens, the phloëm-zone, surrounding the wood, is preserved ; this zone is largely parenchymatous, the elongated elements, presumably forming the true phloëm, occupying only a small space. From some of the best-preserved specimens, it appears that the tissue next the wood was entirely parenchymatous, while the true phloëm lay more to the exterior. In *Lepidostrobus Brownii*, the structure of which is better preserved than that of *L. oldhamius*, a distinct endodermis, separating the stele from the inner cortex, can be traced.

The inner and outer zones of the cortex are usually well preserved in *L. oldhamius*, while the intermediate region has perished—a common condition in the stems of fossil Lycopods. The inner cortex consists of a narrow zone of parenchymatous tissue ; beyond this is the gap representing the position of the wide middle cortex ; the outer cortical zone is usually perfect, and consists of thick-celled tissue, largely made up of fibrous elements.

---

[1] For a full illustrated account of the organisation of these cones see Maslen, " Structure of *Lepidostrobus*," *Trans. Linn. Soc.* vol. v. 1899, and Agnes Arber, " Anatomical Study of the Palaeozoic cone-genus *Lepidostrobus*," *ibid.* vol. viii. 1914.

This zone is continuous on the exterior with the bases of the sporophylls.

The leaf-trace strands, one of which runs out to each sporophyll, have a very steep course, so that a large number, corresponding to several circuits of the foliar spiral, are seen in transverse section. The structure of these bundles, which is sometimes admirably preserved, is normally collateral. The smallest spiral tracheae lie at about the middle of the xylem-strand, as in *Lepidodendron Harcourtii*. The xylem is surrounded by a layer of delicate parenchyma, which on the outer side separates it from the phloëm. After passing through the inner cortex, the whole bundle is further surrounded by a parenchymatous sheath, continuous with the inner cortical tissue. In this condition it traverses the middle zone of the cortex, where the leaf-trace bundles, with their sheaths, are usually the only tissues preserved.

In *Lepidostrobus Brownii*, where the middle cortex is partly preserved, the leaf-trace bundles are connected with the surrounding tissues by trabeculae, analogous to those radiating from the steles in *Selaginella*. In *L. kentuckiensis*, another large cone, of Lower Carboniferous age, this zone is fairly perfect, and shows an interwoven structure, such as has often been observed in the cortex of Lepidodendroid stems.[1] The leaf-traces of *Lepidostrobus* closely resemble those of living Lycopods in structure.[2]

On reaching the outer cortex, where the bundles gradually assume a more horizontal course, the same structure is preserved. Here the sheath, immediately surrounding the vascular strand, has less thick walls than the enveloping cortical tissue. In this region a gap in the tissue constantly appears below each bundle,

[1] Scott and Jeffrey, " On Fossil Plants, showing Structure, from the Base of the Waverley Shale of Kentucky," *Phil. Trans. Royal Soc.* B, vol. 205, 1914, p. 357 (under the name *L. Fischeri*).

[2] See Bower, " On the Structure of the Axis of *Lepidostrobus Brownii*," *Annals of Botany*, vol. vii. 1893.

and accompanies it outwards into the sporophyll. There can be no doubt that this gap was in nature occupied by a delicate parenchyma (sometimes preserved in other species), continuous with that of the middle cortex, and that this tissue, accompanying the leaf-trace, corresponds to the parichnos-strand in the vegetative axis (see pp. 132 and 138).

The sporophylls in *L. oldhamius* are more than a centimetre in length, and stand out almost at a right angle with the axis. Each consists of a long, slender pedicel, terminating in a foliaceous lamina. Near the axis the pedicel is narrow, with a triangular section, while further to the exterior it becomes broader and flatter. It consists chiefly of thick-walled tissue like that of the outer cortex, and is traversed by the vascular bundle, which retains essentially the same structure as in the cortex. The lamina broadens out rapidly at the end of the pedicel, where at the same time it attains a considerable thickness. It turns upwards almost at a right angle with the pedicel, and becomes both narrower and thinner towards its termination. The general form of the lamina is thus lanceolate ; as mentioned above, it has a shorter downward prolongation, rendering the whole somewhat peltate (see diagram, Fig. 74). The structure is simple, the mesophyll consisting of rather small-celled parenchyma, in the outer layers of which the cell-walls are much thickened. The single vascular bundle which traverses the lamina is surrounded by a very well developed transfusion-tissue of short spiral or reticulated tracheides, most abundant where the leaf is thickest. In this respect the sporophyll resembles the foliage-leaf, and in both cases this accessory system of tracheides no doubt served to facilitate the supply of water to the mesophyll.

An interesting feature of the sporophyll is the ligule, the presence of which was demonstrated by Mr. Maslen in *L. oldhamius*. The ligule is seated on the upper surface of the sporophyll, near its distal end, and just where the lamina begins to bend upwards. It is a small pointed body, about half a millimetre in height, with a triangular transverse section, and consists of very small-celled parenchyma. In itself it thus resembles the ligule of the vegetative leaves, but differs in the entire absence of any ligular chamber. In allied forms of strobilus, however, a deep ligular chamber is present. As the discoverer points out, " the position of the ligule in *Lepidostrobus*, with the sporangium between it and the axis, is identical with that in *Selaginella* ; but whereas in the latter genus it is quite close to the axis of the cone, in the former the great elongation of the sporangium, which had taken place in the radial direction, had of course carried the ligule with it, and so the latter comes to be situated near the periphery of the cone, and at a considerable distance from the axis. The whole of the horizontal (sporangium-bearing) portion of the sporophyll thus appears to be homologous with the short leaf-base or cushion on the vegetative stem " [1] (see diagram, Fig. 74, *lg*).

The large, elongated sporangium is seated on the upper surface of the pedicel, to which it is attached throughout almost its whole length, from a point close to the axis, up to the beginning of the lamina (see diagram, Fig. 74). The connection between sporangium and sporophyll thus extends for a long distance in the radial direction, amounting to about a centimetre in large specimens of *L. oldhamius*, but at the same time the attachment is extremely narrow tangentially, so that a radial section of the cone seldom follows the plane of insertion for more than a small part of its length. Hence the connection between the two organs has sometimes been represented as much less extensive than is actually the case. The pedicel is grooved along its upper surface, and into this groove the narrow band of tissue fits, by

[1] Maslen, *Annals of Botany*, vol. xii. 1898, p. 259.

which the sporangium and sporophyll are connected. The large baggy sporangium projects on either side considerably beyond the limits of the pedicel.

The wall of the sporangium, as preserved, consists of a single layer of prismatic palisade-like cells, very characteristic of *Lepidostrobus* sporangia, though in some species the wall has a more complicated structure. Along the lower side of the sporangium, where it is attached to the sporophyll, a pad of delicate tissue rises into its cavity, and spreads laterally for some distance along the interior of the wall. Further, a radial plate of sterile tissue, often subdivided, runs up far into the cavity of the sporangium ; such trabeculae, comparable to some extent with those of *Isoëtes*, occur also in other species. It has been suggested by Bower,[1] that these extensions of the sterile tissue into the cavity of the sporangium may have served to facilitate the nutrition of the developing spores, and may also have contributed to the mechanical support of the sporangial wall. Both points may well have been of importance in spore-sacs of such large size, with so slender an attachment to the subtending leaf.

In *Lepidostrobus oldhamius* and some other forms, only the small spores are known with certainty. They are present in countless multitudes in each sporangium, and are usually found still grouped in fours, with a tetrahedral arrangement. The spores are very minute, about .02 mm. in diameter. From the analogy of other cones of Lepidodendreae there is a strong presumption that *L. oldhamius* was heterosporous, like *Selaginella*, the microspores alone having been identified at present. Several forms are known to have been heterosporous, and it is most probable that all *Lepidostrobi* will prove to be so when we have a more complete knowledge of the

---

[1] " Studies in the Morphology of Spore-producing Members," Part i., *Phil. Trans.* B, 1894. See also Dr. Agnes Arber's paper, above cited, on the genus *Lepidostrobus*.

strobili.[1] Fragments of a heterosporous cone, with large megaspores nearly a millimetre in diameter, have been found in the same beds which have yielded the specimens of *L. oldhamius.*

We will, however, choose as our example of heterospory in *Lepidostrobus* a cone from a lower horizon, named *Lepidostrobus Veltheimianus,* a small species which is very abundant in the plant-bearing beds of the Calciferous Sandstones, near Burntisland, in Scotland. These cones are indistinguishable from those of *Lepidodendron*

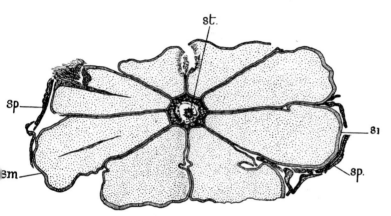

FIG. 75.—*Lepidostrobus Veltheimianus.* Transverse section of cone, through microspore-region. *st,* stele of axis; *sp,* laminae of sporophylls (only partially shown); *sm,* microsporangia; in the two to the left trabeculae are shown. × about 7. S. Coll. 400. (G. T. G.)

Veltheimianum, one of the few *Lepidodendra* which have been found with the fructification still attached to the branches. As this species is extremely abundant in the Calciferous Sandstone Series, of which the Burntisland beds form part, it is almost certain that the cones with structure preserved belong to it. Hence I have ventured to use the specific name *Veltheimianus* for the cones also. For information on this subject, as well as on the identity

[1] In certain cases, the apparently homosporous strobili were doubtless the male fructifications corresponding to the " seed-bearing " cones of *Lepidocarpon,* described below, p. 174.

of *Lepidodendron Veltheimianum* with *L. brevifolium*, Will., I am indebted to Dr. R. Kidston, F.R.S.[1]

This strobilus is only about 1 cm. in diameter, and was probably not more than 4 cm. in length. In general morphology and structure it is essentially similar to *L. oldhamius*, but all the parts are on a smaller scale, and the slender stele of the axis has but little pith (see Fig. 75). The sporophylls have the same general form as in the previous species (Fig. 77), but the pedicels on which the sporangia are seated are relatively flatter and wider. In

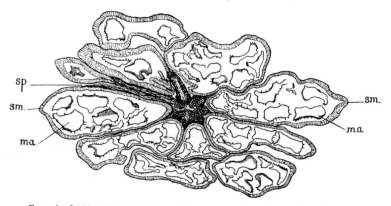

Fig. 76.—*Lepidostrobus Veltheimianus.* Transverse section of cone, through megaspore-region. *sp*, sporophylls (only partially shown); *sm*, megasporangia; *ma*, the spinose megaspores. × about 7. S. Coll. 413. (G. T. G.)

some, at least, of the specimens, their arrangement is in alternating verticils. The heterospory is beautifully shown in several specimens; from the longitudinal sections it is evident that all the upper part of the cone was occupied by microsporangia, and the lower by mega-sporangia, as in most species of *Selaginella* at the present day (Fig. 77). Fig. 75 represents a transverse section from the upper, and Fig. 76 one from the lower part of the cone; the former shows microsporangia, the latter megasporangia only.

[1] This *Lepidostrobus* was described and figured by Williamson in his " Organisation of the Fossil Plants of the Coal-measures," Part iii. 1872, and Part xix. 1893, *Phil. Trans.*

The structure of the sporangium is similar to that of the last species ; the wall consists of narrow prismatic cells, sometimes divided by a transverse septum. From the base of the sporangium a radial plate of tissue runs

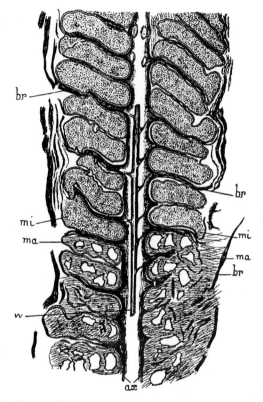

FIG. 77.—*Lepidostrobus Veltheimianus.* Longitudinal section of cone, showing microsporangia above and megasporangia below. *ax,* axis of cone, showing stele (*w*) and leaf-traces, passing out to sporophylls, *br* ; *mi,* microsporangia ; *ma,* megasporangia, containing a few spinose megaspores. × about 4. S. Coll. 1008. (G. T. G.)

up into the cavity, and often forks into two above. This structure may be compared with the trabeculae of *Isoëtes.* It is best shown in the microsporangia, but evident traces of it are present in the megasporangia also. The microspores occur in immense numbers in

their sporangia, and are generally found united tetrahedrally in fours.   They are of small size, not exceeding
about .02 mm. in diameter.   The megaspores are rela-

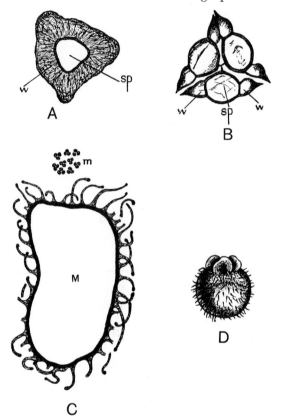

Fig. 78.—Spores of Lepidodendreae. A. *Spencerites insignis.* Spore, showing wing in
surface-view. *sp*, cavity of spore ; *w*, wing. B. Tetrad, in section, showing three
out of the four spores, tetrahedrally arranged. *sp*, cavity of spore ; *w*, wing. A and
B × about 90. C. *Lepidostrobus Veltheimianus.* M, a single megaspore, showing the
blunt spines ; *m*, tetrads of microspores, on the same scale. × about 70. After
Williamson, *Phil. Trans.* D. A single megaspore, probably of *L. Veltheimianus,* showing
spines and lobes of membrane, surface-view. × 15. After Kidston and Bennie.

tively of enormous dimensions, so that they are easily
visible to the naked eye.   Their mean diameter is at
least .8 mm., quite forty times that of the microspores
(see Fig. 78, C).   The number of megaspores in each

sporangium was small, certainly not more than sixteen, and perhaps as few as eight (cf. Figs. 76 and 77). The thick membrane of the megaspores was prolonged on the outside into a number of stout curved spines (see Figs. 76, 77, and 78, C). Detached megaspores of *Lepidostrobus* and allied fructifications are very abundant in the Carboniferous formation, and show a great variety in size and surface-sculpture. Some of these megaspores (which were investigated by Messrs. Kidston and

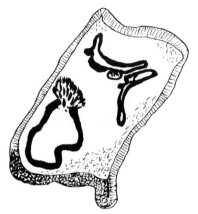

FIG. 79.—*Lepidostrobus foliaceus.* Sporangium, showing three megaspores, on two of which the appendage is visible. × about 18. S. Coll. 2237. (R. S.)

Bennie) appear to be identical with those of *Lepidostrobus Veltheimianus* ; in addition to the spines, these detached specimens show a curious three-lobed appendage to the membrane of the spore (see Fig. 78, D), which very commonly appears in the sections also. It is probable that this structure, which was of very general occurrence in the megaspores of Lepidodendreae, formed a passage for the admission of the microspores or of the spermatozoids produced by them. Microspores are often found entangled among the bristles of the megaspores.

FIG. 80.—*Lepidostrobus foliaceus.* Megaspore (somewhat collapsed) bearing large episporic appendage. × 28. From R. Scott, *New Phytologist.* S. Coll. 1217.

The megaspores of *Lepidostrobus foliaceus,* a Coal-measure species, of which until recently only the microsporangia were known, appear to have numbered not more than four in each sporangium, and possess a curious episporic appendage, comparable to the so-called " swimming apparatus " of *Azolla* [1] (see Figs. 79 and 80).

In favourable cases the prothallus is preserved within

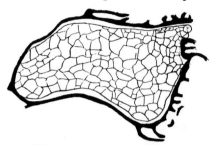

FIG. 81.—*Lepidostrobus Veltheimianus.* Megaspore in section, filled with prothallus, which protrudes somewhat through the opening of the megaspore-wall.   × 50.   S. Coll. 912. (R. S.)

the megaspore. This is sometimes the case in *L. Veltheimianus*, as is well shown in Fig. 81 ; the prothallus is here almost complete, and fills the megaspore. Fig. 82, from a photograph, represents the megaspore and prothallus from a fructification, named *Mazocarpon*, dis-

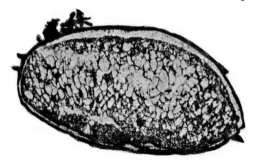

FIG. 82.—*Mazocarpon horense,* Benson. Isolated megaspore filled with prothallus. × about 35.   From a photograph by Mr. W. Tams.   S. Coll. 1756.

tinguished by the fact that the megaspores in the sporangium are embedded in a massive parenchymatous tissue (see p. 213). In other specimens the archegonia are recognisable. M. Renault found megaspores of a *Lepido-*

[1] R. Scott, "On the Megaspore of *Lepidostrobus foliaceus,*" *New Phytologist,* vol. v. 1906.

strobus in which the prothalloid tissue contains flask-shaped cavities, strongly suggestive of archegonia.

The best example, however, is provided by *Lepidostrobus Veltheimianus* itself. In a prothallus of this species Dr. Gordon[1] discovered a well-preserved archegonium, seated on the small-celled part of the prothallial tissue, probably facing the open beak of the megaspore. The archegonium has a short, but well-marked neck, still closed, with evident remains of the canal and central cell (Fig. 83); the whole has essentially the same structure as an archegonium of *Selaginella* or *Isoëtes*.

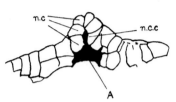

Fig. 83.—*Lepidostrobus Veltheimianus.* Archegonium. A, Central cell; *n.c.*, neck cells; *n.c.c.*, neck canal-cell. × 275. Gordon Coll. 1215. (R. S.)

There is thus every reason to believe that the mode of reproduction in many of the Lepidodendreae agreed closely with that of the heterosporous Lycopods of the present time, but certain other fructifications of the same group attained, as will be explained below (§ 4), a much higher organisation.

3. *Spencerites.*—The chief generic character of *Lepidostrobus*, distinguishing it from most other Lycopodiaceous strobili, is to be found in the great radial elongation of the sporangium, and its attachment by a long and narrow insertion to the upper surface of the sporophyll-pedicel throughout its length. There is another form of Lycopodiaceous cone from the Coal-measures, which differs in this, as well as in other important points, from *Lepidostrobus*, and which has therefore been separated, under the name of *Spencerites*.[2] This type will now be

---

[1] W. T. Gordon, "Note on the Prothallus of *Lepidodendron Veltheimianum*," *Ann. of Bot.* vol. xxiv. 1910.

[2] See Scott, "On the Structure and Affinities of Fossil Plants from the Palaeozoic Rocks, ii. On *Spencerites*," a New Genus of Lyco-

shortly described, and the description will be based, in the first instance, on *Spencerites insignis* (Will.), the smaller of the two known species.

The strobilus, which is from 8 to 10 mm. or more in diameter, is pedunculate, the peduncle bearing scattered bracts. The sporophylls are in some cases arranged in regular alternating verticils, of about ten members each, though a spiral arrangement has also been met with. As Miss Berridge has shown, the sporophyll consists of a narrow pedicel, about 2.5 to 3 mm. long, carrying a thin upturned lamina with a broad fleshy base. The base of the lamina bears a thick dorsal lobe below, and a larger ventral outgrowth above (see Fig. 84). The sporangia are not elongated, but ovoid or spherical, and not in any way attached to the pedicel, but inserted, by means of a short stalk at the distal end, on the upper adaxial surface of the ventral lobe (Fig. 84). No ligule has been observed. The structure of the sporangial wall is also quite different from that of *Lepidostrobus*, for it consists of prosenchymatous cells, elongated in the plane of the wall, and not at right angles to it as in the former genus.

The winged spores are a remarkable feature of the cone (Fig. 78, A and B). They measure about .14 mm. in maximum diameter (not reckoning the wing), and are thus intermediate in size between the microspores and megaspores of a *Lepidostrobus*. They are often found still grouped in tetrads, with a tetrahedral arrangement (Fig. 78, B). Around the equator of each spore runs a broad, hollow, annular wing, formed by the dilation of the cuticle (Fig. 78, A and B). It is probable that this wing served the same purpose as the well-known air-sacs of the pollen-grain in *Pinus* and some other Coniferae,

---

podiaceous Cones, *Phil. Trans. Roy. Soc.* vol. 189, B, 1897. The earlier papers by Williamson are there cited. See also Miss E. M. Berridge, F.L.S., " On two New Specimens of *Spencerites insignis*," *Annals of Bot.* vol. xix. 1905, and the reference to Prof. Lang on p. 173.

namely, to facilitate dispersal by the wind. The form of the air-chamber is, however, quite different, for in *Spencerites* it constitutes a continuous rim all round the spore (Fig. 78, A), while in the Conifer it forms two distinct sacs, one on each side of the pollen-grain. These

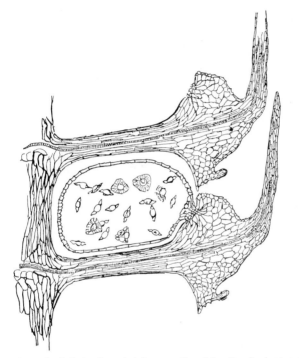

FIG. 84.—*Spencerites insignis.* Somewhat diagrammatic radial section showing two of the sporophylls in connection with the axis. On the lower sporophyll the sporangium is seen, attached at its distal end to the ventral outgrowth ; a few of the winged spores are shown. After Miss Berridge.

spores are thus quite unlike anything known in *Lepido-strobus*, and at once distinguish *Spencerites insignis* from allied fructifications.

Indications of a tissue, or of distinct cells, are frequently found in the cavities of the large spores, but there is reason to suspect that these appearances were caused by the presence of some parasitic organism. No signs of microspores have been detected, and so the homosporous or heterosporous character of the strobilus remains uncertain. A very similar spore (*S. membranacens*) has been described by Dr. Kubart from the Ostrau Coalfield, somewhat older than our Lower Coal-measures.

The anatomy of the axis is of a simple Lycopodiaceous type, with an axial strand of centripetally developed wood ; in some specimens there is a small pith, which is quite absent in others. The leaf-trace bundles passed out more horizontally than in *Lepidostrobus*, having a somewhat arched course in approaching the pedicel. The inner cortex and, in some cases, the phloëm are preserved : the middle cortex has often disappeared, but when present sometimes shows a remarkable structure, consisting of interwoven trabecular filaments, connected with the inner and outer tissues, and with the sheaths of the outgoing vascular bundles. The outer cortex consists of fibrous sclerenchyma, either continuous or forming a network, with a more delicate tissue occupying the meshes through which the leaf-traces passed out to the sporophylls.

The other species, *S. majusculus*, which is larger, has relatively still shorter sporophylls ; as regards the form and insertion of the sporangia, the two species of *Spencerites* nearly agree; in *S. majusculus*, the enlarged base of the lamina, comprising the ventral and dorsal lobes, is highly developed, reaching 3 mm. in tangential width ; collectively these bodies form an almost continuous armour. Here also there is evidence that the lamina possessed a relatively thin distal limb. The spores are smaller in *S. majusculus*, and of different' shape, having the form of quadrants of a sphere, with narrow wings along the angles. Vegetative stems are known, which in structure much resemble the axis of the *Spencerites* cones. They are of the Lepidodendroid type, and have something in common with the stems of *Bothrodendron* (see p. 180).

The insertion of the sporangium by its distal end on a ventral lobe of the sporophyll suggests a comparison with Sphenophyllales, but the absence of any vascular supply to this lobe in the case of *Spencerites* is a serious point of difference.

Lepidostrobus and *Spencerites* are typical Lycopodiaceous strobili, as to the affinities of which no doubt can arise. The well-marked heterospory of some species (possibly of all) shows that these fructifications had reached at least as high a differentiation as the most highly organised Lycopods of the present day. They differ from most recent strobiliferous forms in the mode of insertion of the sporangia, which in existing Lycopodiaceous cones are either axillary (*Selaginella*), or are seated on the sporophyll, usually near the axis [1] (*Lycopodium* and *Phylloglossum*). In *Lycopodium cernuum*, however, there is a certain analogy with *Spencerites*,[2] in so far as the sporangium is borne on the distal part of the pedicel, but there is no ventral outgrowth; the analogy is perhaps nearer with the cone of *Bothrodendron mundum* (see p. 181, Fig. 90). In *Lepidostrobus*, as in the recent, non-strobiliferous *Isoëtes*, the enormous development of the sporangia is due chiefly to radial elongation, and this brings with it a corresponding extension of the base of the sporangium, which is attached to the long pedicel of the sporophyll from end to end. The displacement of the ligule, as described above, affords a good measure of the radial extension of the whole organ. The presence in some cases of trabeculae was no doubt an adaptation to the great bulk of the sporangium.

4. *The Seed-like Lycopodiaceous Fructifications.*—We can well understand that an enormous output of spores must have been necessary in the *Lepidostrobi*, in so far

---

[1] *Psilotum* and *Tmesipteris* are left out of consideration, as it is quite doubtful whether the synangium of these genera is comparable to a single sporangium of the typical Lycopods. See the concluding Chapter.

[2] W. H. Lang, " Preliminary Statement on the Morphology of the Cone of *Lycopodium cernuum*," *Proc. Royal Soc. Edinburgh*, vol. xxviii. Part v. 1908.

as they were heterosporous. For fertilisation and the development of an embryo to take place, it was essential for microspores and megaspores to germinate together, and where these cones were borne on trees, and often at a great height above the ground, the chances must have been enormously against such an association. The successful accomplishment of the reproductive act could only be ensured by the production of a prodigious number of spores, and especially of microspores. It is quite probable, however, that the bristles and other appendages of the megaspores may have served to catch the microspores, and thus secure their presence when dispersal took place.

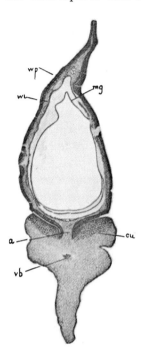

Fig. 85.—*Lepidocarpon Lomaxi.* Sporangium and sporophyll before integument was formed, in tangential section of cone. *cu*, lateral cushions of sporophyll; *a*, base of sporangium; *v.b.*, vascular bundle; *wp*, palisade layer of sporangium; *wi*, inner layer of wall; *mg*, membrane of megaspore or embryo sac. This section does not pass through the abortive spores. × about 12. (G. T. G.) Scott, *Phil. Trans.* S. Coll. 607.

Recent discoveries have shown that the difficulty was met, in some of the Palaeozoic Lycopods, in another way, namely, by the formation of a kind of ovule or seed, which may probably have been fertilised, or at least pollinated, while still on the plant. In *Lepidocarpon Lomaxi*, a cone so closely allied to *Lepidostrobus* that male specimens were formerly regarded by myself and others as a mere variety of *L. oldhamius*, each megasporangium contains a single mature megaspore or embryo-sac, filling almost the whole cavity (Fig. 85), but accompanied by three abortive spores, so that the original number in each sporangium was no doubt four, of which one gained the upper hand over the rest. Around the sporangium, the wall of which was identical in structure with that of a *Lepidostrobus*, the tissue of the bract grew up to form a regular integument, closing in at the top, but leaving a narrow crevice or micropyle (Figs. 86 and 87). This opening, however, differed from the micropyle of ordinary seeds in not being tubular, but forming a long narrow

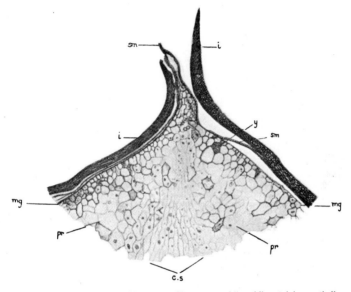

FIG. 86.—*Lepidocarpon Lomaxi.* Upper part of integumented " seed," containing prothallus. *i*, integument ; *sm*, wall of sporangium ; *mg*, membrane of megaspore ; *pr*, tissue of prothallus ; *y*, possible central cell of an archegonium ; *c.s.*, central strand of prothallus. × 20. (G. T. G.) Scott, *Phil. Trans.* S. Coll. 1073.

slit, extending in the radial direction almost the whole length of the sporangium, which was radially elongated, as in an ordinary *Lepidostrobus*. A ligule was prese t, at the distal end, just as in that genus.

When cut at right angles to this slit-like micropyle, the appearance of the sporangium with its integument is altogether that of a seed (see Fig. 87), and detached specimens were long known to science under the name *Cardiocarpon anomalum* of

Williamson [1] (not of Carruthers). The seeds, which attained a great size, became detached, together with the remains of the sporophyll, and in this condition were never suspected of belonging to a Lycopod until their origin had been traced. The prothallus within the megaspore is not uncommonly preserved (see Figs. 86, 87), and is found in the younger stage, before the integument has grown up, as well as in the mature "seeds." The tissue of the prothallus may show a considerable amount of differentiation (see Fig. 86) ; only doubtful traces of archegonia have so far been observed.

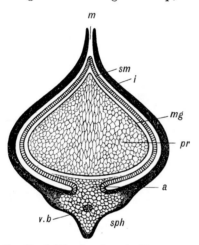

FIG. 87.—*Lepidocarpon Lomaxi.* Diagrammatic section of "seed," tangential to cone. *sph*, sporophyll ; *v.b.*, vascular bundle ; *i*, integument ; *m*, micropyle ; *sm*, wall of sporangium ; *a*, base of sporangium ; *mg*, membrane of megaspore ; *pr*, prothallus. (G. T. G.)

In a microspore-bearing strobilus, probably belonging to *Lepidocarpon Lomaxi*, the microsporophylls developed lateral outgrowths, suggestive of imperfect integuments.

Lepidocarpon Lomaxi, and other undescribed species, belong to the Lower Coal-measures ; the closely similar *L. Wildianum* is frequent in the more ancient Burntisland deposits of Lower Carboniferous age.

The cone of *L. Lomaxi* was first discovered by the late Mr. G. Wild and Mr. J. Lomax, working independently.[2]

[1] " Organisation, etc.," Part viii., *Phil. Trans.* 1877, p. 254, Figs. 117-119 ; Part x. 1880, p. 518, Fig. 64. The identification of these " seeds " with the *Cardiocarpus* of Brongniart is certainly incorrect.

[2] See their note " On a New *Cardiocarpon*-bearing Strobilus," in the *Annals of Botany* for March 1900 ; for the full description see Scott, " On the Seed-like Fructification of *Lepidocarpon*," *Phil. Trans. Roy. Soc.* vol. 194, B, 1901.

Lepidocarpon no longer stands alone among Palaeozoic Lycopods in possessing organs analogous with true seeds. Another instance is afforded by *Miadesmia membranacea*, the vegetative organs of which were discovered by Bertrand in 1894 in the calcareous nodules of the English Lower Coal-measures. The stem is very slender, and the plant appears to have been of herbaceous habit. The stele is of simple structure, with centripetal wood and no pith; the cortex contains trabeculae comparable to those of *Selaginella*. The leaves appear to have been

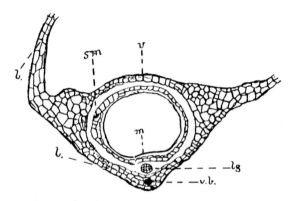

Fig. 88.—*Miadesmia membranacea.* Approximately transverse section of seed-like organ. *l, l,* lamina of sporophyll; *v.b.,* vascular bundle; *v,* velum or integument; *lg,* ligule; *sm,* sporangium-wall; *m,* membrane of megaspore. × about 30. (R. S.) S. Coll. 2237.

borne in four rows; the ligule is remarkably well developed, and the lamina is fringed by a membrane one cell thick, breaking up into uniseriate hairs at the margin. Within the last few years a megasporangiate fructification has been discovered, which is shown, by the structure of the ligule, the fringed margin of the sporophyll, and other characters, to have belonged to *Miadesmia*.[1] The fructifications are borne in a rather lax strobilus. Each sporophyll bears a megasporangium, attached to its

---

[1] Dr. M. Benson, " On a New Seed-like Lycopodiaceous Fructification," *New Phytologist*, vol i. 1902. For the full paper see *Phil. Trans. Roy. Soc.* B, 1908.

upper surface at the proximal end, containing a single megaspore, filling its cavity (Fig. 89). As in *Lepido-carpon*, the megasporangium is enclosed in an integument, which in *Miadesmia*, however, completely roofs in the sporangium above, leaving only a narrow opening or micropyle at the distal end (Figs. 88 and 89). The integument is provided with long tentacles, which, as they project beyond the micropyle, may probably have assisted pollination. The sporangial wall is less developed than in *Lepidocarpon*, the integument having, as it appears, more completely taken over the function of a protective

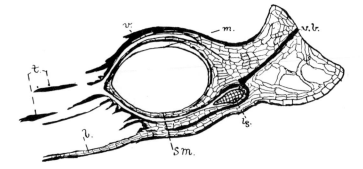

Fig. 89.—*Miadesmia membranacea.* Radial section of seed-like organ. *t*, tentacles; other lettering as in Fig. 88. × about 30. (R. S.) S. Coll. 2240.

organ, and no abortive sister-cells of the single megaspore (in which the prothallus is sometimes present) have been observed. Thus the seed-like character is even more striking in *Miadesmia* than in *Lepidocarpon*. There seems to be no near affinity between the two genera, which differ widely, especially in the insertion of the sporangium and the position of the micropyle, as well as in habit ; in each of them, presumably, the seed-habit was independently evolved.

In both genera the most important difference from true seeds, such as those of the Pteridosperms, consists in the fact that the sporophyll as a whole formed part of the seed-like organ, and was shed together with it.

In other respects—the single megaspore, the integument, and the indehiscent character—the analogies with seeds are complete. In the case of *Miadesmia* the wide lamina of the sporophyll gave the organ the character of a winged seed.

5. *Bothrodendron.* — The genus *Bothrodendron*, of Lindley and Hutton, represents another group of Palaeozoic Lycopods, very near *Lepidodendron*, though differing from it in the surface-characters of the stem. The genus is now well known, and presents several points of interest. On the larger stems, the surface of the cortex is smooth, the leaf-scars are very small, and flush with the surface, for leaf-cushions were not developed. This causes a striking difference in appearance from *Lepidodendron*, though the leaf-scars are in themselves quite similar to those of that genus, showing the usual three prints on the actual scar, with the ligular pit above. On the younger twigs the foliage is sometimes preserved ; the leaves are narrow, and resemble those of a recent *Lycopodium*. The smooth character of the stem-surface has suggested a comparison with a group of the *Sigillariae*, which we shall consider in the next chapter ; some authors have even united these two genera.

The stem of *Bothrodendron punctatum* is commonly found in the Ulodendroid condition, bearing the large, cup-shaped scars described in the last chapter. It has, therefore, been inferred that its cones were in these cases borne on the old wood, but in other species they have been found in connection with small twigs, and it has become very doubtful whether the large *Ulodendron* scars really had any relation to the cones. The strobili borne on the slender branches in *B. minutifolium* are identified by Dr. Kidston with a *Lepidostrobus* described by M. Zeiller under the name of *L. Olryi*, a small cylindrical cone with verticillate sporophylls of the *Lepidostrobus* type. On the whole, there is no reason to doubt the very close affinity of *Bothrodendron* with *Lepidodendron*.

The group is of great antiquity, chiefly occurring in the lower beds of the Carboniferous formation, while species have been described from the Upper Devonian of Ireland and of Bear Island.

The Irish species, *B. kiltorkense*, is now well known, so far as external characters are concerned. The stem has been found by Professor T. Johnson in connection with its Stigmarian root-stock (see p. 217). The arborescent, dichotomous stem bore long, linear-subulate leaves which appear to have been shed early. The cones have been identified by Johnson with the *Lepidostrobus Bailyanus* of Schimper ; they were short, stout strobili, borne terminally on forked twigs. The sporophylls were enormously long (at least 13 cm.), and resembled the foliage leaves. The large sporangium was borne on the thick, spatulate base of the sporophyll. The megaspores, already discovered by Schimper about 1870, number as many as twenty in the sporangium, and are about 1 mm. in diameter. The microsporangia have also been observed.[1]

Bothrodendron is thus among the oldest known genera of Lycopods, and it is therefore of much importance that its internal structure should be recognised. This has been discovered in a Coal-measure species by Mr. J. Lomax, who finds that a stem showing the characteristic external features of a *Bothrodendron* has the anatomical structure of the *Lepidodendron mundum* of Williamson.[2] The structure of *Bothrodendron mundum*, as the species may now be provisionally named, is of a simple Lepidodendroid type. In the larger stems there is a massive pith, surrounded by a comparatively thin zone of centripetal wood with well-marked protoxylem groups ; in the more minute twigs, however, the xylem is solid. A

---

[1] T. Johnson, "On *Bothrodendron kiltorkense*, Haughton, sp., *Scientific Proc. Royal Dublin Soc.* vol. xiii. (N.S.) No. 34, 1913; "*Bothrodendron kiltorkense*, its *Stigmaria* and Cone," *ibid.* vol. xiv. No. 13, 1914.

[2] "Organisation of Fossil Plants of Coal-measures," Part xvi., *Phil. Trans. Roy. Soc.* B, 1889.

characteristic feature is the radial arrangement of the primary tissue of the outer cortex, quite apart from the subsequent formation of periderm. No secondary wood has been observed in the stem, but in a *Stigmaria* described by Prof. F. E. Weiss, probably belonging to the same plant, extensive secondary growth took place (see p. 235).

Shortly afterwards Mr. D. M. S. Watson [1] identified the cone of *Bothrodendron mundum* in structural material.

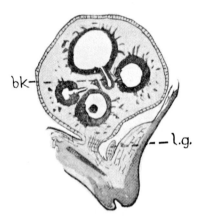

The cone is a minute one, only a few millimetres in diameter, and is hermaphrodite, probably with the microsporangia above and the megasporangia below. The sporophylls are very short in the radial direction (Fig. 90), and the sporangium is attached by a narrow neck of tissue about the middle of the horizontal portion; there is a large ligule in the usual position, *i.e.* in a depression beyond the sporangium.

FIG. 90.—*Bothrodendron mundum*. Sporophyll and sporangium in radial section. Four megaspores are shown. *bk*, beak of a megaspore *l.g.*, ligule of sporophyll. × about 30. S. Coll. 2561. (R. S.)

Each megasporangium was found to contain only four megaspores, which are characterised by their long branched spines and by a prominent beak (Fig. 90). The cone is evidently quite distinct from a *Lepidostrobus*, though apparently nearer to that genus than to *Spencerites*.

It will be remarked that the cones are of a very different character in the three species of *Bothrodendron*

1 " The Cone of *Bothrodendron mundum*," *Mem. and Proc. Manchester Lit. and Phil. Soc.* vol. lii. Part i. 1908.

in which they are known. It may be doubted whether the genus, founded essentially on the superficial features of the stem, is really a natural one.

Bothrodendron is further of interest from the extraordinary mode of preservation in which one of the species, *B. punctatum*, occurs. At Tovarkovo, in the province of Toula, in Central Russia, beds of a peculiar kind of coal, called leaf-coal or paper-coal, have long been known. The seams are about 8 inches thick, and lie near the surface of the ground, only covered by sand. The so-called coal has all the appearance of a bed of excessively thin dead leaves, intermixed only with structureless organic matter of the nature of humic acid. The leafy films, on investigation, have proved to consist entirely of layers of cuticle, belonging to the stems of ancient plants, from which all other tissues had rotted away, ages before. The cuticles are perfectly fresh and pliable, and not in any way fossilised, although geologists are agreed that the bed (which covers an area of many square miles) belongs to the Carboniferous Limestone horizon, in the lower part of the Carboniferous formation. The cuticle is in some cases complete, corresponding to the whole circumference of the stem which it once enclosed ; it is perforated by numerous small round holes, regularly disposed, and corresponding in arrangement with the leaf-traces of a *Bothrodendron*. The cuticularisation had evidently extended to a portion of the vertical cell-walls abutting on the outer skin, for the network of cells is marked out with perfect clearness on the inner surface of the cuticle. Irregular borings, which occur here and there in the membrane, were attributed by M. Renault to the activity of Palaeozoic Bacteria.

The cuticles, when freed from the formless organic matter adhering to them, are of a light brown colour ; they swell up in water, can be stained with aniline dyes, and on chemical analysis prove to have much the same composition as the cuticle of recent plants. That a vegetable tissue should thus have come down to us, fresh and unaltered, from a period more ancient than that of the Coal-measures, is certainly one of the most remarkable among the curiosities of palaeontology.[1]

6. *Pinakodendron.*—This Coal-measure genus appears to be allied to *Bothrodendron*, from which it chiefly differs in the presence of a delicate network of raised lines between the leaf-scars. In one species, *P. Ohmanni*, the fructification has been discovered by Dr. Kidston. He finds that there are no specialised cones ; a part of the stem becomes fertile without any morphological alteration, as in *Lycopodium Selago.* The sporophylls are long and narrow ; a sporangium is seated on the enlarged base of each, as in *Bothrodendron kiltorkense*, but only four megaspores are present in each megasporangium. The sporophylls are quite similar to the ordinary leaves.[2]

[1] See Renault, *Les cuticules de Tovarkovo*, Autun, 1895.

[2] Kidston, " Végétaux houillers dans le Hainaut Belge," *Mus. Royal d'Hist. Nat. de Belgique*, t. iv. année 1909.

CHAPTER VII

LYCOPODIALES—*continued*

Sigillaria and Stigmaria ; Lycopoditeae

I. SIGILLARIA

WE now come to the great genus *Sigillaria*, one of the most extensive and important groups of Palaeozoic plants, and one of those of which the affinities have been most keenly discussed. In geological range the *Sigillariae* are somewhat more restricted than the *Lepidodendra*. The genus, *Archaeosigillaria*, Kidston, of which a species has been described from the Upper Devonian of New York,[1] appears to combine Sigillarian with Lepidodendroid characters ; otherwise they have not been detected with certainty below the rocks at the base of the Carboniferous formation, and scarcely extend above the Permian ; they attain their maximum in the Middle and Upper Coal-measures.

1. *Habit and External Characters.* — The *Sigillariae* must have been among the largest trees of the Palaeozoic forests. A trunk of *Sigillaria reniformis*, found near Saarbrücken, in Germany, *in situ*, was 6 feet in diameter at the base, where its roots were attached. This trunk was only 18 feet high, diminishing towards the top to a

---

[1] See David White, "A remarkable Fossil Tree Trunk from the Middle Devonic of New York," *N.Y. State Museum Bulletin*, 107 ; *Geological Papers, Albany*, 1907.

diameter of about a foot. Other gigantic specimens have a very different form. M. Zeiller [1] described a trunk found at L'Escarpelle, near Valenciennes, in France, which was traced for a distance of 22 metres (over 70 feet). At the lower end it had a diameter of 60 cm. (about 2 feet), which at the upper extremity had only diminished to 50 cm. (1 foot 8 inches). The stem was thus a slender, nearly cylindrical shaft. Both this and other, even longer, trunks, reaching a length of 30 metres (nearly 100 feet) were unbranched. In some cases the large stems are found still clothed with leaves in their upper part. Thus M. Grand'Eury [2] described a stem of *Sigillaria lepido-dendrifolia,* which, for a distance of 3 metres (nearly 10 feet) from the top downwards, was covered by rigid and erect linear leaves, more than a metre in length. The foliage of *Sigillaria* is in some cases scarcely to be distinguished from that of *Lepidodendron,* and, as we shall see below, the agreement extends to histological structure. The stems of *Sigillaria* are often found connected at the base with their subterranean organs, which we will provisionally call roots, though their morphological nature is doubtful, and will have to be discussed later on. These roots (known under the name of *Stigmaria*) are extremely common in the " underclay " of the Coal-measures, immediately below the seams of coal, and no doubt belong to the same plants, the stem and leaves of which have contributed to form the coal itself, the underclay representing the soil in which the trees grew. It is usually, however, impossible to say whether the root-like organs belonged to a *Sigillaria* or a *Lepidodendron.* Fig. 91 shows an enormous specimen of the stump and roots of one of these trees found in a sandstone quarry, of Coal-measure age, at Clayton, near Bradford, in Yorkshire. The actual stump of the tree is here 4 feet 4 inches in diameter, while the whole specimen, including

[1] *Bassin houiller de Valenciennes, flore fossile,* p. 512.
[2] *Flore carbonifère du Département de la Loire,* p. 156.

the forked roots, is almost 30 feet across.   This gigantic
fossil is now set up in the Museum of the Owens
College at Manchester, and affords a striking example of
the scale of Palaeozoic vegetation.   Fragments of other
specimens, which must have been about twice the size
of this one, were found at the same time.

Before going further into the question of the habit
of the Sigillarian trees, it will be necessary to give some
account of the characteristic superficial markings by
which the genus is commonly recognised, and according

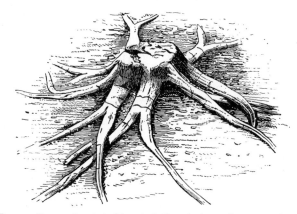

FIG. 91.—Stump and roots (=*Stigmaria ficoides*) of a Lycopodiaceous tree from the ǀ
Coal-measures.   For description, see text.   After Williamson.

to the variations in which, the so-called " species " are
distinguished.

Sigillaria, like *Lepidodendron*, is characterised by the
form and arrangement of the leaf-scars, left on the surface
of the stem after the leaves themselves had fallen.   The
wonderful perfection with which these markings are often
preserved, even on large trunks, is certainly a surprising
fact, and seems to show, either that the growth of the
trees was extremely rapid, or that the Carboniferous
forests were singularly free from epiphytic or parasitic
vegetation.

The leaf-scars of *Sigillaria* are, as a rule, arranged

in conspicuous vertical series, the scars of adjacent series alternating with one another (see Figs. 92-95). The marked longitudinal seriation of the scars affords, in typical cases, the most obvious distinction from the sculpturing of *Lepidodendron*. The scars are not always seated on distinct leaf-cushions, or if such cushions are

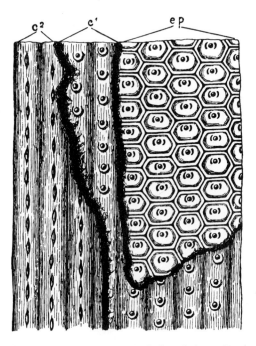

FIG. 92.—*Sigillaria tessellata* (*Favularia* type). Surface of stem. *ep*, external surface, showing leaf-scars, with the prints of the vascular bundle and parichnos; c^1, sub-epidermal surface; c^2, deeper cortical surface, showing "*Syringodendron*" characters. Nat. size. After Schimper.

present they are not much larger than the scars themselves (Fig. 92). The individual leaf-scar has, as a rule, an approximately hexagonal outline, with the angles more or less rounded (see Figs. 92-95). The form of the scar varies much, not only in different species, but on different parts of the same stem; as the stem increased in diameter with age, the scars not only became more widely separated, but were also themselves stretched out in the horizontal direction.

The prints on the scar are essentially similar to those of *Lepidodendron*, and are here also three in number, forming a transverse row, usually a little above the centre of the scar (see Fig. 94). The middle print, which is dot-like, or transversely elongated, is the smallest, but the most important, for anatomical investigation has shown that this alone represents the vascular bundle of the leaf. The two lateral prints are vertically elongated, and are

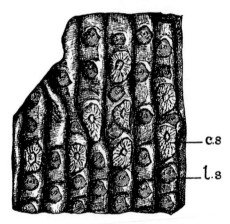

FIG. 93.—*Sigillaria mamillaris* (*Rhytidolepis* type). Surface of stem, showing vertical ribs with leaf-scars (*l.s.*) and scars of the cones (*c.s.*). Nat. size. After Zeiller.

either straight or crescent-shaped, with the concavity directed inwards. These lateral marks are of the same nature as the parichnos of *Lepidodendron*. Immediately above the scar, and sometimes seated in a depression of its upper edge, is another print, which evidently represents the ligular pit (Fig. 94, *lg*). We thus see that, except for trifling details, there is no difference in morphology between the leaf-scars of *Sigillaria* and those of *Lepidodendron*.

When we come to the arrangement of the scars, we meet with considerable variations within the genus;

these variations have been used for the distinction of subgenera, which some authors have even erected into distinct genera. We shall see, however, that in the light of our present knowledge very little, if any, taxonomic value can be attached to these differences, though they are worth noting for descriptive purposes.

In the first instance, the genus *Sigillaria* has been divided into two main series, those with ribbed stems—the *Eu-Sigillariae*, and those without ribs—the *Sub-Sigillariae*. The ribs, characterising the former series, are broad longitudinal ridges, each of which bears a single vertical series of leaf-scars. The ridges are separated by comparatively narrow furrows (Figs. 92 and 93).

The *Eu-Sigillariae* were formerly divided into two subgenera, *Rhytidolepis* and *Favularia* — names which, though no longer of taxonomic significance, may

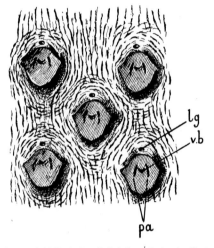

FIG. 94.—*Sigillaria Brardi* (*Leiodermaria* type). Part of surface of stem, showing five leaf-scars. *lg*, ligule; *v.b.*, print of vascular bundle; *pa*, parichnos. × 1½. After C. E. Weiss.

be retained to designate types of surface. In *Rhytidolepis* the ribs, which are often much broader than the leaf-scars borne upon them, are separated by straight vertical furrows. The scars of the same vertical series are in some cases almost contiguous; more often they are separated by considerable spaces (see Fig. 93). The ribs have been looked upon as representing series of fused leaf-bases, a view, however, which is negatived by the observations of Arber and Thomas, who find that the true leaf-bases form bracket-like projections from the ribs, the latter being really part of the cortex. *Rhytidolepis* is the most characteristic form of *Sigillaria*, and the most remote in outward appearance from *Lepidodendron*. The great ribbed stems of this type are a striking and familiar feature of the Coal-flora, and are among the best-known fossil remains.

The other ribbed type of surface—termed *Favularia* by Sternberg—has the ridges separated by zigzag furrows, while a marked transverse furrow intervenes between the adjacent leaf-scars of the same series (see Fig. 92). Here, in fact, each scar is seated on a well-marked hexagonal leaf-cushion, though the arrangement in vertical series is still manifest. The extreme forms of *Rhytidolepis* and *Favularia* are distinct enough, but both may occur on different parts of one and the same stem, connected by intermediate forms, so no systematic value can be attached to the distinction. Generally speaking, the *Eu-Sigillariae* are geologically more ancient than the *Sub-Sigillariae*, and some of the oldest stems known show the *Favularia* type of surface.

The *Sub-Sigillariae*, which are characteristic of the Upper Coal-measures and Permian, agree in the absence of distinct ribs, and have likewise been grouped under two subgenera, to which the same remarks apply as in the case of the previous group. In the *Clathraria* of Brongniart, the surface of the stem is formed by somewhat prominent, contiguous leaf cushions, separated by oblique furrows, each cushion bearing the scar of a leaf (see Fig. 95, which, however, is too much like a *Favularia*). Here the oblique parastichies stand out more conspicuously than the vertical orthostichies, and there is a certain approach to the *Lepidophloios* form of surface, from which, however, the typical *Clathraria* differs in the greater size of the scar relative to the cushion, and in the form of both.

In the other division of *Sub-Sigillariae*, the *Leio-*

dermaria of Goldenberg, there are no prominent leaf-
cushions ; the scars are remote from each other, and
separated by a smooth cortical surface (see Fig. 94).
This form shows some approximation to *Bothrodendron*,
which has even been united with this group of
Sigillariae by some modern authors. The Clathrarian
and Leiodermarian sculpturings may both occur on the
same stem—in fact, the characteristic markings of the
type-species of *Clathraria* and *Leiodermaria* respectively,
S. Brardi and *S. spinulosa*, have repeatedly been
found associated in this way. The two forms of surface
frequently occur in alternating zones on the stem, and
the same is the case with the *Rhytidolepis* and *Favularia*
markings among the *Eu-Sigillariae*. It has been suggested that the crowded leaf-scars characteristic of *Favularia* and *Clathraria* may have coincided with periods of
slow growth, while the more scattered arrangement in
the *Rhytidolepis* and *Leiodermaria* forms may have been
due to seasons of rapid elongation. All these four
types, however, have been regarded, even by some
modern authors, as distinct genera. As a matter of fact,
only the division between *Eu-Sigillaria* and *Sub-
Sigillaria* holds good taxonomically, and even here the
distinction is not always a sharp one, for some forms
of Favularian and Clathrarian [1] surface approach each
other very nearly,[2] and may even occur on the same
stem.

A hundred or more so-called species of *Sigillaria* have
been described, according to the superficial markings,
but they are admittedly of doubtful value at the best.
The genus, however, was evidently a rich and varied one,
though the characters available are altogether insufficient
for the clear limitation of the different forms.

---

[1] Clathrarian *Sigillariae* are also spoken of as *Cancellatae*.

[2] On the subject of the surface-characters of *Sigillariae*, see Zeiller,
"Revue des travaux de paléontologie," *Rev. Gén. de Botanique*, 1897,
p. 404 ; *Éléments de paléobotanique*, Paris, 1900, p. 190.

Just as in *Lepidodendron*, so also in *Sigillaria*, the appearance of the stem was often much changed by the partial destruction of the external tissues, and the various types of more or less decorticated surface noticed under *Lepidodendron* recur here. One very characteristic form may be noticed, to which the name *Syringodendron* has been given. In this, the epidermis and the leaf-scars have perished ; the ribs—if the specimen belonged to the *Eu-Sigillariae*—remain, and are marked by the same prints which occur in the typical leaf-scars. In these cases, the middle print—that marking the leaf-trace bundle—is usually inconspicuous, while the two lateral lines of the parichnos are extremely marked. Corresponding forms of preservation, without the ribbing, occur in the *Sub-Sigillariae*. The *Syringodendron* character may also be found, even on the epidermal surface, at the base of the old stems, where excessive growth in thickness has obliterated the leaf-scars. Fig. 92, from *Sigillaria tessellata*, one of the Favularian forms, shows the surface exposed at three different levels. At *ep* the natural epidermal surface is shown, with the characteristic hexagonal leaf-scars, each of which shows the three prints (representing the vascular bundle and the double parichnos) as described above. On the part marked c^1, the superficial layers, with the leaf-scars, have peeled off, exposing the outer cortex, on which the longitudinal ribs come out more clearly than before. The leaf-trace bundles are still evident ; the two parichnos-scars have united below each vascular bundle, forming a crescent. At c^2 the process of destruction has gone deeper ; a considerable thickness of cortex has broken away, and a deeper layer is laid bare. The ribs are still evident ; the fused parichnos-scars show conspicuously as lenticular outlines, but the vascular bundle within each loop is not visible. This lowest level may be taken as representing the *Syringodendron* surface, though on a small scale. In typical *Syringodendron* the parichnos-prints may be enormously enlarged, reaching a length of more than a centimetre.

In some cases the leaf-scars on the Sigillarian surface are accompanied by other scars, best interpreted as marking the insertion of the fructifications (see Fig. 93, *c.s.*). We will, however, postpone the consideration of these, until we come to deal with the cones themselves.

As regards the habit of the *Sigillariae*, our knowledge is still very imperfect. In some of the forms, forking branches have been observed, though they are not as a rule common ; in stems with the *Rhytidolepis* type of sculpturing no branching has yet been observed. In the unbranched forms the habit appears to have been something like that of the Australian Grass - tree, *Xanthorrhoea*, the tall, upright shaft terminating in a sheaf of long, grass-like leaves. In other cases, as in the Favularian species *S. elegans*, and in *S. Brardi*, of the *Clathraria* group, the stem divided, by successive dichotomy, into a few large branches.

2. *Anatomical Structure.*—Recognisable specimens of *Sigillaria* with structure preserved are comparatively rare ; of late years, however, several new examples have come to light. It is possible that the rarity of specimens with structure, while the structureless casts are so common, may be in part due to the smaller branches not having always been recognised as belonging to *Sigillaria*. The fact, however, would also find an explanation, if branching occurred very sparingly, for, of course, the small branches, rather than the great trunks, are likely, as a rule, to have been preserved in the petrified condition.

The first specimen of a *Sigillaria* showing anatomical structure was described by Brongniart,[1] as long ago as the year 1839, and has played a most important part

[1] " Observations sur la structure intérieure du *Sigillaria elegans*," *Archives du muséum d'hist. nat.* vol. i. 1839.

in the history of fossil botany.   The fragment was
about 4 cm. in diameter, and about 2 cm. long, and
showed a portion of the external surface with its leaf-
scars, as well as the internal anatomy (see Fig. 95).
The superficial characters have rendered it possible to

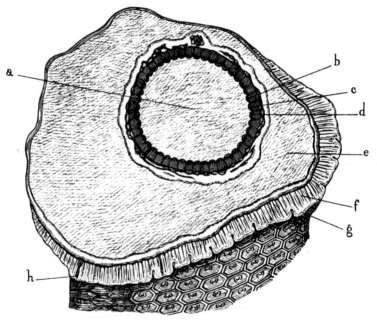

FIG. 95.—*Sigillaria Menardi* (*Clathraria* type). Brongniart's original specimen, showing
transverse section and part of surface with leaf-scars. *a*, pith (perished) ; *b*, primary
wood, forming many distinct bundles ; *c*, secondary wood ; *d*, phloëm-zone ; *e*, middle
cortex (perished) ; *f*, periderm ; *g*, leaf-base ; *h*, foliar bundle. × about 2. After
Brongniart.

identify the specimen as belonging to the form *Sigillaria
Menardi*, one of the *Clathraria* group.[1]   The parts in
which the structure is preserved consist essentially of
the wood and a portion of the outer cortex ; the pith
and the inner region of the cortex have perished (see
Fig. 95).   Fortunately, however, the parts which remain

[1] Brongniart himself referred the specimen to the Favularian species,
S. elegans, but this determination was subsequently corrected by Zeiller
and Renault.

are the most important, as Brongniart pointed out. His whole description, though of so early a date, might still serve as a model for such investigations. The ring of wood is complete, and has a diameter of about 16 mm. The pith was of large size, for the woody zone is only about a millimetre in thickness. It consists of a large number (between forty and fifty) of vascular bundles, each of which is made up of an inner or primary and an outer or secondary portion. The primary strands are distinct from each other, though close together, and are crescent-shaped, as seen in transverse section, with the convex side towards the pith. The small, spiral tracheides are placed on the outer, slightly concave, side of each bundle. The rest of the primary xylem-elements, which are irregularly arranged, and increase in size towards the interior, are reticulated or finely scalariform tracheides.

The secondary zone, which is almost continuous, though showing some signs of division into distinct bundles corresponding to the primary strands, consists of radially arranged scalariform tracheides, and narrow medullary rays of very variable height. The interfascicular rays seem to have been only slightly broader than those opposite the primary bundles. The secondary tracheides, as in the Lepidodendreae, are pitted on their tangential as well as on their radial surfaces ; the smallest elements lie towards the interior, adjacent to the protoxylem of the primary strands.

The leaf-trace bundles, so far as their xylem is concerned, were given off from the outer, concave part of the primary strands, and passed obliquely through the secondary wood ; the preservation only allows of their being traced for a short distance beyond the woody zone. M. Renault found that these leaf-trace bundles are " diploxylic," each consisting of an inner centripetal primary strand, and an outer centrifugal secondary portion continuous with the secondary wood of the

stele.   This character was long regarded as peculiar
to *Sigillaria*, as distinguished from *Lepidodendron*, but
the distinction no longer holds good, for it is not
constant in *Sigillaria*, while, as already mentioned in
Chapter V., Prof. Seward and Mr. Hill found typical
" diploxylic " leaf-traces in a fine specimen of *Lepidodendron Wunschianum*, a plant which may belong more
properly to *Lepidophloios*, but is, at any rate, not a
Sigillaria.   This structure is shown in Fig. 60, p. 127.

The outer cortex, which is alone preserved, consists
of two zones ; the more internal is composed of uniform,
radially arranged tissue, and no doubt represents a
secondary formation, of the nature of periderm, such as
we so constantly find in *Lepidodendron*.   The outer
zone, bearing the leaf-cushions, is simply the primary
external cortex, within which the periderm had formed
(Fig. 95, *f* and *g*).

If we compare the structure of *Sigillaria Menardi*
with that of the Lepidodendreae with secondary
thickening, such as *L. Wunschianum* or *L. brevifolium*,
we find one difference of importance.   The primary
wood in the Lepidodendreae forms a continuous zone,
usually of considerable thickness, while that of *Sigillaria
Menardi* is less in amount, and is broken up into
a ring of distinct and definite bundles.   The latter
difference is striking enough, but, as we shall see, it
does not serve to distinguish *Sigillaria* generically.

The inference which Brongniart himself drew from
the study of the structure of his *Sigillaria* was this :
" The arrangement of the woody tissue in bundles
composed of radial series is a character foreign to all
the Cryptogams ; it is, on the contrary, characteristic
of the Dicotyledons " ; [1] and hence he was led to
conclude, " that the *Sigillariae* and *Stigmariae* constituted a special family, entirely extinct, probably
belonging to the great division of Gymnospermous

[1] " *Sigillaria elegans*," p. 440.

Dicotyledons." [1] This conclusion, which was natural
enough at that time (1839), still has an historical
interest, owing to the dominant influence which the
views of this great investigator long exercised, especially
in his own country. The force of Brongniart's argument
is now, of course, entirely invalidated by the discovery
of a great number of Cryptogams with secondary growth,
and by our knowledge of the Cryptogamic fructification
of *Sigillaria* itself.

In 1875 MM. Renault and Grand'Eury described
some specimens of another *Sigillaria* showing internal
structure ; [2] the superficial characters of the stem
enabled them to identify it as belonging to the
Leiodermarian form *S. spinulosa* ; the latter, however,
as mentioned above, is now known to have been
identical with the Clathrarian *S. Brardi*, so there is no
important distinction, so far as external characters are
concerned, between Renault's and Brongniart's species.
Some authors, indeed, have even united *S. Menardi*
with *S. Brardi*, in which case the two French observers
would have been dealing merely with varieties of the
same species. The anatomy, however, appears to
negative this view ; the two species are probably
distinct, though nearly allied.

In the case of *S. spinulosa* several specimens were
available for investigation, from branches of various
sizes. The primary wood is of about the same thickness
as in the former species, but shows curious variations
in its arrangement. At some points it is broken up
into distinct bundles, quite similar to those of *S. Menardi*
(see Fig. 97), but elsewhere, even in the same transverse
section, it forms a continuous band for a considerable
distance (see Fig. 96). [3] We thus see that the separation

[1] " *Sigillaria elegans*," p. 447.
[2] " Étude du *Sigillaria spinulosa*," *Mém. prés. par divers savants à
l'Académie des Sciences*, tome xxii. 1875.
[3] For the photographs reproduced in these two figures I have to

of the primary xylem-zone into definite strands is not necessarily a character of any taxonomic importance.

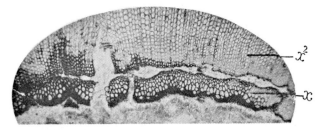

FIG. 96.—*Sigillaria spinulosa.* Part of transverse section of stem, showing primary (x) and secondary (x^2) wood. The former consists partly of separate and partly of confluent bundles. × about 9.

The primary wood was centripetal, and agrees in minute structure with that of *S Menardi.* The secondary zone

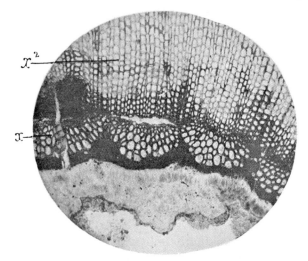

FIG. 97.—*Sigillaria spinulosa.* Part of wood, more highly magnified, showing separate primary strands (x) and secondary wood (x^2). × about 18. Figs. 96 and 97 from photographs by Dr. R. Kidston, F.R.S.

(which in some of the specimens attains a thickness of about 2 cm.) is here perfectly continuous, but otherwise

thank my friend Dr. Kidston, who took them from sections of one of the original specimens.

agrees closely with that of the former species. The leaf-traces arose, in this case also, at the outside of the primary wood, passed through the secondary zone, and then took a nearly vertical course through the inner cortex, which is partially preserved in these specimens. In the outer cortex the bundles assumed a more horizontal direction. In some of the sections they show a diploxylic structure. In this species M. Renault first made the interesting observation that two large lacunae accompanied the bundle on its outward course, one on each side, forming, at the point where they entered the leaf, the two lateral prints on the foliar scar, which are now termed the parichnos. In this and in other species of *Sigillaria* M. Renault subsequently showed that the lacunae, which are surrounded by a definite sheath of radially elongated cells, were filled by a delicate cellular tissue traversed by secretory canals (see Fig. 98, A). The same observer also proved, by anatomical investigation, that the well-known prints on the partially decorticated *Syringodendron* stems are of the same nature, though here much enlarged. The identity of *Syringodendron* with *Sigillaria* thus received fresh demonstration.[1]

In *Sigillaria*, as in *Lepidodendron*, the parichnos-strands start from the inner cortical zone. That their function was in part secretory is highly probable, but the persistence and enlargement of the parichnos on the surface of old stems suggests a respiratory function, like that of lenticels.

The outer cortical layers of *S. spinulosa* have a peculiar structure. There is a broad zone of secondary periderm, but its tissue is not uniform; it is made up of radial anastomosing bands of narrow elongated cells, while the meshes between these bands are occupied by short thin-

---

[1] See also K. H. Coward, "On the Structure of *Syringodendron*, the Bark of *Sigillaria*," *Mem. and Proc. Manchester Lit. and Phil. Soc.* vol. li. Part ii. 1907.

walled cells of greater diameter. As the fibrous bands, which no doubt had a mechanical function, fuse with each other in every direction, they form a network,

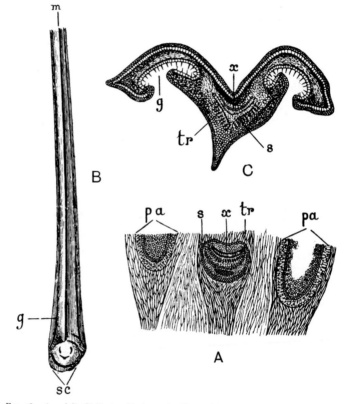

Fig. 98.—A and B, *Sigillaria spinulosa*. A. Tangential section of outer cortex, showing leaf-trace, with the parichnos (*pa*) on either side. In the leaf-trace; *x*, primary xylem; below this the secondary xylem (*tr*) and phloëm, then a sclerenchymatous strand; *s*, sheath of bundle. Magnified. B. Leaf, showing the lower surface, and the scar (*sc*) at base; on the scar the prints of the bundle and parichnos are seen. *m*, midrib of leaf; *g*, one of the stomatiferous furrows. Nat. size. C. *S. latifolia*. Transverse section of leaf. *x*, xylem; *s*, sclerenchyma; *tr*, transfusion-tissue; *g*, stomatiferous furrows, lined with hairs. Magnified. All after Renault.

whether seen in transverse or tangential section. The existence of this highly differentiated secondary cortex, so distinct from the uniform periderm of *S. Menardi*, certainly seems to justify the specific separation of these two forms, even if there were no other diagnostic characters. The fibrous periderm attained an immense development ; fragments 7 or 8 cm. thick are found, and these appear to be only exfoliated laminae of a much thicker bark.

Beyond the secondary cortical zone lies the primary outer cortex, bearing the leaf-bases, where they are preserved. The interest of this species lies chiefly in two points—the transition which it shows between continuous and discrete primary xylem, and the complex character of the secondary cortical zone.

Both in *S. spinulosa* and *S. Menardi* the structure of the leaf-bases has been made out, thanks once more to M. Renault's researches. Towards the exterior of the cushion there is a rather thick-walled hypoderma ; the softer tissue within contains the two parichnos strands already described, and between them lies the vascular bundle (cf. Fig. 98, A). The primary wood forms a narrow transverse band, surrounded by a delicate tissue.[1] The secondary wood is separated by this tissue from the primary xylem ; it forms an arc of radially arranged elements towards the lower side of the bundle. Below this again is a layer of phloëm. Some light is thrown on this peculiar arrangement of the parts of the bundle by the structure of the leaf itself, which was also thoroughly investigated by M. Renault.[2]

The leaves with their structure preserved are in association, but not in actual connection with the stems. In cases, however, such as that illustrated in Fig. 98, B, where the base of the leaf itself shows a characteristic scar, corresponding with those on the stem-surface, there can be no doubt as to the attribution. The general form and structure of the Sigillarian leaf (the species chiefly

---

[1] M. Renault regarded this as primary phloëm, which may be correct, as in the leaf the transfusion-tissue (apparently continuous with the secondary xylem) lies outside the primary phloëm. See *Flore fossile d'Autun et d'Épinac*, Part ii. p. 212.

[2] *Flore fossile d'Autun et d'Épinac*, Part ii. p. 213, Plate xli.

studied was *S. Brardi*, with its variety, *S. spinulosa*) is much like that of a *Lepidodendron*. Here also there are two deep longitudinal furrows on the lower surface, one on either side of the midrib, and it is only on the surface of these furrows that the stomata are found (see Fig. 98, C, *g*). The single vascular bundle appears to have been concentric in structure, the xylem having its spiral elements placed laterally. Below the bundle itself is a double layer of sclerenchyma, beyond which is a band of delicate parenchyma with scattered tracheides. This accessory xylem may be regarded as corresponding functionally to the transfusion-tissue of Coniferous leaves. We have already described the same tissue in the leaves of *Lepidodendron*, where, however, the extra-fascicular tracheides are more abundant, and form a complete zone round the bundle. The transfusion-tissue of the Sigillarian leaves was at first regarded by M. Renault as secondary xylem, but he afterwards withdrew that view, considering that the true secondary wood is limited to the leaf-trace, where it passes through the cortex of the stem. It seems, however, to be clear that the secondary xylem and the transfusion-tracheides are continuous one with another ; the relations of the tissues require further investigation.

The mesophyll is lacunar in the neighbourhood of the stomatiferous furrows ; elsewhere it is described as consisting of transversely elongated elements, which may have enabled the leaf to roll up its lamina, and thus diminish transpiration. There is a band of sclerenchyma below the epidermis, except in the stomatiferous furrows. The stomata are of the ordinary kind ; they are accompanied on the epidermis of the furrows by multicellular hairs (Fig. 98, C, *g*). The whole arrangement of the tissues of the leaf is suggestive of a plant occasionally exposed to drought, but we must remember that the plants of salt marshes assume in many respects a xerophytic habit.

It will be seen that the leaves of the species of *Sigillaria* in question agree nearly, though not exactly, in structure with those of *Lepidodendron*, as described above in Chapter V. The differences between them are such as are often found even among species of the same genus ; the resemblances, taken in conjunction with the other characters, are undoubtedly indicative of near affinity.

It appears probable that the leaves of *Sigillaria* were separated from the stem by the formation of a definite abscissile tissue.

So far we have dealt exclusively with the structure of the Sub-Sigillarian group. Our knowledge of the anatomy of the *Eu-Sigillariae* has until recently been extremely meagre, but is now much augmented. A fragment of stem with Favularian surface was described by Williamson [1] in 1871, but except as proving the presence of a·secondary zone of wood, and of a periderm, the investigation yielded little result. The same author described at the same time, under the name of *Diploxylon*, a vascular cylinder which he afterwards referred to *Sigillaria reniformis*, one of the *Rhytidolepis* group (Williamson, *l.c.* Figs. 33 and 34). In this stem there is a perfectly continuous zone of primary wood, with a crenulated outer margin, beyond which is a much broader layer of secondary xylem. The first really good English example of a stem of the *Rhytidolepis* type, with structure preserved, was a specimen which came many years ago into the hands of Professor Boyd Dawkins, and has not yet been fully described. [2] The specimen is a fragment only, forming a segment of the stem, but it includes the whole thickness of the tissues from the pith to the outer surface (Fig. 99). The latter is ribbed in the characteristic manner of *Rhytidolepis*, and there appears to be no doubt of its

---

[1] " Organisation of Fossil Plants of Coal-measures," Part ii. 1872.

[2] For photographs of this specimen, one of which is reproduced in Fig. 99, I am indebted to Mr. A. Gepp of the British Museum, Natural History Department.

belonging to a *Sigillaria* of that type. From the inner margin of the wood to the exterior surface of the ribs the radius of the specimen is about 18 mm. The zone of primary xylem, which is less than a millimetre in thickness, is quite continuous as far as it can be traced. Its outer edge, where the smallest elements are placed, is crenulated, just as in Williamson's specimen, referred to above. The secondary zone of wood, which has the usual structure, is about 4 mm. thick, and has an un-

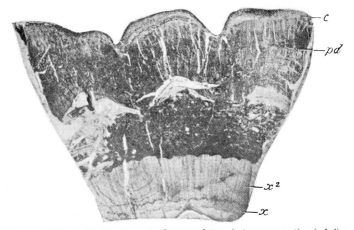

Fig. 99.—*Sigillaria* (*Rhytidolepis* type). Segment of stem, in transverse section, including three ribs. *x*, crenulated primary wood ; x^2, secondary wood ; *pd*, periderm ; *c*, outer cortex. ×3. From a photograph by Mr. A. Gepp.

dulating outer surface, corresponding to the crenulations of the primary zone. This latter character may serve to distinguish a *Sigillaria* from a *Lepidodendron*, but too much stress must not be laid on it. The inner cortex is imperfectly preserved ; the outer bark consists chiefly of a thick zone of radially seriated periderm (Fig. 99, *pd*), beyond which a narrow band of primary cortex (*c*) abuts on the surface of the ribs. The leaf-traces are ranged in vertical rows corresponding to the ribs of the cortex. The xylem-strands of the leaf-traces start from the *depressions* of the crenulated primary wood, just as in *Sigillaria Menardi* or *spinulosa*, and in Williamson's specimen mentioned above. It is thus evident that each concave segment of the continuous primary wood, in the *Rhytidolepis* type of stem, corresponds to one of the distinct bundles, as shown in the Sub-Sigillarian forms previously described.

A more perfect specimen of the stem of a ribbed *Sigillaria* (probably *S. elongata*), from the Hardinghen coal-field, in the Pas de Calais, was described by the late Professor C. E. Bertrand (*Annals of Botany*, December 1899). His more complete observations agree essentially with the short account just given of an English specimen. Professor Bertrand pointed out that the ribbed *Sigillaria* is in certain respects intermediate in structure between the *Sub-Sigillariae* and the *Lepidodendra* with secondary growth.

More recently Dr. Kidston has given a full account of the structure of a petrified specimen of *Sigillaria elegans* from the Lower Coal-measures of Yorkshire.[1] This is a Favularian species ; the characteristic leaf-scars are shown quite plainly on the surface of the specimen. The structure of the stele is essentially the same as in the form already described, and here also the leaf-traces invariably start from the base of the furrows of the crenulated primary wood. The medullary rays are one cell thick, and of varying height ; their cells, as in *Lepidodendron*, sometimes show scalariform markings. The leaf-trace has a distinctly mesarch structure, and is without any secondary xylem. The structure of the bodies known as " cone scars " shows them to be the bases of small lateral branches, which may well have borne the fructifications (see p. 208).

Subsequently the structure of certain species of the *Rhytidolepis* group was fully investigated by Kidston and by Arber and Thomas [2] in material from the Coal-

[1] Kidston, " On the Internal Structure of *Sigillaria elegans*," *Trans. Roy. Soc. of Edinburgh*, vol. xli. Part iii. 1905.

[2] Kidston, " Prelim. Note on Internal Structure of *Sigillaria*

measure nodules. In *S. mamillaris* (see Fig. 93) the structure is almost identical with that of the Favularian *S. elegans* ; in *S. scutellata* the crenulations of the primary wood are comparatively slight (Fig. 100). On the whole the wood structure in both is the same as that above described. Arber and Thomas find that in *S. scutellata*

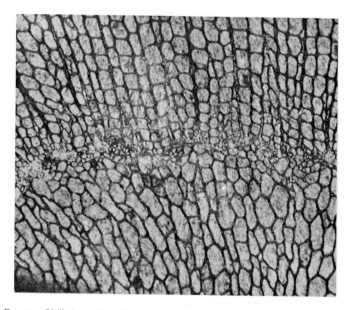

FIG. 100.—*Sigillaria scutellata.*—Transverse section of a portion of the wood, showing primary xylem below and secondary xylem above. The protoxylem-groups lie at the outer border of the primary xylem. × about 50. From a photograph lent by the late Dr. E. A. Newell Arber, F.G.S. S. Coll. 2300.

the periderm was formed on the inner side of a meristematic zone which was active periodically. The ribs consist largely of the phelloderm, but were probably already present in the primary condition of the stem. The authors were able to demonstrate the presence of a ligule and ligular pit on the leaf-base. The most remark-

---

mamillaris and *S. scutellata*," *Proc. Roy. Soc. Edinburgh*, vol. xxvii. Part iii. 1907; Arber and Thomas, " On the Structure of *Sigillaria scutellata*, etc.," *Phil. Trans. Roy. Soc. London*, series B, vol. 200, 1908.

able point, however, which they and Dr. Kidston observed is, that in traversing the phelloderm the leaf-trace divides into two ; in the leaf-base the two xylem-strands are wide apart. This applies to both species.

In 1879 Renault described, under the name of *Sigillariopsis Decaisnei*,[1] a small stem, with leaves attached, from the Permian of Autun ; the stem resembles that of *Sigillaria Menardi* in structure, but the wood contains pitted as well as scalariform tracheides ; the leaf is traversed by two parallel vascular bundles, which only

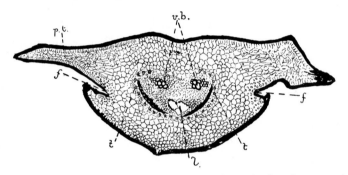

FIG. 101.—*Sigillariopsis sulcata.* Transverse section of leaf. *v.b.,* the xylem-groups of the double vascular bundle ; *l,* lacuna, representing secretory tissue ; *t, t,* transfusion-tissue, forming a horse-shoe, surrounding the double bundle, but open above ; *p.t.,* palisade tissue on the upper side and flanks of the leaf ; *f, f,* stomatiferous furrows. × 22. S. Coll. 2272. (R. S.)

fuse towards the tip. These characters are altogether exceptional among Lycopods, but in other respects the structure is quite of the Lycopodiaceous type. Leaves occur in the nodules of the British Coal-measures which agree with those of Renault's plant in possessing two distinct vascular bundles, though presenting some specific differences. In all other respects their structure is that of a Sigillarian leaf (see the details in Fig. 101). The name *Sigillariopsis sulcata* [2] has been given to the English

[1] *Structure comparée de quelques tiges de la flore carbonifère,* Paris, 1879, p. 270.

[2] Scott, " On the Occurrence of *Sigillariopsis* in the Lower Coal-measures of Britain," *Ann. of Bot.* vol. xviii. 1904.

species, for the leaf has two stomatiferous furrows, as in *Sigillaria* or *Lepidodendron*. *Sigillariopsis*, which corresponds to a part of *Sigillaria*, is interesting from its analogies, in certain points, with the structure of some of the Coniferae, with which, however, an affinity is improbable. There is good evidence that the British *Sigillariopsis* was borne on the stem known as *Sigillaria scutellata* (or some closely allied species), in which, as Kidston and Arber and Thomas have shown, the double leaf-traces are quite similar in structure to the double bundle of the leaf. It thus appears that the *Sigillariopsis* type of leaf probably occurred both on Eusigillarian and Subsigillarian stems. The double bundle is an important character, and may prove to be of generic value.

3. *Fructifications.*—Our examination of *Sigillaria* has shown us, up to the present point, a very close agree ment with *Lepidodendron*, as regards the external morphology and the anatomy of stem and leaf. It is, however, on the character of the fructification that the determination of the systematic position of the genus must ultimately depend. This knowledge we owe primarily to M. Zeiller, who in 1884 first demonstrated the nature of the cones of *Sigillaria*.[1] Before that date several specimens had been described as Sigillarian fructifications, and some, as it has turned out, rightly so, but evidence of identification was not forthcoming. This was supplied by M. Zeiller, for the peduncle of one of the cones described by him is partly clothed by acicular leaves or bracts, and where these have become detached, the leaf-scars are found to lie in vertical rows on the ribbed surface, and to correspond very closely to the markings on the stem of definite species of *Sigillaria*, of the *Rhytidolepis* type. This correlation having once been effected, it became possible to identify various other specimens as

[1] " Cônes de fructification des Sigillaires," *Ann. des sci. nat.* (*Bot.*), ser. vi. vol. xix. 1884,

cogeneric, and the genus *Sigillariostrobus*, as the fructi-fication of *Sigillaria* is called, now includes several species. The cones are often of large size, reaching a diameter of about 6 cm. (*S. nobilis*) and a great length. None of the French specimens were complete, but Dr. Kidston has since described a complete cone, from the Yorkshire coal-field, 9 inches long. All the known Sigillarian cones agree in having long peduncles clothed with acicular bracts. The fertile part bears large, crowded sporophylls, arranged spirally, or in alternating whorls. The form of the individual sporophylls varies in the different species; thus in *S. Tieghemi* (which shows *Rhytidolepis* markings on the peduncle) it is broadly lanceolate and contracted at the base to a narrow claw, so that only a small round scar is left on the axis when the sporophyll has become detached. The short claw is approximately horizontal in direction, while the lamina is bent more or less sharply upwards. In other species, the lamina is prolonged into a fine point, and may be toothed or ciliate at the margins (see Fig. 102, A, from one of the English species discovered by Dr. Kidston [1]). M. Zeiller was not able to observe the sporangia in any of his cones (with the exception of a doubtful form to be mentioned immediately). In several specimens, however, he found groups of large spores, obviously megaspores, lying on the upper surface of the sporophylls, as if they had been set free by the breaking down of the sporangial wall. Though the specimens were not petrified, and their internal structure was thus not preserved, it was found possible to isolate and carefully examine the carbonised megaspores. They are spherical, and of large size, ranging from 1 to 2.25 mm. in diameter in the various species. The cell-wall generally shows three radiating lines, corresponding, no doubt, to the limits of the sister-cells in the same tetrad. The membrane may either be smooth or echinulate, according to the species.

[1] Kidston, " On the Fossil Flora of the Yorkshire Coal-field," second paper, *Trans. Roy. Soc. Edinburgh*, vol. xxxix. Part i. 1897.

M. Zeiller has also described a small cone, under the name of *Sigillariostrobus Crepini*,[1] in which the sporangia, but not the spores, can be recognised. In this form, the sporangia appear to be attached at their distal ends to the spoon-shaped laminae of the sporophylls. In dimensions and general organisation this cone agrees very nearly with *Spencerites insignis*, described in the last chapter. The relation of *S. Crepini* to *Sigillaria* is, however, not quite beyond doubt.

The observations of M. Zeiller established the Cryptogamic nature of *Sigillaria*, for the fructifications were clearly those of a heterosporous member of the Lycopodiales. Dr. Kidston, in his memoir above cited, has made further important additions to our knowledge of these strobili, for in certain forms of *Sigillariostrobus*, which he has described, from the Coal-measures of Yorkshire, he has been able to demonstrate the form and position of the sporangia, and to obtain at least indications of the presence of microspores in some of them. The sporangia were observed in longitudinal section on the fractured surface of a specimen which had been split down the middle ; for it must be remembered that in no case has an undoubted cone of *Sigillaria* been found with the tissues actually petrified, though *Mazocarpon* (see p. 213) may be of that nature. The sporangia prove to have been oval bodies with their long axis directed radially, and were seated each on the horizontal pedicel of the sporophyll, to which the sporangium was to all appearance attached along the whole of its lower surface (Fig. 102, B). The sporangial membrane also appears, so far as the state of preservation allows us to judge, to have been continuous with the upturned laminar portion of the sporophyll, or possibly it may have been covered in by an indusium, as in *Isoëtes*. The sporangia contain large megaspores, with an echinulate membrane (see Fig. 102, C). It would

---

[1] Zeiller, *Bassin houiller de Valenciennes, Flore fossile*, p. 605, Plate lxxvii. Fig. 3, 1888.

appear, therefore, that the sporangia of *Sigillaria*, in their form and mode of insertion, resembled those of *Lepidostrobus*, while differing from those of *Spencerites* or of *Sigillariostrobus Crepini*, which should perhaps be removed from its present genus.

A fine granulation, strongly suggesting the presence of small crowded micro-spores, was observed by the same investigator in the sporangia of another specimen, which at the same time showed distinct megaspores in other parts. If this indication is to be relied on, it follows that *Sigillariostrobus*, like so many forms of *Lepidostrobus*, bore both kinds of spore on the same cone.

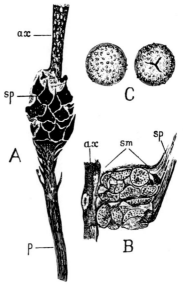

The discovery of the fructification of *Sigillaria* affords an explanation of certain scars which have long been known to occur occasionally on the stems, either between the vertical rows of leaf-scars, or scattered among them in the same series.

FIG. 102.—A. *Sigillariostrobus rhombibracteatus*, Kidston. Part of cone, showing the pedicel (*p*) with sterile bracts. *sp*, sporophylls; *ax*, axis exposed, showing scars of sporophylls, ¾ nat. size. B and C. *S. ciliatus*, Kidston. B. Part of axis (*ax*) with sporophylls (*sp*) and megasporangia (*sm*) seen in radial fracture. × 3. C. Echinulate megaspores. × about 7. All after Kidston.

These scars occur on all forms of Sigillarian stem. Fig. 93 (p. 188) represents them (*c.s.*) on the surface of *S. mamillaris*, which is of the *Rhytidolepis* type. Each scar has a central print, no doubt corresponding to a vascular strand, the structure of which has been demonstrated by Dr. Kidston in the case of *S. elegans* (see p. 205). In one case, small leafy shoots, the dimensions of which agreed well with those of the peduncles of the cones, are said to have been ·found seated on the scars. It is therefore reasonable to assume that we have in these marks the prints left by the deciduous cones after their fall. It would follow that the fructification must have been borne on the large stems (for it is on such that the scars occur), and not on small terminal branches. This conclusion is quite in agreement with the unbranched or little-branched character of the Sigillarian stems. The occurrence of Ulodendroid scars on stems referred to Clathrarian Sigillariae (*e.g. S. discophora*) may be mentioned here, though their relation to the cones is open to doubt (see p. 147).

The controversy as to the systematic position of *Sigillaria* has gradually died out since the discovery of the manifestly Cryptogamic fructifications of the genus. The view, long maintained by Brongniart and his school, that *Sigillaria*, or at least the smooth-barked species, belonged to the Gymnosperms, no longer has any basis. The recent discovery of the seed-like fructifications of certain Palaeozoic Lycopods might at one time have been used in support of this position, but there is at present no evidence that any of the Sigillariae possessed organs of this kind.

We may take it as now definitely established that *Sigillaria* was a genus of highly developed Lycopodiaceous Cryptogams, having the closest affinities with *Lepidodendron*. The difficulty, in fact, is rather to find constant distinctions between the two genera, than to prove their relationship.[1]

It is not probable that *Sigillaria* had even a remote affinity with the Cycads, the family with which Brongniart and his followers endeavoured to connect it. As we shall see later on, there is strong evidence for tracing the origin of the Cycadales from quite a different phylum, namely that of the Pteridosperms.

---

[1] The family Lepidodendreae is thus most naturally regarded as including the genus *Sigillaria*.

The question of a possible affinity between the Palaeo-zoic Lycopods generally and certain of the Coniferae, an hypothesis advocated by some modern writers, will be considered in the concluding chapter.

Mazocarpon. — This remarkable fructification has recently been investigated by Dr. M. Benson ;[1] it was described by her as " the structural *Sigillariostrobus,*" and regarded as exhibiting the internal structure of cones of that genus. The best known species is *Mazo-carpon shorense,* Benson, from the coal-balls of Lancashire and Yorkshire. The cone, in the main features of its organisa-tion, is of the usual Lycopod type, bearing a general resemblance to a *Lepidostrobus.* The axis, which is somewhat hex-agonal in transverse sec-tion, has a narrow ring of centripetal xylem ; numerous leaf-traces are given off, one to each sporophyll. The bracts are usually ill-preserved ;

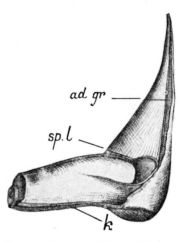

Fig. 103.—*Mazocarpon.* Diagram of the sporo-phyll and megasporangium, from a model. *ad.gr.,* adaxial groove of sporophyll; *k,* keel; *sp.l.,* distal lamella of the sporangium. After Dr. M. Benson.

they were evidently detached easily from the cone-axis. The single sporangium, seated in the typical manner, on the upper side of the pedicel (Fig. 103), has the usual palisade layer on its outer surface, but in every other respect is peculiar. The megasporangia are the better known and will be first described. The wall is produced into a thin distal flange or lamella. The cen-tral or sub-archesporial pad is persistent and enormously

[1] " *Mazocarpon,* or the Structure of *Sigillariostrobus,*" *Ann. of Bot.* vol. xxxii. 1918.

developed, occupying all the middle part of the sporangium (Fig. 104) ; it is connected below with the bract, from which tracheides extend into its substance, forming a transfusion tissue. The inner layers of the sporangial wall are likewise thick and persistent, so that the megaspores are embedded in a mass of tissue, like sausages in a roll (hence the name, from μάζα, a loaf) (Fig. 105). The megaspores are very large, reaching at least 2 mm. in length ; in section they commonly appear

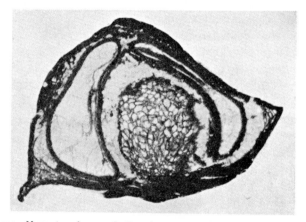

Fig. 104.—*Mazocarpon shorense.* Section of megasporangium, tangential to the cone, showing the central pad, with a megaspore on each side. At the base the remains of the sporophyll are seen. × about 24. S. Coll. 2282. From a photograph by Mr. W. Tams.

sausage-shaped ; the true form was in some cases that of a hollow crucible, but seems to have varied considerably.

The megaspores are ranged in a single series round the central pad ; in a section tangential to the cone, two megaspores are commonly seen, one on each side of the pad (Fig. 104) ; the total number was no doubt variable ; Dr. Benson finds that the maximum was 8. The meaning of the curved shape of the megaspore is that the concave side fitted on to the central pad ; in the middle of the concave side is the open beak of the megaspore, within which traces of the archegonia have been recognised (Fig. 106).

The occasional good preservation of the prothallus has already been noticed (p. 168 ; Fig. 82). The thick wall of the megaspore, especially on its convex side, is studded

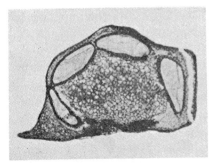

Fig. 105.—*Mazocarpon shorense.* Oblique section of megasporangium, showing four megaspores in section, and the membrane of a fifth (below); central pad and sporangial wall well-preserved. × 12. Manchester Coll. R. 758. From a photograph by Dr. M. Benson.

with short spines or pegs, which interlock with the surrounding tissue.

The megasporangium with the remains of the bract readily became detached from the cone ; it seems to have also broken up naturally into fragments. It is common

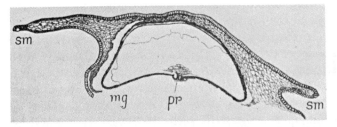

Fig. 106.—*Mazocarpon shorense.* Detached portion of a fragmented megasporangium. *mg,* the single, boat-shaped megaspore ; *pr,* remains of prothallus, opposite beak of megaspore ; *sm,* sporangial wall, showing lamella on each side. × 24. S. Coll. 1800 A. (G. T. G.)

to find a single megaspore with its portion of sporangial tissue still attached to the convex side (Fig. 106), the fragments having broken away from the central pad of the sporangium. Such single-spored units are aptly described as " seed-like bodies " by Dr. Benson.   From the position of the megaspore in the sporangium, it seems evident that fertilisation can only have been effected after fragmentation took place.

The megasporangia and their fragments are common in the Coal-balls ; the microsporangium, no doubt a more transitory structure, is at present known from a single specimen only, carefully investigated by Dr. Benson.   The sterile tissue is even more developed than in the megasporangium ; the microspores are restricted to comparatively small areas, more or less separated by irregular trabeculae.   The spores are often in tetrads ; they average about 75 $\mu \times$ 50 μ in diameter, and are thus larger than the microspores of a *Lepidostrobus*, but smaller than the spores of *Spencerites*.

Mazocarpon, then, was a highly differentiated heterosporous cone, with special provision for the nutrition of the megaspores, which evidently germinated while still in connection with sporangial tissue.   The great development of sterile tissue in the microsporangium remains unexplained.

In a Lower Carboniferous species, *M. pettycurense*, Benson, the megaspores seem to have been more numerous than in the Coal-measure forms.

Mazocarpon is clearly distinct from *Lepidostrobus* ; in no species of the latter is there anything like the development of sterile sporangial tissue which characterises the new genus ; the form of the megaspores is also quite peculiar. The Coal-measure specimens of *Mazocarpon* are very commonly associated with *Sigillariopsis sulcata*, now known to be the leaf of a *Sigillaria*, and occasionally with portions of Sigillarian stems.   The bracts of *Mazocarpon* were evidently shed readily from the axis of the cone, and according to Dr. Kidston this feature was also character. istic of *Sigillariostrobus*.   In Dr. Benson's paper a close comparison is made between *Mazocarpon* and *Sigillariostrobus*, and the conclusion is reached that the former is a Sigillarian cone with structure preserved.[1] There is much to be said for this view, but in the present state of our knowledge it seems premature to venture on an identification of the two genera.

II. STIGMARIA

1. *Habit and External Characters.*—The subject of the roots or other subterranean organs, both of *Lepidodendron* and *Sigillaria,* has been postponed so far, because it presents considerable difficulty, and we are not even now in a position to distinguish the roots of the one genus from those of the other.[2] Yet *Stigmaria ficoides,* which includes most of the specimens in question, is the very commonest of all fossils in the English Coal-measures, and other strata of similar horizon, and its outward appearance is familiar to every one who has paid the least attention to fossil remains. The *Stigmariae,* which are ordinarily preserved as structureless casts, are long, more or less cylindrical or slowly tapering bodies, varying in diameter from an inch or so up to more than two feet. The surface is marked all over with quincuncially arranged circular scars. Each scar is depressed, with a raised margin ; within the scar is a second, much smaller circle, in the centre of which a raised point can be detected in good specimens (Fig. 107). The scars mark the insertion of the appendages, which are often found *in situ,* radiating out in all directions, and forming approximately a right angle with the main axis (see Fig. 107). The appendages have been found to reach a length of 12 or 15 inches ; they have a nearly cylindrical, but gradually tapering form, and are slightly constricted at the base. Their dimensions are small compared with those of the main axis, scarcely reaching a diameter of half an inch, while they are often quite slender.

---

[1] Benson, " *Mazocarpon,*" *l.c.* Part ii.

[2] The morphological character of these organs is considered below, p. 236. The word " root " is used here in a physiological sense.

The main *Stigmariae* themselves attained an immense length ; one was traced by the late Prof. W. C. Williamson for a distance of 37 feet 4 inches from its base ; in this length it twice forked, but the only branch which could be followed to its full extent measured about 28 feet, from the second dichotomy to its end. At the base of the whole, the diameter was no less than 32 inches, which diminished to a mere point at the extremity of the long branch. This specimen appears to be the largest *Stigmaria* which has been found in actual connection with the

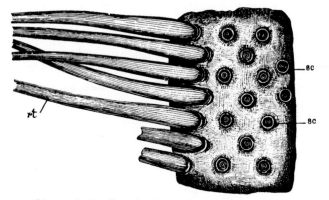

FIG. 107.—*Stigmaria ficoides.* Part of surface, showing the rootlet-scars (*sc*) to some of which the rootlets (*rt*) are still attached. Reduced. After Schimper.

tree-stump to which it belonged ; detached specimens have been described of much greater length.

Up to the year 1839 there seems to have been no good evidence as to the nature of *Stigmaria*, though the probability of its being the root of *Sigillaria* was recognised by some investigators, as, for example, by Brongniart. In 1839, during the construction of the Manchester and Bolton Railway, the stumps of several large fossil trees were discovered at Dixon Fold, with four great dichotomous roots radiating from the base of each trunk. The distinctive characters of these trees and their roots, however, could not be determined. A few years later a number of similar trees were found by Binney at St. Helen's and at Dukinfield, in Lancashire. Their trunks showed the characteristic Sigillarian markings, while the branches of the forked roots bore the Stigmarian scars.[1] Thus the proof was first given that *Stigmaria* is identical with the subterranean parts of the Sigillarian trees, a conclusion which has been confirmed by various later observations. Subsequently, other specimens of *Stigmaria* were found in connection with tree-trunks, which showed the markings, not of *Sigillaria*, but of *Lepidodendron*. Specimens of this kind were first observed in the Coal-measures of Nova Scotia, by Richard Brown, soon after Binney's discoveries in England, but there was some doubt as to whether Brown's trees were rightly identified as *Lepidodendron*. Other cases, however, observed in Germany and in England, seem to leave no doubt that the *Stigmariae* formed the subterranean organs of *Lepidodendron* as well as of *Sigillaria*. It is not even possible to distinguish specifically between those of the two genera ; the name *Stigmaria ficoides* does duty for both, and though other species have been distinguished, we are rarely able to correlate their diagnostic characters with those of the stems. One or two special cases, on which rather more light has been thrown, will be mentioned after the common " species " has been dealt with. In the meantime, we may take *Stigmaria ficoides* as representing the " roots " of various *Lepidodendron*, as well as of various *Sigillariae* of the ribbed division.

The mode of connection between the *Stigmaria* and its Sigillarian or Lepidodendroid stem has been shortly noticed above (p 186, Fig. 91). This has now been observed in a great number of specimens, and the main features appear to be constant. There is never a tap-root forming the direct downward continuation of the vertical stem ; the Stigmarian roots are always given off laterally

---

[1] See Williamson, " Monograph of *Stigmaria ficoides*," Palaeontographical Society, 1886.

from the base of the stem, and there are always four of them to start with, the four occupying at their attachment the whole circumference of the trunk, which ends abruptly between them ; its under surface is marked by a cruciate furrow, corresponding to the lines of junction of the Stigmarian roots.	Each of these main roots forked at least twice, and if the first dichotomy took place very near the base, their number may appear to be greater than four.	Whether the stem be large or small, the arrangement is just the same ; thus in the Clayton specimen shown in Fig. 91, the stump of the stem is more than 4 feet in diameter, while in another figured by Williamson in his Monograph it only measures 6 inches.	The angle at which the Stigmarian roots pass off from the stem is variable.	Sometimes they take a nearly horizontal direction from the first ; in other cases they first strike sharply down at an angle of 50° or 60°, and only begin to take a more horizontal course at some distance from the main trunk.

The Stigmarian roots, as mentioned above, are especially abundant in the clay underlying the coal-seams, to which the name " Stigmarian clay " has been given by English geologists ; they are, however, by no means limited to this position.	The conditions must often have been more favourable for the preservation of these underground organs than for that of the aërial stem ; hence it is not surprising that in some Carboniferous beds on the Continent, *Stigmariae* are found without any corresponding remains of *Sigillaria* or *Lepidodendron*. It is still uncertain whether *Stigmaria* when living ever occurred except in connection with aërial stems.	The *Stigmaria*, with its appendages, manifestly performed the functions of a root, taking up food from the soil. A rich soil seems to have suited it, for the Stigmarian rootlets burrowed in every direction through the mass of decaying vegetation which formed the organic material of the calcareous nodules.	They occur in countless numbers, crowded together and penetrating every kind of vegetable fragment—stem, leaf, root, or cone, so that the first lesson a beginner has to learn, in studying the microscopic structure of coal-plants, is to avoid confusing these intruders with integral parts of the organs which they invade. We may form some idea of the conditions under which the *Stigmariae* grew, from the analogy of weeds growing on a leaf-mould heap, and sending their roots in all directions through the decaying vegetable mass beneath them; only, in the case of the *Stigmaria*, the weeds are represented by gigantic trees. Special care is necessary in the frequent cases where the rootlets led a kind of cannibal existence, burrowing into roots and rootlets of their own kind. Such cases have deceived even practised observers; thus Göppert described an intruding rootlet, found in the pith of a Stigmarian axis, as part of the structure of the latter, and this elementary blunder misled several of his successors, until Williamson set the matter right.

2. *Anatomical Structure.*—We have now to consider the internal structure of *Stigmaria* and its appendages; our description will be based in the first place on the common type *S. ficoides*, which is by far the best known.

The main axis of *Stigmaria* consisted of a well-developed vascular cylinder, surrounded by cortex and periderm (see Fig. 108). The centre of the stele was occupied by a fair-sized pith, the tissue of which is rarely found preserved, except in the outer part, next the wood. Possibly the pith may have been fistular during life. The wood forms a broad zone, divided up into bundles by the principal medullary rays (Fig. 108, *x*). These bundles constantly anastomose laterally with each other, forming a network, in which the principal rays occupy the meshes. Throughout almost the whole thickness of the woody zone, a regular radial arrangement of the elements prevails; there is no sharp distinction between primary and secondary xylem, but at the inner end of each wedge the elements are smaller and less regular than elsewhere. Good radial sections show that the spiral tracheides are placed at the extreme inner edge of the wood, next the pith, so that in this form of *Stigmaria* centripetal wood was entirely absent. This is a rather surprising ana-

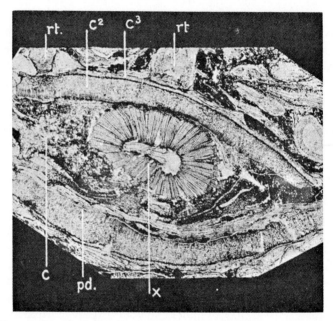

Fig. 108.—*Stigmaria ficoides.* Transverse section of a small specimen. *x*, zone of wood, radially seriated throughout; *c*, middle cortex, only partially preserved; *pd*, periderm; *c²*, outer primary cortex; *c³*, hypodermal zone of cortex; *rt*, bases of rootlets; free rootlets are also shown. × 3½. From a photograph by Mr. L. A. Boodle. Spencer Coll. 147 (now S. Coll. 1465).

tomical peculiarity, considering that the centripetal primary wood is one of the chief structural characters of Lycopods, both recent and fossil. The case of *Stigmaria ficoides* is not, however, without analogy within the class. Thus, in the creeping stem of *Selaginella spinosa*, the first-formed tracheides are central, so that the whole of the wood is centrifugally developed. The same is the case in the hypocotyl and rhizophores of *S. Kraus-siana* and other species.[1] In both plants the upper parts of the axis have the normal structure, with centripetal xylem, just as in the case of the Sigillarian or Lepido-dendroid stems to which *Stigmaria ficoides* belonged. As we shall see presently, the absence of centripetal wood does not hold for all forms of *Stigmaria*.

The bulk of the xylem in *S. ficoides* consists of radially arranged scalariform tracheae, the pits occurring on the tangential as well as on the radial walls of the elements (Fig. 109). In addition to the principal rays, numerous narrow secondary rays traverse the wood ; they may consist of a single radial row of cells, or may be several cells in height ; usually they are one cell thick, sometimes more (Fig. 109, *m.r*). It is an interesting fact that the rays consist partly of spirally or reticulately thickened elements, presumably tracheides, a peculiarity which, as we have seen, is very general in the secondary wood of Lepidodendroid stems.   There is here an obvious analogy with the complex organisation of the medullary rays in the Abietineae, though the two structures no doubt arose quite independently.

The regular radial seriation of the secondary xylem-elements is sometimes interrupted by the intercalation of a tangential band of much smaller tracheides, beyond which the regular formation of large elements recom-mences. These interruptions no doubt point to a break in the activity of the cambium, but the small-celled layers are not always continuous, and cannot be regarded as marking annual rings. To use Williamson's words : " The meristemic activity of the cambial layer may have manifested itself irregularly rather than periodically." [2] At the exterior of the wood, some remains of the cambium can sometimes be traced, passing over externally into a

---

[1] See the papers by Bruchmann and Harvey Gibson, cited on p. 237.
[2] " Monograph of *Stigmaria ficoides*," p. 17.

zone of delicate tissue, more or less radially arranged, and consisting, as shown by longitudinal sections, of elongated elements. This was no doubt the phloëm. On its outer margin is an imperfectly preserved lacunar zone, such as often occurs in a corresponding position in

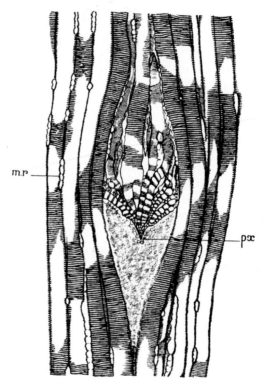

Fig. 109.—*Stigmaria ficoides.* Part of tangential section through wood, showing an outgoing rootlet-bundle. All the tracheides are scalariform. *m.r.,* medullary rays; *px*, protoxylem of rootlet-bundle. The top of the figure is directed towards the base of the *Stigmaria.* × 40. Spencer Coll. 150 (now S. Coll. 1469). (G. T. G.)

the stems of *Lepidodendron.* The middle cortex (Fig. 108, *c*) is never perfectly preserved, but where parts of it remain, it appears to have the same curious trabecular structure, as if made up of interwoven filaments, which we so often find in the same region in *Lepidodendron.* In

some specimens the preservation of the outer cortex is
very perfect (see Figs. 108 and 110). The primary
structure of this region can only be observed in fairly
young examples (Fig. 108, c^2). Most of its thickness is
made up of a very uniform large-celled parenchyma.
On the external surface is a hypodermal zone of smaller
cells, marked off from the rest of the cortex by a narrow

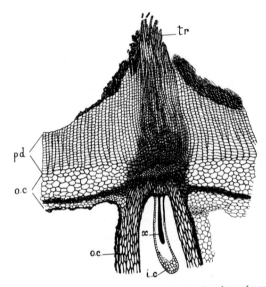

FIG. 110.—*Stigmaria ficoides.* Part of transverse section, to show base of a rootlet. *pd*,
periderm of main axis; *o.c.*, outer cortex (including hypoderma) of main axis and of
rootlet; *i.c.*, inner cortex, *x*, xylem of rootlet; *tr*, tracheides passing out to rootlet.
× about 15. (G. T. G.)

band of dark tissue, probably sclerotic (Figs. 108, c^3,
and 110).

Periderm-formation set in early, and the older specimens were provided with an immensely thick bark,
fragments of which are among the " common objects "
of the coal-balls. The development of periderm (Figs.
108 and 110, *pd*) began in a deep-seated layer of the outer
cortex, and appears to have gone on for some time, chiefly
in the centripetal direction, so far at least as one type is

concerned, for it is here on the inner edge of the secondary cortical zone that remains of the delicate phellogen can be traced. In another type the periderm consists of two zones, an outer, wide-celled, irregular portion, and an inner, smaller-celled and more regular region; here the phellogen appears to have been between the two.[1] The tissue thus formed cannot have been of the nature of cork, for the outer tissue shows no sign of withering, and some of its cells had sometimes undergone tangential division, as if starting a new, more external phellogen. In many of the Carboniferous plants the formation of secondary cortex played a much more important part than is usually the case in recent vegetation, and though we use the words " periderm " and " bark," it is certain that many of the structures thus indicated were very different in nature and function from the recent tissues which answer to them morphologically. A characteristic feature of the Stigmarian bark is the great tangential dilatation of the more external peridermal cells.

The above must suffice for a general account of the anatomy of the Stigmarian axis; it remains to describe its appendages, and their relation to the parent organ.

As already mentioned, the appendages, which we will call simply *rootlets*, following Williamson's terminology, are arranged in quincuncial order on all parts of the Stigmarian surface (see Fig. 107). The vascular strand of each rootlet, so far as its xylem is concerned, starts from the inner, primary margin of the wood of the main axis, and bends sharply outwards, taking a nearly horizontal course through the secondary xylem. Every principal ray is traversed by one of these rootlet-bundles, which appear in tangential sections of the axis as tongue-shaped bodies, with the point projecting freely into the lenticular cavity, left by the decay of the ray, while the base is continuous with the adjacent wood

[1] See Kisch, " Periderm of Fossil Lycopodiales," *l.c.* p. 294.

(see Fig. 109). The orientation is such that the free point (protoxylem) of the rootlet-strand is directed towards the *apex*, while its connection with the wood is towards the *base* of the main axis.[1] Thus the water absorbed by the rootlet would have been directly conducted through the wood of the main organ, to the aerial stem.

The xylem of the rootlet was increased to some extent with the growth of that of the main axis, for the strand becomes larger as we follow it outwards through the secondary wood. In the ill-preserved middle cortex the rootlet-bundles are often met with, and here their course seems to have approached more nearly to the vertical. The parenchyma immediately surrounding the bundle is often preserved when the general cortical tissue has perished. In this region the sectional form of the xylem of the rootlet is triangular, with protoxylem at the apex. At the opposite side the phloëm can sometimes be recognised.

On entering the outer cortex the bundle again takes a more horizontal course. It is here surrounded by a well-marked zone of tissue, in which layers corresponding to the inner and outer cortex of the free rootlet can already be distinguished. In passing through the periderm the parenchymatous tissues of the base of the rootlet kept pace, by tangential divisions, with the growth of the surrounding secondary zone (Fig. 110).

Fig. 110 shows, in longitudinal section, the structure of the rootlet at its base, where it is just escaping from the cortex of the principal axis, which is shown in transverse section. At its attachment, the rootlet is a solid structure with its tissues complete, but as soon as it becomes free the inner and outer cortex are separated by a wide lacuna, in which only slight remains of the probably

---

[1] Thus in Fig. 109 the growing point of the *Stigmaria* would have lain in the *downward*, and its base in the *upward* direction, as the figure is drawn.

trabecular tissue, which once occupied it, can be traced. The outer cortex is continuous with that of the main organ, the hypoderma extending over from one to the other without change (Fig. 110, *o.c.*). The inner cortex, enclosing the vascular strand, is seated directly on the solid tissue of the transitional region. The continuity of the outer tissues from the main axis to the rootlet is, however, only partial. In the original condition, as Dr. Lang has found, the rootlet, though it cannot be called endogenous, is somewhat deeply seated on the outer cortex, having broken through the most external layers. In older specimens these layers are often lost, and the insertion of the rootlet then appears to be superficial, as in Fig. 110.

We have now to describe the characteristic structure of the free rootlet, but may first point out how the anatomy of its base exactly accounts for the configuration of the scars on the ordinary Stigmarian surface (compare Fig. 107 with Fig. 111). The outer cortex answers to the raised external rim of the scar; the lacunar middle zone to its depressed surface; the inner cortex to the internal circle of the scar; and the vascular strand itself to the minute central point seen in the latter, when especially well preserved.

The rootlets of *Stigmaria ficoides* are absolutely the commonest specimens among the petrified material of the calcareous nodules. Their structure is on the whole very uniform, though their dimensions vary greatly, the diameter ranging from a centimetre to a millimetre or less. The external cortex, which is generally well preserved, is several cells in thickness, and is often divided into an outer and inner zone by a band of thick-walled tissue. Sometimes the inner zone as a whole has thicker walls than the outer (Fig. 115), but often there is an entire absence of differentiation (Fig. 111). These distinctions may possibly turn out to be of specific value, but at present we have no clue to their significance. As we have already seen, all the layers of the cortex in the rootlet are continuous with the corresponding tissues of the main *Stigmaria*, and present similar characters. The outermost layer of the rootlet is sometimes papillose, but no true root-hairs have been observed.

Indications of tangential division are sometimes found in the cells of the external cortex, which may thus have undergone some slight secondary increase in thickness. Within this external zone we almost always find a wide

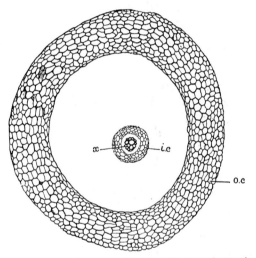

FIG. 111.—*Stigmaria ficoides.* Transverse section of rootlet, in usual state of preservation. *o.c.*, outer cortex ; *i.c.*, inner cortex ; *x*, xylem. × 16. S. Coll. 113. (G. T. G.)

empty space, from which all tissue has perished. It is rare, except at the base of the rootlet, to find any remains of the middle cortex, which must once have bridged the gap. Occasionally, however, especially in young rootlets, some thin-walled tissue is still preserved in this region, or a single, stout trabecula may connect the inner with the outer cortex (Fig. 113).

The internal cortex forms a ring, of very small size compared with the outer layer, and immediately encloses the vascular strand (Figs. 111-115). As, after the decay of the intermediate tissue, there was nothing to keep the internal cortex in place, we seldom find it in its natural central position; usually it is more or less excentric. It consists of a few layers of delicate parenchyma; an endodermis has not yet been distinguished.

We now come to the vascular strand, which occupied the central position in the whole structure. As a rule

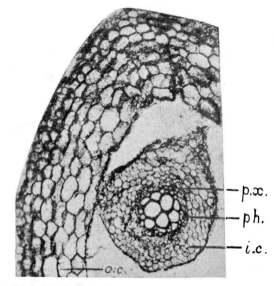

FIG. 112.—*Stigmaria ficoides.* Part of transverse section of rootlet, to show monarch structure. *px*, protoxylem, at one corner of the thick-walled strand of wood; *ph*, phloëm, which thins out opposite the protoxylem; *i.c.*, inner cortex; *o.c.*, part of outer cortex. × about 50. From a photograph by Dr. Bousfield. S. Coll. 114.

the wood only remains; occasionally, as in the specimen shown in Fig. 112, the delicate tissue which no doubt constituted the phloëm, and perhaps the pericycle also, is preserved. We will consider the xylem first. It consists of a small strand of tracheides with a somewhat triangular transverse section (Figs. 111-115). One angle is more prominent than the others, and is in contact with the surrounding parenchyma (Figs. 112-114, *px*). At this angle the smallest elements are situated, and longitudinal sections show that they alone are spirally thickened; the remaining elements of the xylem are scalariform. It is therefore clear that the rootlet had only a single group of protoxylem, and thus, if we are to adopt the terminology usual in the case of roots, must be termed monarch. This conclusion is confirmed by the comparison of rootlets at various stages of growth, which always show the first differentiated tracheae at one angle only, never at three. So far as the English specimens are concerned, there can be no doubt that in *S. ficoides* all the appendages agree in having a monarch vascular strand.

A remarkable feature in the structure of the Stigmarian rootlet was fully investigated by Professor F. E. Weiss, F.R.S.[1] Renault in 1882 had described rootlets with a very delicate vascular strand given off from the stele, and had regarded this as indicating a mode of branching distinct from the usual dichotomy. Professor Weiss confirms this observation (on which some doubt had been cast), but finds that the vascular strands in question have no connection with branches. They consist of spiral tracheides, and start from the protoxylem, pass out, obliquely or horizontally, through the middle cortex, enclosed in a sheath or traversing a trabecula, and terminate in connection with an extensive patch of tracheidal tissue in the outer cortex (Fig. 113); the tracheides here form a network, associated with wide, thin-walled cells. As Professor Weiss says: " The vascular strand and the transfusion cells in which it terminates form a special means of conducting water from the peripheral to the central tissues of the rootlet, a means which is rendered necessary by the development

---

[1] " On *Xenophyton radiculosum* and on a Stigmarian Rootlet," *Mem. and Proc. Manchester Lit. and Phil. Soc.* vol. xlvi. 1902 ; " The Vascular Branches of Stigmarian Rootlets," *Ann. of Bot.* vol. xvi. 1902 ; " The Vascular Supply of Stigmarian Rootlets," *ibid.* vol. xviii. 1904.

of the middle cortex into an air-conducting tissue or space."

When the phloëm is preserved, it appears to be thickest at the side remote from the protoxylem-angle, extending also along the flanks of the xylem, but not round the point (see Fig. 112, *ph*). It must be remembered, however, that in the state of preservation of these specimens the phloëm cannot be distinguished with certainty from pericycle or from cambium.

The elements of the wood do not, in the ordinary cases,

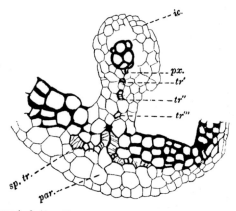

Fig. 113.—*Stigmaria ficoides.* Transverse section of rootlet, showing vascular bundle and part of cortex ; *i.c.*, inner cortex, connected by a parenchymatous bridge with the outer cortex ; *px*, protoxylem ; *tr'*, *tr''*, *tr'''*, three portions of vascular strands running to outer cortex ; *sp. tr.*, spiral tracheides of outer cortex ; *par.*, patch of large-celled parenchyma. × 67. After F. E. Weiss. Hick Collection (Manchester), 75.

show any radial arrangement, and are no doubt to be regarded as primary. In exceptional cases, however, we find an addition of radially arranged secondary wood (see Fig. 114, x^2), and where this is the case the secondary tissue is always limited to the side remote from the protoxylem, thus affording yet another indication of monarch structure. The formation of secondary wood, though rare in the free rootlets, is commonly found in the rootlet-trace, where it passes through the cortex of the main axis.

The branching of the rootlets was by dichotomy. A

transverse section of a rootlet at the point of bifurcation is shown in Fig. 115. The plane of division passes through the protoxylem, and coincides with the plane of symmetry of the bundle. The dichotomous branching is an obvious point of agreement with the roots of modern Lycopods.

Something may now be said of other forms of *Stigmaria*, differing in certain respects from the specimens grouped under *Stigmaria ficoides*.

Xenophyton radiculosum, a fossil described by Mr. T.

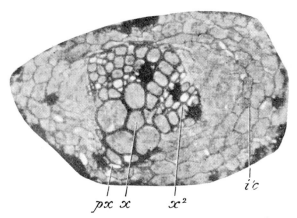

px x   *x²*

FIG. 114.—*Stigmaria ficoides.* Transverse section of central part of rootlet, to show secondary thickening of wood. *x*, primary xylem; *px*, protoxylem; *x²*, secondary xylem, limited to one side of bundle; *i.c.*, inner cortex. × nearly 100. From a photograph by Mr. L. A. Boodle. Will. Coll. 651.

Hick in 1891,[1] has been shown by Professor F. E. Weiss, in agreement with a suggestion of Williamson's, to be a *Stigmaria*. The pith and the whole of the cortex are preserved, giving the specimen a very different character from that of the ordinary *S. ficoides*. The wood, which is little developed, appears to be wholly centrifugal, as in that species. The rootlet-bundles take a steeply acropetal course, like leaf-traces, and secondary paren-

[1] Hick, "On a New Fossil Plant from the Lower Coal-measures," *Journal Linnean Society*, vol. xxix. 1892.

chyma is formed about them in passing through the middle cortex, which has a similar structure to that of *Lepidophloios fuliginosus*, the plant to which Professor Weiss believes this *Stigmaria* to have belonged. Within the periderm there are strands of secretory cells, as in so many Lepidodendroid stems. It was in a rootlet, attributed to the same plant, remarkable for the perfect preservation of the middle cortex, that Professor Weiss first observed the radial vascular strands, thus confirming Renault's previous statement.

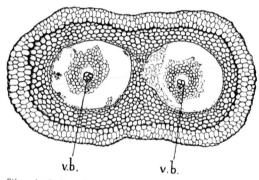

FIG. 115.—*Stigmaria ficoides.* Transverse section of rootlet, showing dichotomy. The outer cortex, differentiated into two zones, is still continuous, while the inner cortex of the two branches has completely divided. *v.b.*, the two monarch vascular bundles. × 25. S. Coll. 172. (G. T. G.)

As mentioned above, the absence of centripetal primary wood from the main axis is not constant in *Stigmaria*. M. Renault[1] found this tissue in various cases, and notably in a *Stigmaria* which he attributed to *Sigillaria Brardi*. Here the centripetal wood is very distinct, though of no great thickness. It forms more or less separate bundles, so that the structure is not unlike that of the corresponding part of the aërial stem.

Another species with centripetal wood, the *Stigmaria flexuosa* of Renault, is regarded by Solms-Laubach[2] as

[1] *Flore fossile d'Autun et d'Épinac*, Part ii. p. 226, Plates xxxviii.-xl.
[2] *Über Stigmariopsis*, Jena, 1894.

having very probably belonged to the fossil called *Stigmariopsis*, a form which differs in the shape of the scars from the ordinary *Stigmaria*, and which is characterised by its well-marked medullary casts, resembling those of a Calamite, though of course without the nodal constrictions. Solms-Laubach, from the geological distribution of *Stigmariopsis*, suggests that it may have constituted

FIG. 116.—*Stigmaria*, sp. Transverse section of an axis, showing pith and large-celled centripetal primary xylem, with broad zone of secondary wood. At the top of the figure the bundle of a rootlet is seen. × 24. From a photograph lent by Professor F. E. Weiss.

the underground organs of the *Sub-Sigillariae*, while the typical *Stigmariae* belonged to *Eu-Sigillariae* as well as to *Lepidodendron*. This, however, is not yet established, and, in fact, there are few questions in fossil botany more difficult than that of the relation of *Stigmaria* to its stems.

Professor F. E. Weiss has described a very interesting *Stigmaria*, from the nodules of the Lower Coal-measures, which possesses a perfectly distinct centripetal primary xylem, surrounded by a wide zone of secondary wood. This fossil was originally described by Williamson as an advanced condition of the stem of *Lepidodendron* (now *Bothrodendron*) *mundum*. It is probable that it really belongs to that plant, representing its root or rhizophore. The primary wood gives the axis its stem-like character, but it is shown to be of the nature of a *Stigmaria* by the structure of the cortex and by the bases of rootlets attached to it. The rootlet-bundles are remarkable for having, usually, a mesarch xylem, with secondary growth on all sides, instead of on the outer side only, as in *S. ficoides*. In passing through the cortex these bundles are connected with groups of reticulate tracheides, which probably served for water-storage.[1] If this *Stigmaria* is rightly attributed to *Bothrodendron mundum*, of which Mr. Watson has now described the cone, that plant will become the most completely known of the Palaeozoic Lycopods.

3. *Morphology*.—It only remains to consider very briefly the morphological nature of *Stigmaria* and its appendages. If we call *Stigmaria* a " root," it is chiefly on physiological grounds that the term is used. The main axis of *Stigmaria ficoides* has in no respect the structure of a root ; in fact, this species, in the absence of centripetal wood, departs from typical root-structure more widely even than the aërial stems themselves. Other forms of *Stigmaria*, though they may possess centripetal wood, are no more root-like in structure than the Sigillarian stem. The arrangement of the appendages (which, in the rare cases where the growing end is preserved, are found to have converged to form a kind of bud at the apex of the main Stigmarian axis) is unlike that of rootlets, nor does their origin seem to have been endogenous. (See, however, p. 228.)

[1] Weiss, " A *Stigmaria* with Centripetal Wood," *Ann. Bot.* vol. xxii. 1908.

On the other hand, the appendages agree so exactly in structure and in the dichotomous mode of branching with the monarch roots of the allied recent genera *Isoëtes* and *Selaginella*,[1] that it seems impossible to doubt their homology. Some authors have regarded the appendages as modified leaves, a view which was primarily suggested by their arrangement on the axis. Recent discoveries have tended somewhat to increase the analogies with leaves ; the so-called transfusion-tissue of the Stigmarian rootlet (see above, p. 231) has been compared with that of the leaf, though the two tissues differ as much in arrangement as they no doubt did in function. Quite recently Professor Weiss has found, in connection with the rootlet-trace of the Stigmarian *Xenophyton*, a strand of cells analogous to the parichnos of the leaves, but situated on the opposite side of the bundle (next the xylem instead of next the phloëm).[2] Such resemblances as these do not count for much in establishing an homology, as Professor Weiss points out. On the other hand, the course of the rootlet-traces in *Xenophyton*, as already mentioned, is remarkably like that of the leaf-traces in the stems of Lepidodendreae.

The arguments in favour of the root-nature of the appendages are their dichotomous branching, monarch structure, general resemblance to the root of allied recent

---

[1] In the Stigmarian appendages the position of the phloëm, which appears to have formed an arc on the side of the strand remote from the protoxylem, agrees exactly with that in the roots of these recent plants. Cf. Bruchmann, *Selaginella spinulosa*, Plate i. Fig. 13, 1897 ; Farmer, " On *Isoëtes*," *Ann. Bot.* vol. v. Plate v. Fig. 4, 1891 ; Scott and Hill, " Structure of *Isoëtes Hystrix*," *Ann. Bot.* vol. xiv. Plate xxiv. Fig. 30, 1900. See also W. H. Lang, " Studies in the Morphology of *Isoëtes*," I., *Manchester Memoirs*, vol. lix. No. 3, 1915 ; C. West and H. Takeda, " On *Isoëtes japonica*," *Trans. Linn. Soc. (Bot.)* vol. viii. 1915. For information on the structure of rhizophore and root in many species of *Selaginella*, see Harvey Gibson, " Contributions towards a Knowledge of the Anatomy of the Genus *Selaginella*, Part iv. The Root," *Ann. Bot.* vol. xvi. 1902.

[2] Weiss, " The Parichnos in the Lepidodendraceae," *Mem. and Proc. Manchester Lit. and Phil. Soc.* vol. li. 1907.

Lycopods, and the occurrence of secondary thickening. In favour of their homology with leaves we have their quincuncial arrangement (see Fig. 107), bud-like convergence at the apex, the transfusion-tissue and parichnos, and the course of the rootlet-traces. There is no analogy among the Lycopodiales for such a modification of a leaf, but the water-leaves of *Salvinia* might be cited as remotely comparable. The presence of leaf-like characters in the Stigmarian appendages may be in part the survival of a more primitive morphology, but on the whole it seems evident that they are the same organs as the roots of recent Lycopods. Even if their origin were exogenous, it would offer no hindrance to this interpretation, for we know that among recent Lycopods, as in *Selaginella* and *Phylloglossum*, roots may arise exogenously.[1]

What view, then, are we to take of the organs which bore the appendages ? They are, as we have seen, often very different from typical roots. Neither, however, do they show the characters of rhizomes ; they bear no leaves, only rootlets, and we have no convincing proof that they gave rise to aërial stems, though it is possible that they may have done so. Those *Stigmariae*, however, the relations of which are the most clear, are evidently appendages of the aërial stems, and not their parent organs. How those stems arose in the first instance, whether directly from the embryo, or from some creeping form of axis, of which, as a rule, no traces remain,[2] is at present an unsolved problem.

It appears, then, that the main *Stigmariae* cannot be classed morphologically either as roots or rhizomes.

[1] Van Tiegham et Douliot, " Origines des membres Endogènes," *Ann. des sci. nat. (Bot.)*, ser. vii. vol. viii. p. 552, 1888 ; Bower, " On the Development and Morphology of *Phylloglossum Drummondi*," *Phil. Trans.* ii. 1885.

[2] M. Grand'Eury maintains the latter view. See his *Bassin houiller du Gard*, p. 236 ; also " Sur les sols de végétation fossiles des Sigillaires et des Lepidodendrées," *Comptes rendus*, t. cxxxviii. 1904. See also Lignier, " Interprétation de la souche des *Stigmaria*," *Bull. de la Soc. Bot. de France*, t. lx. 1913.

The leafless rhizomes of *Psilotum* and *Tmesipteris* offer but a poor analogy, for they bear no roots or other appendages, except hairs. The best analogy we can find for the Stigmarian organs is in the rhizophores of *Selaginella*. These, like the former, are leafless branches, having no other function than to bear the roots ; they may also be regarded as being themselves modified roots. In some cases, as we have seen above (p. 222), their structure shows some slight approximation to that of *Stigmaria ficoides*. The position of the rhizophores on the stem is, it is true, very different in the two genera, but this is not an insuperable difficulty, for we are not assuming a strict homology, but rather suggesting a parallel modification.

It may be suggested that the terminology most in harmony with the facts would be to call the main axis of *Stigmaria* a rhizophore, and its appendages roots. Considering, however, that even in existing Lycopods, as notably in *Lycopodium* itself, the differentiation between root and stem is often far less sharp than in other vascular plants,[1] we need feel no great scruple in applying the terms roots and rootlets to the Stigmarian organs, as was constantly done by Williamson, their chief investigator. Some further suggestions will be considered in Chapter XV.

III. LYCOPODITEAE

Under this name are included certain fossil Lycopods, occurring from the Devonian onwards, which appear from their habit to have been herbaceous plants. One such herbaceous Lycopod — *Miadesmia* — has already been described in connection with its seed-like fructification (p. 177). As a rule, the Lycopoditeae are only known as impressions, but in favourable cases the essential morpho-

---

[1] On this subject see C. E. Jones, " Morphology and Anatomy of the Stem of the Genus *Lycopodium*," *Trans. Linn. Soc. ser.* ii. vol. vii. 1905 ; G. Wigglesworth, " Young Sporophytes of *Lycopodium complanatum* and *L. clavatum*," *Ann. of Bot.* vol. xxi. 1907.

logical features can be recognised in these carbonised specimens. The plants, which until recently were all included in the genus *Lycopodites*, branched dichotomously, and have quite the habit of recent Lycopods ; in some the leaves are uniform, as in most species of *Lycopodium*, while in others they are ranged in four rows, two of large and two of small leaves, just as in many species of *Selaginella*. This character is not, of course, sufficient in itself to establish affinity ; within the last few years, however, the reproductive organs have been investigated in certain species and a clear relationship to *Selaginella* shown to exist. The genus *Selaginellites* has been founded by Zeiller for species known to have been heterosporous. *S. Suissei*, Zeiller,[1] from the Upper Coalmeasures of Blanzy in France, has a dichotomous stem, with four rows of dimorphic leaves of the type of the tetrastichous Selaginellas. The strobili are of considerable size, 8-10 mm. in diameter by 15 cm. in length, with the sporophylls in numerous vertical series. The sporangia of the upper part of the cone contain numerous microspores, 40-60 μ in diameter, while those of the lower part are megasporangia, each of which contains from sixteen to twenty-four megaspores, about ten times the diameter of the microspores (500-650 μ). Both kinds of spore have an equatorial ring or collar. The chief differences from *Selaginella* are in the numerous series of sporophylls, as compared with the tetrastichous vegetative leaves, and the relatively large number of megaspores in the sporangium, while in *Selaginella* they do not exceed four. M. Halle, in his valuable paper on fossil herbaceous Lycopods,[2] describes a Coal-measure species (*S. elongatus* (Goldenberg)), likewise with dimorphic foliage, in which the sporangia appear to arise

[1] Zeiller, " Bassin houiller et permien de Blanzy et du Creusot," Fasc. ii., *Flore fossile*, 1906, p. 140. M. Zeiller's observations were first published in 1900.

[2] Halle, " Einige krautartige Lycopodiaceen paläozoischen und mesozoischen Alters," *Arkiv för Botanik*, Stockholm, 1907.

in the axils of ordinary leaves, no strobilus being differentiated. Microspores were not observed, but some of the
sporangia were found to contain from twenty to thirty
spores, about 450 μ in diameter, so there can be no doubt
that the species was heterosporous ; the absence of a
specialised strobilus is interesting, as no such case is
known among recent *Selaginellas*. We may find an
analogy in *Pinakodendron* (p. 183). Another species of
similar age, investigated by M. Halle, *S. primaevus*
(Goldenberg), is remarkable for its close agreement with
the recent genus. In this case definite terminal strobili
are differentiated ; the sporophylls as well as the leaves
of the smaller branches are uniform and spirally arranged
(as in *Selaginella spinosa*), though it is possible that
dimorphism may have occurred in the main stems. The
most interesting point is that each megasporangium
contained four tetrahedrally arranged megaspores (400-
500 μ in diameter), just as in the living Selaginellas.
Thus the *Selaginella* type, if not the actual genus, is
shown to date from Palaeozoic times. The species *S.
Suissei* and *S. elongatus* may represent a less advanced
condition, but it must be remembered that *Miadesmia*,
a contemporary or older genus, went far beyond any
other known herbaceous Lycopods in the specialisation
of its megasporangia. Nothing certain is known, as yet,
of any homosporous type of Lycopoditeae. If, however,
the Rhaetic plant *Naiadita* is rightly referred to Lycopodiaceae, we may have an example from the Mesozoic,
for the spores, which are found grouped in tetrads in the
sporangia, have a diameter of 80 μ, and only one kind
has been observed.[1]

Conclusion

We have now completed our survey of the Palaeozoic
Lycopods, a group remarkable for the high development

[1] See Miss I. B. J. Sollas, " *Naiadita lanceolata*," *Quart Journ. Geol.
Soc.* vol. lvii. 1901, p. 307.

which they attained, both in vegetative and reproductive characters. The anatomical complexity of the Lepidodendreae was clearly correlated with the arboreal habit, which was then so prevalent. Apart from this, the structure, so far as the primary tissues are concerned, was on the whole of a simple type—simpler than that of the majority of recent Lycopods. The remarkable morphology of the subterranean organs (*Stigmaria*) may possibly indicate a somewhat primitive stage in the differentiation of root and shoot, though it may also be interpreted as a special modification, due to the peculiar conditions of growth. The morphology of the vegetative organs, even in the highly organised Lepidodendreae, is not in itself inconsistent with the view that the Lycopods are among the most primitive of Vascular Plants, if we except the early Devonian Psilophytales (Chapter X.).

On the other hand, the reproductive organs were generally of a very advanced type. With the still doubtful exception of *Spencerites*, it appears that all Palaeozoic Lycopods, of which the reproduction is known, were heterosporous, and this applies, so far as our information extends, to the herbaceous as well as the arboreal forms. *Lepidocarpon* among the latter, and *Miadesmia* among the former attained, in the evolution of an organ closely analogous to a true seed, a higher level than any existing members of the Class, and rivalled the Spermophytes themselves.

Recent discoveries appear to show conclusively that *Selaginella*, at all events, had no direct connection with the Lepidodendreae, but sprang from a distinct and equally ancient herbaceous stock. If any modern member of the Class can claim affinity with the Tree Lycopods of the Palaeozoic, it would appear to be the greatly reduced genus *Isoëtes*.[1] *Lycopodium*, on the other hand, certainly bore no near relation to any of the Carboniferous forms in which the nature of the spores

---

[1] See concluding chapter of book.

has been determined. It has been suggested, however, that the ancient type *Asteroxylon*, one of the Psilophytales, may have had some relation to *Lycopodium* (see Chapter X.).

In spite of the high organisation of the Palaeozoic Lycopods, it is very doubtful whether they have any true affinity with the Seed-plants which some of them simulate, but this is a question which may best be postponed to the concluding chapter.

CHAPTER VIII

THE FERNS

Fronds ; Fructifications ; Anatomy

WE have now reached the fourth of the classes, or *phyla*, under which the Vascular Cryptogams—recent and fossil—naturally group themselves. This fourth phylum is that of the Filicales, or Ferns in the widest sense ; among all the Pteridophyta it is this stock which holds the strongest position at the present day. The Lycopods are unimportant now, compared with what they once were ; the Equisetales survive only in one single genus ; the Sphenophyllales disappeared altogether about the close of the Palaeozoic period.[1] But the Ferns form one of the most prominent groups among living vegetation, numbering, on a recent computation, no less than 149 genera and 6200 species.

Not many years ago all palaeobotanists held that the Ferns were even more important in Palaeozoic times than they are at present, in fact that they were the dominant class of plants at that period. According to the estimates of the systematists the Ferns constituted almost exactly half of the total number of species known from the Carboniferous rocks. Since then, however, the position has completely changed, so much so that the late Professor Zeiller, speaking of the Lower Carboniferous Flora, said that the Ferns, " though they were probably not entirely absent, occupied an altogether subordinate

---

[1] Unless we regard the Psilotaceae as their last surviving remnant ; see the concluding chapter of the book.

rank." [1] The ground for this radical change of view is to be found in the recognition of an extinct class of seed-bearing plants, the Pteridosperms, to which, as it now appears, the majority of the supposed Palaeozoic Ferns really belonged. This class coincides, at least in part, with the Cycadofilices, already recognised in the first edition of this book, but has proved to be much more extensive, and also more remote from the Ferns, than was realised at that time.

The reduction in the number of the true Ferns becomes more marked, the earlier the period to which we go back. " The Westphalian [2] Flora," according to Professor Zeiller, " is already less rich in true Ferns than the Stephanian,[3] and one might almost raise the question whether in the epochs of the Culm [4] and Devonian, Ferns really existed." The Pteridosperms, in fact, appear to be actually older than the majority of the known Ferns, though certain groups of the latter, such as the Botryopteridaceae, to be subsequently described, are doubtless of great antiquity.

From the characters of the frond alone (the part most commonly preserved) it is now impossible to say whether a given Palaeozoic plant belonged to the true Ferns or to the Fern-like Seed-plants.

It is probable that the impressions of " Fern-fronds," often preserved in such exquisite beauty in the strata of the Coal-measures, are better known to the non-botanical observer than any other specimens of fossil plants. The character of such leaves has specially lent itself to this mode of preservation, and as regards form and venation, nothing more perfect could be desired than many of the impressions from the Carboniferous and other strata.

[1] Zeiller, " Une nouvelle Classe de Gymnospermes : Les Ptéridospermes," *Rev. Générale des Sciences*, 16me année, 1905.

[2] Middle and Lower Coal-measures.

[3] Upper Coal-measures.

[4] Lower Carboniferous.

Almost all the well-known genera of conspicuous Fern-like fronds have now, however, fallen under suspicion. In several of them the presence of seeds has been actually demonstrated, in many others all the probabilities point the same way, but there is good reason to believe that some of these artificial form-genera include true Ferns as well as Seed-plants of similar habit. It will therefore be necessary, before going further, to say something of the fronds hitherto attributed to Ferns.

1. *Fronds.*—Brongniart was the first to construct a regular system of classification of the Fern-like plants, based entirely on the form and venation of the leaf, and since his time this system has been further elaborated, so that any fossil " Fern-frond " can now be referred to a provisional genus and species, according to its conformation and the course of its veins. The same system can be, and has been, applied to recent Ferns, and has, of course, proved to be purely artificial.

It would be quite useless for us to go into the distinctive characters of these provisional genera, which, while they are of the greatest use to those working practically at fossil floras, tell us nothing by themselves as to affinities. It will be sufficient to explain two or three of the principal generic names, which will frequently recur in our subsequent descriptions.

One of the largest of the artificial genera is that named by Brongniart *Pecopteris*, which includes many of the most striking Carboniferous " Fern-fronds," and is of special interest, because a good deal is known as to the fructification and anatomical structure of various plants which possessed this type of leaf. It is certain that some of its members were seed-bearing plants, but there is still a strong probability that others were true Ferns. The characters are thus given by M. Zeiller, whose diagnosis I have somewhat abridged :—" Fronds generally tripinnate, often quadripinnatifid or quadripinnate, more rarely bipinnate only. *Rachis of diverse orders naked between the pinnae,* or bearing pinnules between the latter. *Pinnules attached to the rachis by their whole breadth,* usually very broad, *contiguous,* sometimes more or less confluent, with parallel or slightly convergent margins, usually entire, more rarely lobed or dentate; apex usually obtuse, sometimes acute. *Median nerve distinct,* extending almost to the apex of the pinnule; *secondary nerves* pinnately arranged, *always springing*

Fig. 117.—*Pecopteris (Dactylotheca) dentata.* Part of a frond, with the matrix. Reduced. From a photograph by Mr. W. Hemingway.

from the median nerve, with which they make a wide angle, and not directly from the rachis ; sometimes simple, sometimes dichotomous." [1] The more essential characters are indicated by italics.

Among recent Ferns this form of frond is best represented by some of the Tree-ferns (Cyatheaceae). Fig. 117, illustrating the species *P. (Dactylotheca)* [2] *dentata,*

[1] *Bassin houiller et permien d'Autun et d'Épinac, Flore fossile,* Part i. 1890, p. 41.
[2] The second generic name, *Dactylotheca,* is based on the fructification, which happens to be known in this species. It may be Pteridospermous (see Fig. 119, C).

will give a sufficient idea of the habit of a *Pecopteris* frond, though the true affinities of the plant are doubtful. There is good evidence that some of these fronds were really borne by Tree-ferns of the Carboniferous epoch, belonging, however, to a family quite distinct from that which includes our recent arborescent Ferns. A considerable variety of fructifications has been found in connection with fronds of the *Pecopteris* type ; in many cases the reproductive characters point to an affinity with Marattiaceae, but in others they are of quite a different nature.

The important form-genus *Alethopteris*, which comes near *Pecopteris* in foliar characters, is postponed to a future chapter, because there is reason to believe that all, or almost all, the species belonged to seed-bearing plants. The same remark applies to *Neuropteris*. We will therefore pass on to another of the great frond-genera, *Sphenopteris*, the characters of which are as follows :—" Fronds generally tripinnate or quadripinnate, more rarely bipinnate ; pinnules usually small, *contracted at the base*, with a more or less narrow pedicel, habitually divided into acute or rounded lobes, which are themselves contracted into a wedge towards their base. Nervules simple or branched, forming acute angles both with the median nerve and with their own branches." [1]

Generally speaking, the habit of the species of *Sphenopteris*, a most heterogeneous group, may be compared with that of members of the recent genera *Asplenium* or *Davallia* (see Fig. 193, Chapter XI.). The *Sphenopteris* type of frond is of great interest, not only on account of the elegance of its varied forms, but also from the fact that a great variety of fructifications, both Filicinean and Pteridospermous, have been referred to it.

The genus *Diplotmema*, Stur, as limited by Zeiller,[2] differs from *Sphenopteris*, only in the fact that the primary

[1] Zeiller, *Bassin houiller et permien, l.c.* p. 30.
[2] *L.c.* p. 37.

pinnae are forked, dividing into two similar branches, each of which is repeatedly subdivided, after the manner of *Sphenopteris*.

In some species of *Sphenopteris* the main rachis is itself forked. These species, as well as *Diplotmema*, no doubt represent the foliage of Pteridosperms, but some other Sphenopterid fronds are known to have borne fructifications referable in all probability to Ferns (*e.g. Oligocarpia, Corynepteris*).

It will, of course, be understood that there are many other form-genera to which Fern-like fronds are referred by systematists ; the enumeration of these would serve no purpose here. Full accounts of the artificial system of classification will be found in any of the manuals of fossil botany. Some other types of frond will be referred to in describing the Pteridosperms, for in the majority, as mentioned above, the evidence, either direct or indirect, indicates that the leaves in question belonged to seed-bearing plants. The well-known example of the recent *Stangeria*, which, when first discovered, was referred to the Fern-genus *Lomaria*, already showed plainly enough that Fern-like foliage is not necessarily any proof of close affinity with Filicineae.[1]

Before leaving the subject of the fossil Fern-like fronds, we may briefly mention the curious stipellar outgrowths, or adventitious pinnae, as they have been called, which occur on the rachis of many of these leaves, and are usually known as *Aphlebiae*. These bodies, when detached from the frond, have been described as independent genera of Ferns, or even as Fucoid Algae, and when found *in situ* have sometimes been interpreted as epiphytic Hymenophyllaceae. There is, however, no longer any doubt that they formed part of the fronds on

[1] It is now generally admitted that there is a remote relationship between the Cycadaceae (to which *Stangeria* belongs) and the Ferns, so that the occasional resemblance in the leaf-characters is not wholly without significance. The question is discussed at length in the following chapters.

which they occur. The Aphlebiae are present in considerable numbers, along the rachis and its branches, in various forms of *Sphenopteris, Pecopteris, Neuropteris,* etc. They are common to fronds which were probably those of true Ferns, and to leaves which belonged to Pteridosperms. In some cases the Aphlebiae are entire, orbicular or spathulate, in others they are finely divided in a dichotomous or pinnate manner. They usually differ entirely in form from the normal pinnae of the frond to which they belong, but in some cases transitional conditions have been observed. The position of these organs shows that they are not directly comparable with the stipules of the Marattiaceae ; the best analogy which has been suggested for them is with the feathery outgrowths which occur on the base of the rachis in the recent Cyatheaceous Fern *Hemitelia capensis.* In this case, as in that of the fossil forms, they were at one time described as independent parasitic Filmy Ferns.[1] M. Zeiller has pointed out that somewhat similar anomalous pinnae are also produced on the rachis of various species of *Gleichenia,* at the point where the frond resumes its growth after a period of rest. The peculiar Aphlebiae of the Botryopteridaceae are considered in Chapter IX.

2. *Fructifications.*—We will now endeavour to gain an idea of the nearer affinities of some of the fossils which there are still grounds for referring to the class Filicales. The evidence from the fructification, when available, was formerly considered decisive, but we shall find that this is no longer necessarily the case (see p. 262); anatomical characters, if carefully interpreted, may carry equal weight.

A few of the chief forms of fructification attributed to Palaeozoic Ferns will now be considered, in relation, where this is possible, to the form and structure ⸀ the fronds on which they were borne. Certain special groups, in

[1] See Schenk, "Palaeophytologie" (in Zittel's *Handbuch der Palaeontologie,* vol. ii. 1890), p. 141.

which our knowledge of the plant as a whole is more complete than usual, will be dealt with later on (Chapter IX.).

In the majority of cases, fossil fructifications referable to Ferns have been found on specimens preserved as impressions. In favourable instances such specimens may show something of the structure, as well as the form of the reproductive bodies, for spores and the walls of sporangia usually have more or less cuticularised membranes, so that they withstand decay, and may often be found in a recognisable form in the carbonaceous layer coating the surface of the impression. In other cases, again, petrified fructifications have been found, and here, of course, the evidence as to structure is far more satisfactory, though the petrified specimens are usually fragmentary, and hence difficult to correlate with those in which the external characters are shown.

It has been customary, for some time past, to divide living Ferns into two main series—the Eusporangiatae and the Leptosporangiatae—according to the development of the sporangium, which arises from a group of cells in the former, and from a single cell in the latter series. The distinction, though not so absolute as was at first supposed, coincides well enough with natural divisions, for the only two Eusporangiate families—the Marattiaceae and the Ophioglosseae—are very distinct from any of the Leptosporangiate groups.[1] In the living flora the latter enormously outnumber the former, as regards both genera and species. In dealing with fossil specimens it is, of course, impossible to study the development of the sporangium, and our judgment as to affinities must necessarily be based on the mature characters. The sporangia of the Marattiaceae and Ophioglosseae are, on the whole, of relatively large size, attached to the frond by a broad base, with a wall more than one cell thick, and

[1] See, however, Professor Bower's arrangement, given below, p. 369.

without a definite annulus, though its place may be taken by a small group of thickened cells. In the former of the two families, we have also to consider the grouping of the sporangia, which are often united together in each sorus to form a synangium. Among the Palaeozoic plants with a Fern-like fructification we find a surprisingly large proportion which present these characters, or some of them, and it was hence inferred, apparently with good reason, that in those early days the Eusporangiate section of Ferns, now so restricted, was predominant. It is especially the Marattiaceae to which this conclusion applied ; the Ophioglosseae have not been determined, from the earlier strata, with any degree of certainty.

We will first consider a few representative fructifications of the Marattiaceous type, postponing the question whether they actually belonged to Ferns of that family or not, and will begin with one in which very definite confluent synangia were present.

This fructification, to which the generic name of *Ptychocarpus*, Weiss, has been given, was borne on leaves of the *Pecopteris* form ; the species described is *P. unitus*, Brongn., from the French Coal-measures.

The fructification of *Ptychocarpus unitus* was borne on the ordinary frond. The sporangia are grouped six to eight together, in circular sori ; the sporangia of each sorus or synangium are united laterally among themselves, and are at the same time adherent to the central receptacle, which rises up in the middle of the group (see Fig. 118, C). The synangia are ranged in one or two series, along each side of the median nerve of the fertile segment (Fig. 118, A). They are prominent and shortly-stalked bodies (Fig. 118, B), which often became detached entire from the surface of the pinnule. As shown by the transverse section, each sporangium has a wall, or rather perhaps a tapetum, of its own, but the whole sorus is embedded in a delicate tissue, which is quite continuous round the periphery (Fig. 118, C). The receptacle is traversed by a vascular strand. The spores in each sporangium are numerous and very small, measuring only from 18 to 20 μ in diameter. There is no trace of an annulus. M. Renault, to whom our detailed knowledge of this fructification is due, conjectured,

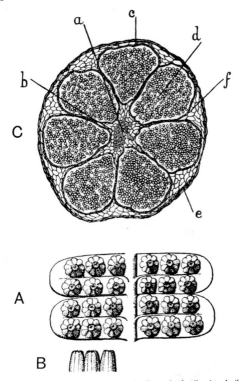

FIG. 118.—*Ptychocarpus unitus.* Fructification. A. Part of a fertile pinnule (lower surface), showing numerous synangia. B. Synangia in side-view. A and B × about 6. After Grand'Eury. C. A synangium, in section parallel to the surface of the leaf, showing seven confluent sporangia. *a*, bundle of receptacle; *b*, its parenchyma; *c*, tapetum; *d*, spores; *e, f*, common envelope of synangium. × about 60. After Renault.

with much probability, that each sporangium discharged its spores through an apical pore. In general characters, the *Ptychocarpus* fructification approaches most nearly to that of the recent genus *Kaulfussia*, in which the synangia are also circular, but there are many differences in detail. In *Kaulfussia* the interior of the synangium is hollowed out into a cup, into which the sporangia open, dehiscence taking place on the inner face of each sporangium. In the fossil genus there is no central depression, and, as the entire synangium was embedded in a continuous enveloping tissue, dehiscence could only have taken place at the apex. The fructification of *Ptychocarpus unitus* is, however, a good example of a typical Marattiaceous synangium, and affords strong evidence as to the affinities of the plant.[1]

Mr. Watson some years ago described, under the name *Cyathotrachus altus*, a synangium of Lower Coal-measure age, differing from *Ptychocarpus* in its taller shape, in having a cup-like central depression, and in the presence of tracheides at the base of the sporangia ; in the two latter characters it approaches *Kaulfussia*. The specimens were isolated, but were associated with a pinnule, probably of a *Pecopteris*. There is a presumption in favour of Marattiaceous affinities, but the same doubts apply here as in other cases of the kind.[2]

The important genus *Asterotheca* resembles *Ptychocarpus*[3] in the fact that in each sorus the sporangia are grouped in a ring around the receptacle, but the receptacle is short, the sporangia are usually from three to six only in number, and are less closely united to one another. The sori are ranged on the under surface of the pinnule in two rows, one row on each side of the median nerve (see Fig. 119, A). The individual sporangia are ovoid in shape, and there is reason to believe that when ripe they separated from' each other, bending outwards from the central receptacle, and dehiscing by a longitudinal opening on the inner side of each sac. Certainly some of the

[1] See Renault, *Bassin houiller et permien d'Autun et d'Épinac*, Part ii. p. 9.

[2] D. M. S. Watson, " On a ' Fern ' Synangium from the Lower Coal-measures of Shore, Lancashire," *Journal R. Microscop. Soc.* 1906, Part i.

[3] These genera are founded solely on the fructification, and are thus likely to represent more natural groups than those based on the form and venation of the frond. See Stur, " Zur Morphologie und Systematik der Culm- und Carbonfarne," *K. Akad. d. Wiss.* Vienna, 1883.

preparations show quite clearly that the sporangia are

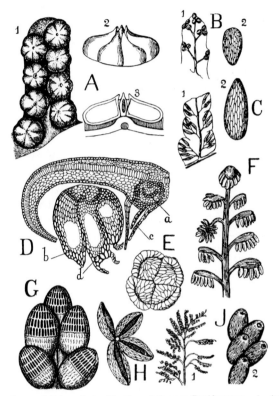

FIG. 119.—Group of Palaeozoic fructifications of Ferns or Pteridosperms. A. *Asterotheca* (probably Marattiaceous). 1. Fertile pinnule showing eight synangia. Enlarged. 2. Synangium in side-view ; 3. in section (diagrammatic). After Stur. B. *Renaultia*, Zeiller (affinities doubtful). 1. Pinnule, showing sporangia on veins. Nat. size. 2. Single sporangium. Enlarged. After Zeiller. C. *Dactylotheca* (affinities doubtful). 1. Pinnule, showing sporangia on veins. Nat. size. 2. Single sporangium. Enlarged. After Zeiller. D. *Sturiella*, Weiss (cf. *Corynepteris*). Transverse section of pinnule, showing a synangium. *a*, vascular bundle of pinnule ; *c*, hairs ; *b, d*, annulus of confluent sporangia. ×8. After Renault. E. *Oligocarpia* (cf. Gleicheniaceae). Sorus in surface-view. Magnified. After Stur. F. *Crossotheca* (♂ of Lyginopterideae). Fertile pinna, bearing several pinnules with sporangia. Enlarged. After Zeiller. G. *Senftenbergia* (cf. Schizaeaceae). Tip of fertile pinnule, showing five annulate sporangia. Magnified. After Renault. H. *Hawlea* (probably Marattiaceous). Synangium, after dehiscence of the sporangia. Magnified. After Stur. J. *Urnatopteris* (affinities doubtful). 1. Part of fertile pinna. Nat. size. 2. Sporangia, enlarged, showing apical pores. After Kidston.

separate down to the base of the synangium. Forms with the sporangia distinctly separate are, however, regarded by Stur as constituting a different genus, to which he has given the name *Hawlea* (see Fig. 119, H). It thus appears that in *Asterotheca* and allied fructifications, the cohesion of the sporangia was much less perfect than in the living Marattiaceous genera *Kaulfussia*, *Danaea*, and *Marattia*.

A number of species with fronds of the *Pecopteris* type are known to have borne the fructifications of *Asterotheca*. They are chiefly characteristic of the Upper Coal-measures and Permian.

The genus *Grand'Eurya* of Stur is interesting from its resemblance to the recent *Angiopteris*. The fructifications in question were first described by Renault from silicified specimens, and referred by him to two species of *Pecopteris*, *P. oreopteridia* and *P. densifolia*.[1] The sporangia are inserted along either side of the *lateral* veins of the fertile pinnules, and appear to be quite free from each other. There is, however, some indication of a grouping of the sporangia in fours. Thus in *Grand' Eurya Renaulti* of Stur (attributed to *P. oreopteridia* by Renault) there are usually eight sporangia belonging to each lateral vein, and forming apparently two quadrate groups of four each. On account of the latter arrangement, Zeiller attributed these species to the genus *Asterotheca* ; in *Grand'Eurya* there seems to be no formation of synangia, but Zeiller considered that this condition, as in *Hawlea*, is only due to age.

Another genus, *Scolecopteris*, also belonging to *Pecopteris* according to its foliar characters, has the same arrangement as in *Asterotheca*, but the synangia are stalked, and the sporangia long and sharply pointed at the apex. Fructifications of *Scolecopteris* have been found in a silicified condition, and their structure has thus been more thoroughly investigated than is usually possible. In one species, *S. polymorpha*,[2] the large tripinnate fronds bear

---

[1] Renault, *Cours de bot. fossile*, t. iii. 1883, p. 110, Plate 19.
[2] Renault, *l.c.* p. 116, Pl. 20, Figs. 1-10 (*Pecopteris polymorpha*).

two long rows of sori on the lower surface of each pinnule. The sporangia in each sorus are four in number ; they are free for the greater part of their length, which reaches about 4 mm. ; at their base they are attached to the surface of the pinnule, and on their inner side to a short receptacle, not more than one-third as long as the spor-

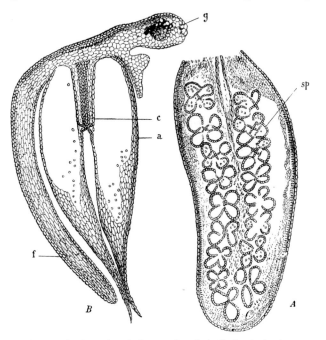

Fig. 120.—*Scolecopteris polymorpha.* A. Lower surface of a fertile pinnule, showing numerous quadrisporangiate synangia (*sp*). Note the cruciform receptacle at the centre of some of the synangia. × about 8. B. Transverse section of half a pinnule, passing through a synangium. *g*, vascular bundle of pinnule ; *f*, infolded margin of pinnule ; *a*, wall of sporangium ; *c*, receptacle, fused to the sporangia. × about 18. After Renault.

angia (see Fig. 120). The receptacle is described by M. Renault as having a cruciform transverse section, each arm of the cross corresponding to one of the four sporangia constituting the synangium (see Fig. 120, A, *sp*). Each of the long, pointed sporangia has a wall with thickened cells on its free outer surface, but on the inner side the wall is thin. It is probable that this unequal thickness of the wall caused the dehiscence of the sporangium on the inner side, and thus worked in the same way as the annulus of ordinary Ferns. The margins of the pinnule were incurved, so as to partly cover in the sori. Another species of *Scolecopteris*, *S. elegans*, was investigated many years ago by Strasburger.[1] The sporangia are here smaller, and there are often five in each sorus. Towards the base they are confluent with one another, and with the central receptacle ; higher up they become free, and dehiscence appears to have taken place on the inner side, where the sporangial wall was thinnest. Strasburger's remarks on the affinities of this fossil may be quoted, for they apply to the genus as a whole, and express the view still generally held. " Zenker's *Scolecopteris elegans*, according to the formation of its sorus, certainly belongs to the Marattiaceae, and, in fact, comes nearest the genus *Marattia* in the form of the sporangia of which the sori are composed, while it approaches the genus *Kaulfussia* in the circular grouping of the sporangia, and finally resembles the genus *Angiopteris* in the fact that the sporangia become free in their upper part. In the mode of dehiscence of the individual sporangia, *Scolecopteris* agrees with all three genera mentioned, but the similarity to *Marattia* is again the most striking, to which it also bears the greatest resemblance in the structure of the sori."

So far as the pedicellate sori are concerned, the agreement is especially close with the subgenus *Eupodium* of *Marattia*.

In the genus *Dactylotheca* of Zeiller, another of the *Pecopteris* group (see Fig. 119, C), the sporangia are somewhat similar in form to those of *Scolecopteris*. They are, however, completely independent of one another ; each sporangium is placed singly over a lateral vein. The line of dehiscence can be recognised, but there is no trace of an annulus; it is mainly on this ground that *Dactylo-*

---

[1] *Jenaer Zeitschrift für Naturwissenschaft*, vol. viii. 1874.

theca and various other genera with separate sporangia have been placed in the Marattiaceae. For example, in the genus *Renaultia* of Zeiller [1] (see Fig. 119, B), the ovoid sporangia are independent, isolated, or grouped in small numbers at the extremity of the nerves. In this case there is an indication of a rudimentary annulus, like that of the recent *Angiopteris*, at the apex of the sporangium. *Renaultia*, Zeill., was the fructification of certain species with fronds of the *Sphenopteris* type.

It must be confessed that in such cases the reference to Marattiaceae has always rested on very slender evidence. Where no synangium is formed, and the sporangia are not even grouped in definite sori, we really have very little to go by, in default of anatomical evidence, for the mere absence or rudimentary development of the ring is of course no proof of Marattiaceous affinities. The position of genera such as *Dactylotheca* and *Renaultia* is entirely doubtful, and it is quite possible that their fructifications may really be of the nature of microsporangia, the plants being in that case Pteridosperms and not Ferns.

Among the Palaeozoic plants with definite synangia, the circular or radiate type of synangium, now limited to the genus *Kaulfussia*, seems to have prevailed. In the genus *Danaeites*, however, which includes some Pecopteroid forms from the Coal-measures, the synangia were linear in shape, and appear to have closely resembled those of the recent genus *Danaea*. In this case the sporangia were arranged in a double row along each secondary nerve of the fertile pinnule ; they were sunk in the tissue of the lamina, and fused laterally with one another, the constituent sporangia each dehiscing by an apical pore. The agreement with the recent genus was thus remarkably exact.

---

[1] *Hapalopteris* of Stur, whose genus *Renaultia* (*Sturiella*, Weiss ; Fig. 119, D) is quite different, having typical synangia. The nomenclature of these fructifications is lamentably involved. For *Hapalopteris schatzlarensis* see p. 267.

The forms hitherto described bore their sporangia on the ordinary vegetative fronds, as is the case with a majority of the Ferns at the present day. A considerable number, however, of the Palaeozoic Fern-like plants were dimorphic, the sporangia appearing on fertile leaves, or parts of the leaf, quite different in form from the sterile foliage.

Many of these dimorphic fronds no doubt belonged to Pteridosperms and not to Ferns. Thus a species of *Crossotheca* (Fig. 119, F) has been shown by Dr. Kidston to be the male fructification of *Lyginopteris* (Chapter XI.) ; *Calymmatotheca* is now known to represent a condition of the seed-bearing apparatus of the same genus ; *Urnatopteris* (Fig. 119, J) is probably, like *Crossotheca*, a microsporangiate fructification. Some examples of dimorphic fronds in plants which appear really to come under the head of Ferns will be given in the next chapter in describing the Botryopteridaceae.

Before leaving the supposed Marattiaceous fructifications we may shortly refer to a genus which combines Marattiaceous characters with those of other families. This is the *Sturiella* of Weiss (*Renaultia* of Stur). The structure of the leaf and sorus was worked out by Renault [1] from silicified specimens. The frond was of the *Pecopteris* type, though its form is not completely known, as the specimens were fragmentary. The sori are ranged in two series on the pinnule, along either side of its median nerve. Each sorus constitutes a synangium, for the five sporangia of which it consists are fused at the base, and attached by a short common pedicel to the lower surface of the pinnule (see Fig. 119, D). Hence their arrangement is altogether that of a Marattiaceous Fern. The structure, however, of the individual spor-

---

[1] *Cours de botanique fossile*, vol. iii. p. 122, 1883. M. Renault named the species *Pecopteris intermedia*. Stur appropriately founded the genus *Renaultia* for its reception, but this generic name was adopted slightly earlier by Zeiller for another fructification, above mentioned.

angia is peculiar, for the free end of each is capped by an apical annulus of large thick-walled cells, which also extends for some distance along the outer side of the sac (Fig. 119, D, *b*, *d*). The annulus is accompanied by multicellular hairs.

The leaf was a thick fleshy one, with a layer of palisade-cells, but the most characteristic anatomical peculiarity is the horse-shoe bundle of the midrib (Fig. 119, D, *a*). Authorities differ as to the systematic position to be assigned to this curious Fern. Stur, relying on the characters of the sorus, placed it among Marattiaceae, near *Asterotheca* and *Scolecopteris*, while Zeiller rejected this attribution, on account of the well-marked annulus. The latter feature suggests a comparison with Schizae-aceae or Osmundaceae, but Zeiller left the position of the genus an open question. On the whole, the balance of characters seems to weigh on the side of Marattiaceae, for there is no reason why the annulus, still represented at the present time in *Angiopteris*, should not have been more highly developed in some Palaeozoic members of the family. A relation, through *Corynepteris*, to the Zygopterideae is also possible (see next chapter, p. 328).

This brings us to yet another genus, *Senftenbergia*, of still more dubious affinities. Several species have been included under this genus, the foliage of which was of the Pecopteroid type. The sporangia are inserted singly over the lateral nerves of the pinnules, near their outer end, so as to form a marginal series. There is thus no formation of synangia, or even of definite sori (see Fig. 119, G). In the typical species there is a definite apical annulus, several cells in width. *Pecopteris exigua*, referred to *Senftenbergia* by Stur, has no annulus, and appears to be a *Crossotheca* (see Chapter XI.). The sporangia of *Senftenbergia* find their nearest parallel in the Schizaeaceae, to which family Corda, the discoverer of the genus, referred it. The pluriseriate structure of the annulus has been brought forward as an argument against this view, but in *Lygodium,* among recent Schizaeaceae, the annulus, as Zeiller pointed out, is often more than one cell in breadth.

Upon the data available, it remains impossible to determine the position of the genus. The analogy with *Angiopteris,* on which Stur, who maintained the Marattiaceous affinities of *Senftenbergia,* laid stress, appears remote. There is, however, some evidence that in the fossil genus the sporangial wall was several cells in thickness, a character which points in the direction of Marattiaceae.

Sporangial characters, like any other characters, are, in fact, insufficient *by themselves* to determine the position of a genus in a doubtful case.

The evidence for the Marattiaceous affinities of such genera as *Ptychocarpus, Asterotheca, Scolecopteris,* and *Danaeites,* in which the fructification is in the form of synangia borne on the ordinary foliage, is still generally accepted, and is much strengthened by the presence, at similar horizons, of stems (*Psaronius*) with some Marattiaceous anatomical characters. Any doubt there may be arises from two considerations : (1) Practically all the fructifications in question were borne on *Pecopteris* fronds, and one species referred to *Pecopteris* (*P. Pluckeneti*) is now known to have been a seed-bearing plant (see Chapter XIII.) ; (2) a species of *Crossotheca,* formerly regarded as a Marattiaceous genus, has been shown by Dr. Kidston to be the male fructification of the Pteridosperm *Lyginopteris,* and the *Crossotheca* type occurs in species of *Pecopteris* (e.g. *P. exigua*) as well as in *Sphenopteris.* Even typical " Marattiaceous " synangia, such as those of *Scolecopteris,* are remarkably like other fructifications (*Telangium Scotti,* Benson) which there is reason to regard as microsporangia. Hence the question has arisen, whether all the supposed synangia of Marattiaceae may not represent the microsporangia of Pteridosperms, a suggestion which has been supported by the remarkably close agreement between the stamens of the Mesozoic Bennettiteae and the fertile fronds of Marattiaceae (see Chapter XV.). On the whole, however, the balance of evidence, if we also take the anatomical data into account (see below, p. 268), is still decidedly in favour of the view that a considerable group of Marattiaceous Ferns existed in Carboniferous times, side by side with Pteridosperms of similar habit. The former are mainly, though not exclusively, characteristic of the Permian and Upper Coal-measures, and are not known to extend to the Lower Carboniferous.

As regards the other Eusporangiate family there is little to say. A couple of genera, *Rhacopteris* and *Noeggerathia*, formerly referred by Stur to the Ophio-glosseae, were more probably the microsporophylls of Pteridosperms. A fructification resembling that of an *Ophioglossum* has been described by Renault, from the Permo-Carboniferous of Autun, under the name of *Ophioglossites*. We shall find in the Botryopteridaceae —to be described in the next chapter—a group which, in certain characters, bears a resemblance to Ophio-glosseae, though very different in other respects.

There is some slight evidence for the existence in Palaeozoic times of Ferns allied to Gleicheniaceae. As Professor Bower has pointed out, " the type of sorus " in *Gleichenia* " is that of the Marattiaceae." [1] Hence, on soral characters alone, it would not be possible to distinguish between a fossil fructification of this family and one of the Marattiaceae with free sporangia arranged circularly. The genus *Oligocarpia* of Göppert, with Sphenopteroid foliage, bore such sori, which in surface view certainly look wonderfully like those of a *Gleichenia* (see Fig. 119, E). Each sporangium shows a transverse or somewhat oblique annulus, much as in that genus ;

---

[1] " Studies in Morphology of Spore-producing Members," Part iv., *Phil. Trans. Roy. Soc.* vol. 192, B, p. 38, 1899.

though some authors have denied that the apparent annulus is really distinct from the rest of the sporangial wall, the inspection of the specimens, especially those of *O. robustior*, Stur, leaves no doubt that the former interpretation is correct. Dr. Kidston, however, finds that the annulus is really bi- or triseriate, and the relation to Gleicheniaceae therefore more remote. Zeiller, who supported the Gleicheniaceous affinities of this genus, further cited certain isolated sporangia, which have been found in the Quartz of Autun, as having unmistakably the characters of that family.

Sporangia with a transverse annulus, much like that of the Hymenophyllaceae, have been observed on the fronds of some Sphenopteroid Ferns from the Coal-measures (*Hymenophyllites quadridactylites*), but the evidence as to their position on the leaf is not sufficient to place the affinities of these fossils beyond doubt. The Devonian genus *Archaeopteris* or *Palaeopteris*, the type-species of which, the famous *A. hibernica*, is characteristic of the Old Red Sandstone of Ireland, was once referred by some authors to the Hymenophyllaceae, by others to the Marattiaceae, but is now regarded by Dr. Kidston as most probably a member of the Pteridospermeae.

The anatomical evidence for the existence of Palaeozoic Osmundaceae is now well established ;[1] in addition, it is not at all uncommon to find isolated sporangia in the petrified material, which might well be of that nature. The presence of a lateral group of enlarged cells, resembling the annulus or areola of Osmundaceae, is a frequent feature. Professor Bower many years ago drew attention to the Osmundaceous character of certain Carboniferous sporangia ;[2] some of the sporangia of this type no doubt

[1] See the work of Kidston and Gwynne-Vaughan referred to below (p. 278).

[2] " Is the Eusporangiate or the Leptosporangiate the more Primitive Type in the Ferns ? " *Annals of Botany*, vol. v. 1891. The *Sarcopteris Bertrandi* of Renault also has Osmundaceous characters (see *Cours de bot. foss.* vol. iii. p. 129, Plate xxi. Figs. 12-15).

belonged to the Botryopteridaceae described in the next chapter.

In the calcareous specimens showing structure, from the British Carboniferous strata, sporangia like those of Ferns are frequent enough, but unfortunately they are usually isolated, so that it is impossible to tell what was their arrangement, or to determine the nature of the leaf on which they were borne. The specimens, however, prove the frequency, in Palaeozoic times, of free sporangia not grouped into synangia. They also prove that the presence of an annulus of some kind was almost as common

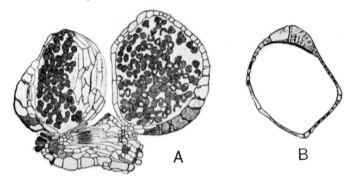

FIG. 121.—*Pteridotheca Williamsonii.* A. Two sporangia seated on a pinnule, showing the attachment. Annulus in oblique section, incompletely shown ; numerous spores present. S. Coll. 2252. B. Sporangium in transverse section, showing the biseriate annulus. S. Coll. 215. × about 60. From drawings by Mr. L. A. Boodle, F.L.S.

then as now, though the form of the annulus was, no doubt, different from that usual among recent Ferns. The generic name *Pteridotheca* may conveniently be used provisionally for such unassigned petrified sporangia, of Palaeozoic age, as possess an annulus or other characters indicating Filicinean affinity. In Figs. 121 and 122 certain Fern-sporangia from the English Coal-measures are represented.[1]

In Fig. 122 we have a section passing through a

[1] The Figure and description of *Pteridotheca Butterworthii*, given in previous editions, are omitted, some doubt having arisen as to the connection between the sporangia and the subjacent tissue.

large sorus, or rather a group of sori. The plane of the
section was no doubt approximately parallel to that of
the fertile frond, which was highly compound and
apparently of the *Sphenopteris* type, the lamina being
well developed, like that of a vegetative frond rather

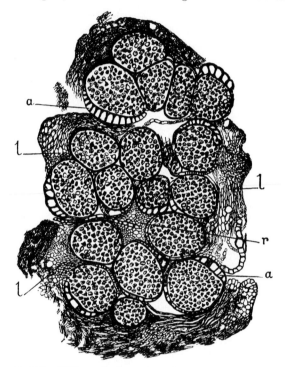

Fig. 122.—*Pteridotheca Williamsonii.* Group of annulate sporangia, seen in section, parallel
to surface of frond. The sporangia contain numerous spores ; at *a*, the annulus is
specially clear. *l, l, r,* parts of tissue of the fertile pinnules. × 36. S. Coll. 215 (Coal-
measures). (G. T. G.)

than a specialised sporophyll. The pinnules are much
incurved, and the sporangia are seated on their margins.
In the section figured, several pinnules, cut in various
planes, are shown. The sporangia are sessile, with a
multicellular base (Fig. 121, A), and are of nearly spherical
form, except where their sides are flattened by mutual
pressure. The most striking feature of the sporangia,

which contain numerous smooth tetrahedral spores, is the extreme distinctness of the annulus, which, when cut lengthways (Fig. 121, A ; Fig. 122, *a*), quite suggests that of a Polypodiaceous Fern, and contrasts sharply with the small cells of which the remainder of the wall is composed. The annulus was evidently longitudinal or somewhat oblique, rather than transverse ; it agrees in detailed structure with the annulus of recent Ferns, especially in the thinness of the external cell-walls, and the gradual thickening of the radial walls from without inwards ; transverse sections of the annulus show, however, that it was regularly two cells in width (Fig. 121, B), thus differing from that of any recent Ferns. Specimens of this fructification, which I have named *Pteridotheca Williamsonii*, are of frequent occurrence in the coal-balls of the Lower Coal-measures, and the preservation is often remarkably perfect. There is every reason to believe that it belongs to a true Fern, though it would be futile to seek for any near affinities with recent families.

A second species, in which the sporangia are ranged in long rows on the infolded pinnules, may be called *P. seriata*. Dr. Kidston's genus *Boweria*,[1] founded on the *Hapalopteris schatzlarensis* of Stur, appears to have the same structure as *Pteridotheca*. The sporangia are borne on the slightly reduced pinnules of a Sphenopterid frond ; the specimens are carbonaceous impressions, from a somewhat higher horizon than that of the coal-balls yielding *Pteridotheca*.

Postponing any further discussion of the extent and character of the Palaeozoic Fern-flora to the end of the following chapter, we will now pass on to consider some cases in which the anatomical structure is preserved, and affords evidence of Filicinean affinities. We will first discuss an important group of stems in which the structure appears to be of a Marattiaceous type.

[1] Kidston, " Les Végétaux houillers rec. dans le Hainaut belge," Brussels, 1911, p. 31.

3. *Anatomy* [1]—*Psaronius.*—Among the Fern-like remains from the Permo-carboniferous strata, and especially from their upper beds, specimens resembling Tree-ferns, in habit not altogether unlike those of the present day, are conspicuous. Some of these plants were of great size, with a stem reaching, it is said, as much as 60 feet in height.

The arrangement of the leaves on these trunks showed more variety than exists among living Tree-ferns. Thus, in the genus *Megaphytum* of Artis, the tall, somewhat slender stem bore the fronds in two vertical series, as shown by the distichously arranged leaf-scars, which were of large size, having a transverse diameter of 8 or 10 and a height of 5 or 6 cm. There was thus a certain superficial and deceptive resemblance to large specimens of *Ulodendron*, with which the older authors sometimes confused these stems. This phyllotaxis is apparently unknown among arborescent or erect Fern-stems of the present age, though frequent in the case of prostrate rhizomes. In other Palaeozoic Tree-ferns the leaves were ranged in four vertical rows, while in others, again, and these the most numerous, a spiral polystichous disposition prevailed, as in the arborescent Ferns of the present day. To guard against misconception, it may be well to say at once that the Palaeozoic Tree-ferns only resembled those of the present day in general habit ; their affinities doubtless lay in a direction quite remote from that of the Cyatheaceae.

The polystichous stems, in which the external surface, bearing the foliar scars, is shown, are known by the name of *Caulopteris*, while a separate generic name, *Ptychopteris*, is applied to stems in another state of preservation, in which the cortex has been stripped off and the vascular system exposed. Lastly, yet another genus had been founded for those stems of Tree-ferns which are preserved

[1] See P. Bertrand, " L'Étude anatomique des fougères anciennes," *Progressus Rei Botanicae*, vol. iv. 1911.

in a petrified condition, so as to retain their internal structure ; the latter, whatever the disposition of their leaves may have been, are embraced under the common name *Psaronius*. We have thus a curious example of palaeontological nomenclature, for one and the same stem, according to its mode of preservation, may be placed in any one of the three " genera," *Caulopteris* (or *Megaphytum*, as the case may be), *Ptychopteris*, or *Psaronius*. If the foliage and fructification were taken into account, still other generic designations would come into requisition. Yet these anomalies are unavoidable, for it is rarely possible to identify the same species through its different states of fossilisation.

For our present purpose, the name *Psaronius* is the most suitable, as it is with the anatomical structure of the stem that we are specially concerned.

The specimens of *Psaronius*, which are characteristic fossils in the Permian beds of Saxony and Central France, were perhaps the earliest known of any fossil vegetable remains with structure preserved. They were quite familiar objects, even to the general public, in the eighteenth century, for, owing to the beauty of their surface when cut and polished, they became, for a time, favourite articles of ornament, under the name of " Staarsteine." [1] The markings, to which they owed their popularity, depend on their anatomical structure.

The genus contains a great number of described species, and though some may have merely a palaeonto-logical value, many no doubt represent real distinctions among the plants when living. The species from the Upper Coal-measures and Permian agree in having a highly complex polystelic organisation, comparable to that of the most highly differentiated Fern-stems of our

[1] " Starling-stones," from the speckled surface. The technical name *Psaronius* has the same origin. These names were originally applied especially to specimens consisting of the roots ; those showing the long, curved steles of the stem used to be called " Wurmsteine " (*helmintholithi*).

own day. The structure of the *Psaronii* has been worked out in a most elaborate manner by Corda, Göppert, and Stenzel in Germany, and by Zeiller and Renault in France. A very full description, covering many species and forming a model of fossil anatomical investigation, is that given by M. Zeiller in the first volume of the magnificent work, so often referred to, on the fossil flora of Autun and Epinac.[1] M. Zeiller, discarding the somewhat complex methods of arrangement of earlier authors, classifies the members of the genus according to their phyllotaxis, ranging them in three groups—the Polystichi, with numerous vertical series of leaves ; the Tetrastichi, with four such series ; and the Distichi, with only two. The illustration in Fig. 123 is taken from a member of the Tetrastichous division ; this group is the least important of the three in number of species, but the form selected, *Psaronius brasiliensis*, Brongn., shows the anatomical structure with remarkable clearness. This fossil, as its name shows, came from Brazil, and, though its source is still uncertain, is probably of Permian age, like the majority of the European species.

The stem, as in all the *Psaronii*, is made up of two well-defined regions — a central portion, including the whole of the vascular system proper to the stem, and a broad peripheral zone of tissue, traversed throughout by innumerable adventitious roots, seen in approximately transverse section in our figure. In this case the limit between the two regions is sharply defined, by an almost continuous band of sclerenchyma. The immense development of the peripheral zone of roots is a most characteristic feature of the genus *Psaronius*. Most authors used to regard the zone in which the roots are embedded as form-

[1] Corda, *Beiträge zur Flora der Vorwelt*, Prague, 1845 ; Göppert, "Die fossile Flora der permischen Formation," *Palaeontographica*, vol. xii. 1864 ; Stenzel, "Ueber die Staarsteine," *Nova Acta*, vol. xxiv. 1854 ; Zeiller, *Bassin houiller et permien d'Autun et d'Épinac*, vol. i. 1890 ; Rudolf, "Psaronien und Marattiaceen," *K. K. Akad. d. Wiss. Vienna*, 1905 ; Stenzel, "Die Psaronien," *Beitr. z. Paläont. u. Geol. Österreich-Ungarns*, 1906.

ing part of the cortex of the stem, as in the Marattiaceae, in which the adventitious roots arise near the apex of the stem, and grow down through the cortical tissues for a long distance before they become free.[1] There are two difficulties in applying this interpretation to *Psaronius*. The connection between the roots and the surrounding tissue is much more intimate here even than in Marattiaceae, and the root-zone is never traversed by the leaf-traces, as it should be if it belonged to the primary cortex. It was therefore acutely suggested by Farmer and Hill in 1902[2] that the embedding tissue in *Psaronius* may be formed by the compacted hairs of the roots themselves; the filamentous character of the tissue lent support to this explanation, which has turned out to be essentially the correct one. On the other hand, the evident continuity between the tissue in question and the true cortex appeared to favour the older view. Stenzel's explanation was that the embedding tissue is a secondary zone, developed *pari passu* with the growth of the roots after the leaves had fallen. The question, however, received further investigation at the hands of the late Count Solms-Laubach,[3] whose work confirms in general the interpretation of Farmer and Hill, showing that the tissue in which the roots are embedded is not a cortex, but consists entirely of filamentous outgrowths (multicellular hairs) arising chiefly from the roots themselves, but in part also from the stem (see p. 273).

In the central region, the stem, we see at once that the vascular system is remarkably complex, consisting of a great number of regularly disposed steles, usually much

[1] See the well-known longitudinal section of the stem of *Angiopteris evecta in* Sachs's Text-book and other manuals.

[2] J. B. Farmer and T. G. Hill, " On the Arrangement and Structure of the Vascular Strands in *Angiopteris evecta*," *Ann. of Bot.* vol. xvi. 1902, p. 382.

[3] Solms-Laubach, " Der tiefschwarze *Psaronius Haidingeri* von Manebach in Thüringen," *Zeitschrift f. Botanik*, iii. 1911, p. 721; also F. Pelourde, "Observations sur le *Psaronius brasiliensis*," *Ann. des Sci. Nat. (Bot.)* sér. ix. t. xvi. 1912.

elongated in transverse section, but varying greatly in size and form. At two opposite points (Fig. 123, F1 and F2) outgoing leaf-traces are shown. The leaves appear to have been decussately arranged, but those of the same pair were not precisely at the same level. At F2 the open curve of the outgoing stele is very evident; at F1, which is cut nearer its exit, the trace is apparently divided into two, and the sclerenchymatous zone has almost

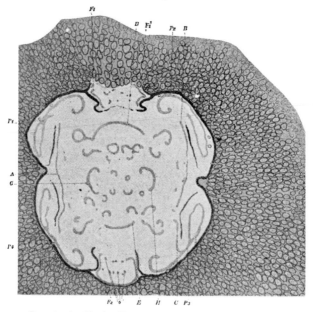

FIG. 123.—*Psaronius brasiliensis.* Transverse section of stem. The whole of the true stem, containing the vascular bundles, is shown, together with a great part of the outer zone with innumerable adventitious roots. F1, F2, leaf-gaps. For detailed description, see text. The round objects at *o* are accidental perforations. Reduced. After Zeiller.

closed in behind it. Stenzel found, however, that the two arms of the leaf-trace always form part of a single horse-shoe or elliptical bundle.

A and B, at the sides of the figure, are the steles from which the leaf-traces of the next pair of leaves will be supplied, while D and E will give off, at a still higher level, the traces for the pair lying above F1 and F2.

These four bands, corresponding in position to the four orthostichies of leaves, may be called the *reparatory* steles. At the four diagonal corners we see four very long and curved steles (P1-P4), the " peripheral steles " of Zeiller, which have an important part to play. For one thing, it is from them that the adventitious roots take their rise ; such roots are shown at several places between the peripheral steles and the sclerenchyma, or just passing through the latter. The peripheral steles are further concerned in the emission of the leaf-traces, for they anastomose with the reparatory steles immediately below the point where the leaf-trace passes out from the latter. Thus at C a branch is seen springing from the peripheral stele P3 to join the reparatory stele B.

The numerous internal steles—G, H, etc.—form a cauline system, the members of which, however, anastomose both among themselves and with the more external steles.

The whole subject of the vascular system of the *Psaronii* has been worked out by Zeiller, Stenzel, and Rudolf with a degree of completeness which could hardly have been exceeded if they had been dealing with recent instead of with fossil plants. We have here only given the main results for this particular species, which, however, may serve very well as a type of the rest.

The more minute histology has also been worked out with a fair amount of detail. The steles have the typical concentric structure, each consisting of a band of wood surrounded by phloëm. The xylem is composed of scalariform tracheides with or without xylem parenchyma, according to the species.

The ground tissue is mostly parenchymatous, but internal sclerotic bands occur below the leaf-gaps (see Fig. 123, on the right and left).

The broad zone of roots surrounding the stem may be divided into two regions : in the outer region the roots are free from one another ; in the inner, wider area they

are embedded in and held together by the dense, filamentous tissue, formerly interpreted as cortical. The
structure of the roots is somewhat different in the two
regions. The external, free roots have an inner, more or
less lacunar cortex, then a band of sclerenchyma, and
finally a parenchymatous outer cortex, bounded by an
epidermis. In the inner, embedded roots this outer
cortex appears to be absent ; the sclerenchymatous zone
is the outermost, except where the cells have grown out
to form the filamentous interstitial tissue. By the study
of specially clear sections Solms-Laubach was able, for the
first time, to demonstrate the origin of this tissue. It
consists of closely packed, multicellular filaments or hairs,
which on the whole, subject to many deviations, take a
radial course. It is only at their inner ends that the
filaments are actually in organic continuity with the
cortex of the roots (Fig. 124). At the external ends they
abut on the next outer roots which happen to lie in their
way, and apply themselves closely to them, often being
bent and somewhat swollen at the extreme ends (Fig. 124).
It follows from these facts that the filaments arose from
the outer side of each root, growing thence in an outward
direction until stopped by coming into contact with a
root further to the exterior. The whole mass is closely
welded together, to form a practically continuous tissue.

Thus the origin of the interstitial tissue among the
roots is explained ; it springs from the roots themselves,
as Farmer and Hill suggested. The innermost zone,
lying between the stem-surface and the nearest roots, was
found to have a similar origin, but here the filaments
arise from the surface of the stem, growing out until they
meet with a root on which to abut. Thus the continuity
of the interstitial tissue with the true cortex is explained.
The cauline and radical filaments, which between them
build up the continuous matrix of the root-zone, are quite
similar in structure ; the tissue is peculiar, so far as is
known, to *Psaronius* ; it appears to find its nearest

analogue in the hyphal complexus of the Fungi and certain Algae.

In *Psaronius* generally the vascular structure of the

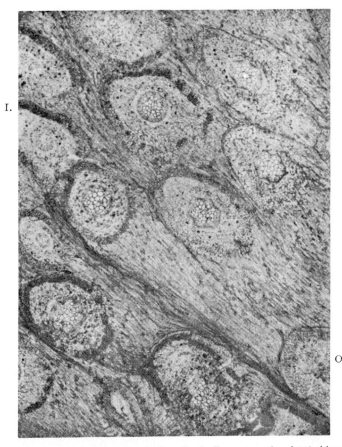

I.

O

FIG. 124.—*Psaronius*. Unnamed species from Brazil. Transverse section of part of inner root-zone, showing several 6-9 arch roots, embedded in filamentous tissue. O, outer ; I, inner side. The filaments arise from the outer side of each root and abut on the inner side of the next root. ×about 7. S. Coll. 2756 (from Solms Coll. 592). From a photograph by Mr. W. Tams.

roots is polyarch ; in the particular species, *P. brasiliensis*, the number of xylem-angles is usually five or six. Phloëm and cortex are sometimes quite well preserved (Fig. 124), and in the latter, secretory sacs or canals are conspicuous. The roots strongly recall those of Marattiaceous Ferns now living.

A species, *P. Renaulti*, occurring in the roof-nodules of the Lower Coal-measures of Lancashire, is interesting from its exceptional antiquity and from the simplicity of its structure.[1] The stem in this species contains a single annular stele, enclosing a large pith, and interrupted only at the exit of the leaf-traces, the sole instance, at present known, of a solenostele in a Palaeozoic stem. The phloëm, with its large sieve-tubes, is well shown in good specimens on both sides of the wood, and the protoxylem can be recognised, forming a number of small groups on the inner edge of the xylem, which is thus endarch (Fig. 125). Its position in the numerous steles of the more complex species may be similar, but requires further investigation.

P. Renaulti may provisionally be regarded as the most primitive member of the genus. It is interesting to find that in this simple species the structure of the root-zone in all respects agrees with that in the more advanced forms investigated by Solms-Laubach. In a specimen probably referable to *P. Renaulti*, Mr. Butterworth made the interesting discovery that some of the roots show a well-marked formation of secondary wood. A similar peculiarity has since been observed in some Permian species. These are the only instances in which any trace of secondary tissues has been observed in the *Psaronii*; Solms-Laubach found that their presence in the root was connected with the insertion of the rootlets.

The petioles of these Ferns have occasionally been found apart from the stems, and bear the generic name of *Stipitopteris*. They are identified by the comparison between their transverse section and the marks on the leaf-scars of the *Psaronii* in the *Caulopteris* condition.

---

[1] A polystelic *Psaronius* from the Lower Coal-measures has more recently come to light, showing that the group had already attained a considerable degree of complexity at that relatively early period.

It appears that the petiole usually received a single large bundle with a horse-shoe section, the opening being on the upper side, with the free ends either strongly incurved or replaced by a distinct strand, lying within the curve of the main bundle.

M. Grand'Eury, in his researches on the Coal-flora of the Loire,[1] found the stems of *Psaronius, in situ,* standing

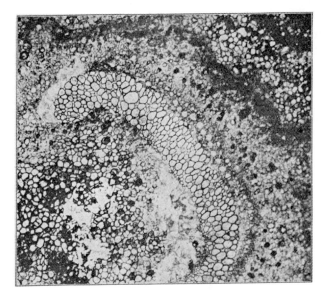

Fig. 125.—*Psaronius Renaulti.* Part of transverse section of stem, showing a portion of the solenostele. On the left is the edge of a leaf-gap. In the stele, note the protoxylem-groups on the inner edge of the wood. The phloëm, with large sieve-tubes, is well preserved on the outer side. The dark elements in the pericycle are secretory sacs. × 13. S. Coll. 2174. From a photograph by Mr. Tams.

erect and rooted as they had grown. From the evidence of constant association he has no doubt that their fronds were of the *Pecopteris* type, and identical with those on which fructifications such as *Asterotheca* and *Scolecopteris* were borne. This conclusion, which is confirmed by M. Renault's studies on the anatomy of certain *Pecopteris* leaves, would tend to show that the *Psaronii* were the stems

[1] *Flore carbonifère du Département de la Loire,* 1878, pp. 78-98.

of arborescent Marattiales, and there is little doubt that this was their general affinity. There are, of course, various differences in structure, as, for example, in the great development of the sclerenchymatous tissues and in the single leaf-trace, points in which *Psaronius* diverges widely from the recent family.

The work of Rudolf on the anatomical relations between *Psaronius* and the Marattiaceae on the whole confirmed the long-established view of their affinity ; the common characters are to be found chiefly in the course of the vascular strands and in the structure of the roots, to which, as it now appears, the endarchy of the steles in the stem may be added. It must, however, be pointed out that the discovery of the true nature of the tissue enclosing the roots shows that in this respect there was no analogy with the recent family. The evidence afforded by the *Psaronius* stems, taken in conjunction with that derived from the synangic fructifications, seems to leave little room for doubt that true Ferns with some Marattiaceous affinity formed an important constituent of the Permo-carboniferous Flora, especially towards the close of that period. Where anatomical evidence is not available, it is, however, extremely difficult to distinguish between true Ferns of this group and plants more probably belonging to the Pteridospermeae.

Osmundaceae

The work of Kidston and Gwynne-Vaughan[1] has thrown great light, from the anatomical side, on the geological history of this family. The fossil specimens fall naturally into two groups : those of Tertiary and Mesozoic age, which are included in the genus *Osmundites*, and those from the Permian, of which the most important genera

---

[1] R. Kidston and D. T. Gwynne-Vaughan, " On the Fossil Osmundaceae," Parts i.-iv., *Transactions of the Royal Society of Edinburgh*, vols. xlv., xlvi., xlvii. 1907–1910, and vol. l. 1914.

are *Zalesskya* and *Thamnopteris* ; in structure, as well as in antiquity, there is a considerable gap between the two groups.

Certain species of *Osmundites*, both Tertiary and Mesozoic, show essentially the same anatomical structure as the recent genera *Osmunda* and *Todea*. There is a ring of collateral vascular bundles, with a continuous zone of phloëm, the xylem forming a network around a large pith ; the leaf-traces pass out singly from the lower edge of each mesh, which thus constitutes a leaf-gap, interrupting the whole thickness of the xylem-ring. The leaf-trace, in transverse section, has the form of an arc or horse-shoe, concave inwards, with a number of protoxylem-groups along the inner side ; the phloëm surrounds the xylem. Traced downwards, the bundle contracts, the internal phloëm dies out, and the protoxylem-groups are reduced to one, which, after the trace has entered the vascular ring, assumes a mesarch position, the xylem closing on behind it ; it then disappears ; there is no protoxylem proper to the stem. The trace unites, on either side, with a reparatory strand.

Such is essentially the vascular structure of various species of *Osmundites*, e.g. the Tertiary *O. schemnitzensis* [1] and *O. Dowkeri*,[2] and the Jurassic *O. Gibbiana*,[2] from New Zealand. Another New Zealand Jurassic fossil, *O. Dunlopi*,[2] while resembling the recent *Todea* in general structure, has the peculiarity that the leaf-gaps do not completely interrupt the xylem-ring, but leave its inner zone continuous—showing some approach towards the protostelic structure of earlier types. On the other hand, the *O. skidegatensis* [2] of Penhallow, from the Lower Cretaceous of Queen Charlotte Islands, British Columbia, has a more complex structure than any recent species.

The preservation is astonishingly perfect ; the plant shows well-developed internal phloëm, continuous through

[1] Kidston and Gwynne-Vaughan, *l.c.* Part iv. 1910.
[2] *L.c.* Part i. 1907.

the leaf-gaps with the external phloëm-zone (Fig. 126). In fact this Mesozoic species comes very near to realising the dictyostelic type of structure, which Jeffrey regards as ancestral to the simpler forms which alone survive. Penhallow's species may, however, quite as well be interpreted, in agreement with Kidston and Gwynne-Vaughan, as marking the culminating point, on a lateral

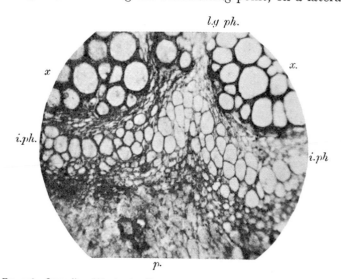

FIG. 126.—*Osmundites skidegatensis*. The inner margin of a portion of the vascular ring, showing the internal phloëm. *x*, part of xylem of two bundles ; *i.ph.*, internal phloëm ; *p*, pith ; *l.g.ph.*, phloëm in leaf-gap. × about 80. After Kidston and Gwynne-Vaughan.

line of descent, in the anatomical elaboration of the Osmundaceae. *O. Carnieri*,[1] a Paraguay species, of doubtful age, appears also to have had a completely dictyostelic structure. As is well known, some approach to this condition is still found in the recent *Osmunda cinnamomea*.

O. Kolbei, Seward,[2] a South African species, of Wealden age, is of interest in two respects : first, the leaf-trace

[1] Kidston and Gwynne-Vaughan, *l.c.* Part v. 1914.
[2] *L.c.* Part iv. 1910.

departs without immediately interrupting the xylem-ring, the leaf-gap only opening out at a somewhat higher level ; and secondly, the pith contains scattered tracheal elements. This latter point is of considerable importance, for a mixed pith forms a welcome transition to the proto-stelic structure of the Permian forms. The medullary tracheides are shorter and wider than those of the xylem-ring, and are not limited to any one part of the pith. Sinnott's objection that these elements might have belonged to the xylem of intrusive roots, burrowing in the pith, appears to be inconsistent with the observed facts.[1]

When we come to the Permian species we find a great change of structure, so much so that while an affinity to Osmundaceae is clear, it is possible that these forms may ultimately require a family to themselves.[2] The three species of which the stem-structure is known are *Zalesskya gracilis*, *Z. diploxylon*, and *Thamnopteris Schlechtendalii* (Figs 127, 128), all from the Upper Permian of the Ural, in Russia. The structure is very similar in all three. In the *Thamnopteris*[3] the preservation of the stem is sufficiently complete to show that wood extended to the centre, no pith existing ; the structure was thus proto-stelic. The wood, however, manifests a striking differ-entiation ; while the outer zone consists of ordinary, elongated, scalariform tracheides, all the central part is made up of wide, short elements with reticulate walls (Fig. 128). Their arrangement shows that they arose by the transverse subdivision of long, procambial cells. This specialisation of the inner xylem as a tissue appar-ently adapted for water-storage recalls the structure of *Lepidodendron selaginoides*, and will be met with again in *Diplolabis* (p. 317) and in *Megaloxylon*. In *Thamno-*

---

[1] Sinnott, " Some Jurassic Osmundaceae from New Zealand," *Ann. of Bot.* vol. xxviii. 1914, p. 475.

[2] Kidston and Gwynne-Vaughan, *l.c.* Part iv. p. 466, 1910.

[3] *L.c.* Part iii. 1909.

pteris, as in *Diplolabis*, there is no trace of xylem-paren-
chyma ; the woody cylinder is perfectly solid.

Where a leaf-trace is about to depart, a protrusion
appears on the outer border of the xylem (Figs. 128, 129).

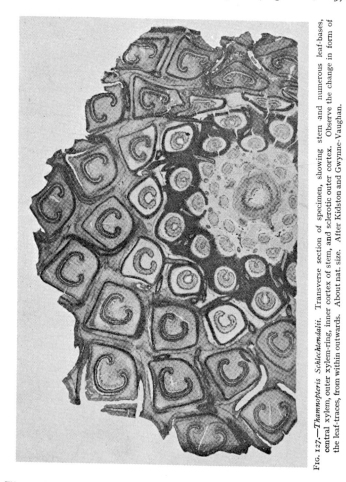

FIG. 127.—*Thamnopteris Schlechtendalii*. Transverse section of specimen, showing stem and numerous leaf-bases, central xylem, outer xylem-ring, inner cortex of stem, and sclerotic outer cortex. Observe the change in form of the leaf-traces, from within outwards. About nat. size. After Kidston and Gwynne-Vaughan.

There is no interruption even of the outer zone, and no
depression is formed when the trace becomes free. As a
rule the xylem of the leaf-trace contains, as it leaves the
stele, a single central protoxylem—the structure is here

mesarch. As it passes outwards, a little parenchyma appears on the adaxial side of the protoxylem, and ultimately the xylem opens out on this side, the structure thus becoming endarch before the trace leaves the stem.

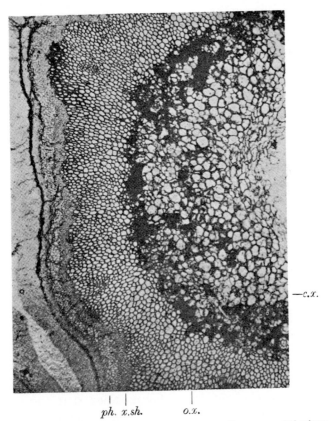

—*c.x.*

ph. x.sh.   *o.x.*

FIG. 128.—*T. Schlechtendalii.* Portion of stele in transverse section. *c.x.*, central xylem ; *o.x.*, outer xylem-ring ; *x.sh.*, xylem-sheath ; *ph*, phloëm ; the protoxylem of a leaf-trace is seen in the outer xylem-ring near the top. × 13. After Kidston and Gwynne-Vaughan.

The protoxylem now divides into two, and later further divisions take place and the bundle assumes the horse-shoe-form characteristic of the order, with a number of protoxylem-groups on its inner concave surface. The successive phases are shown in the diagrams, Fig. 129. Occasionally there are two protoxylem-groups from the start.

The fact that the departing trace maintains a mesarch structure for some time after it has become free from the stele is important ; it will be remembered that in the later Osmundaceae this structure is only found at a point where the bundle forms part of the xylem-ring of the stele. As the trace passes further out it assumes in all respects the structure of a typical Osmundaceous foliar bundle, including the presence of secretory sacs in the pericycle. It is the organisation of the outer region, the cortex and petiole-bases, which establishes the relationship to the recent family. *Thamnopteris Schlechtendalii* is a magnificent fossil, 12 cm. in diameter, including the numerous leaf-bases still attached to the stem (Fig. 127).

The structure of the two species of *Zalesskya* [1] is essentially similar. Here too the evidence indicates that the xylem was originally a solid mass, though the central part is not preserved ; there is the same differentiation into an outer conducting zone and an inner core of wider, probably water-storing tracheides. In *Zalesskya gracilis*, and possibly in *Z. diploxylon* also, the leaf-trace, as in *Thamnopteris*, departs from the stele as a mesarch strand, only assuming endarch structure further out on its course.

It appears then that the Osmundaceae were represented, in Upper Permian times, by plants with a protostelic type of structure in the stem ; this structure, however, was already so far modified that the central xylem had become adapted to the storage rather than the conduction of water. In the later Osmundaceae this tissue is replaced by pith, while the remaining outer ring of wood becomes more and more identified with the leaf-trace system. The continuous zone of phloëm, persisting in recent Osmundaceae, may perhaps be regarded as the last relic of the original protostelic organisation.

---

[1] Kidston and Gwynne-Vaughan, *l.c.* Part ii. 1908.

There is little to show how the transition from proto-stelic to medullate structure took place. Prof. Jeffrey

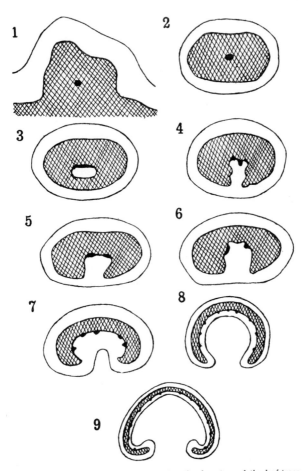

Fig. 129.—*T. Schlechtendalii.* Diagrams illustrating the departure of the leaf-trace. The black marks represent the protoxylem. 1, trace leaving stele; 2, just free, with central protoxylem; 3, parenchymatous island appears; 4, 5, xylem opens on inner side; 5, protoxylem divides; 6, division of protoxylem completed; 7, it divides further; trace becomes curved; 8, 9, still further divisions of protoxylem and increasing curvature of trace, initiated by the xylem. After Gwynne-Vaughan and Kidston.

and his school believe that a dictyostelic condition with internal phloëm (such as is shown in *Osmundites skide-*

gatensis) intervened, or was contemporary with the protostelic forms, and that it gave rise by reduction to the existing type. On the other hand, Kidston and Gwynne-Vaughan hold that the medullate stem with collateral bundles arose directly from protostelic ancestors, by conversion of the central xylem into pith ; on this view the complex structure of *O. skidegatensis* is a special further elaboration, not on the direct line of descent of the recent forms. This interpretation is supported by the case of the Wealden *O. Kolbei*, where the observation of medullary tracheides may indicate a transition from the protostelic to the completely medullate condition.

In almost all the fossil species, of whatever period, the adventitious roots are found, inserted either on the leaf-traces or on the stele itself, in the neighbourhood of a departing trace. The structure of the roots is almost invariably diarch, and essentially similar to that of the roots in the recent members of the Order.

The wide distribution of fossil Osmundaceae is of interest. Species of *Osmundites* are recorded from England, Hungary, Spitzbergen, North and South America, South Africa and New Zealand ; the Permian genera are all from Russia.

The relation of the Permian Osmundaceae to still earlier Palaeozoic Ferns will be considered in the next chapter.

CHAPTER IX

THE FERNS—*continued*

The Botryopteridaceae—Summary on the Ferns

I. BOTRYOPTERIDACEAE

AMONG fossil plants generally, and in particular among those which may still be regarded as Ferns, it is only in rare cases that we are able to describe a plant as a whole, giving a connected account of all its organs. Where the evidence is such as to allow of even an approach to this desirable end, the fossil-botanist must regard himself as peculiarly fortunate.

For this reason the group of the Botryopteridaceae has long claimed a special interest among Palaeozoic Filicales, for in several members of this order the structure of all the important organs is fairly well known, and we have good evidence for connecting them together. Within the present century the interest in this group has been greatly enhanced owing to the importance which now attaches to authentic Palaeozoic representatives of the class of Ferns, and especially to such representatives as appear to have in certain respects a primitive character.

The group, as we shall see presently, was an extensive one in Palaeozoic times, and in several genera there is evidence as to the reproductive as well as the vegetative organs.

Our knowledge of the anatomy of the Botryopteridaceae has made remarkable progress during the last ten years, thanks chiefly to the investigations of Dr. Paul Bertrand, Dr. Gordon, and Dr. Kidston.

In the earlier editions of this book the name Botryopterideae was used, in accordance with Renault's nomenclature, for the order as a whole, of which Renault was the founder. In more modern work it has become customary to restrict this designation to one of the two families regarded as constituting the order. The name Inversicatenales, based on certain peculiarities in the foliar bundle, is employed by Dr. Bertrand for the whole group. We here maintain the original name, in the form Botryopteridaceae, in the general sense, dividing the order into the families Zygopterideae and Botryopterideae, to which we must now add a third, the Anachoropterideae.

A. Zygopterideae

This family now includes a considerable number of generic types, the old genus *Zygopteris*, founded by Corda in 1845, having been much subdivided, and other genera added. Our present conception of the extent of the family, as determined by anatomical characters, is principally derived from the work of Dr. P. Bertrand, though some points remain doubtful.

The genera which we include in the Zygopterideae are as follows : *Clepsydropsis*, *Ankyropteris*, *Botrychioxylon*, *Metaclepsydropsis*, *Diplolabis*, *Asteropteris*, *Asterochlaena*, *Dineuron*, *Etapteris*, *Corynepteris*, *Zygopteris* (in the restricted sense), and *Stauropteris*. The position of *Tubicaulis*, placed in this family by Bertrand, is open to question.

The seven genera which come first in this list are those in which the structure of the stem as well as that of the frond is known. The genera *Ankyropteris*, *Metaclepsydropsis*, *Diplolabis*, and *Etapteris* were all at one time included under *Zygopteris*, now confined to a single, not very well known species, which retains the old generic name on grounds of priority.

1. *Ankyropteris.*—It will be convenient to begin with *Ankyropteris*, one of the best known genera, at least as regards the vegetative organs. *Ankyropteris* was founded, as a sub-genus of *Zygopteris*, by Stenzel in 1889, and was re-defined and raised to generic rank by P. Bertrand [1] in 1909 ; several species have been described, but in some of them the structure of the petiole only is known ; our knowledge of the stem extends to four species : *A. Brongniarti* (Ren.),[2] from the Permian of Autun, in France ; *A. scandens* (Stenz.),[3] from a similar horizon in Bohemia and Saxony ; *A. Grayi* (Will.),[4] and *A. corrugata* (Will.),[5] from the Lower Coal-measures of England. *A. scandens* and *A. Grayi* were regarded by Williamson, in spite of the difference in geological age, as identical. The anatomical description will be based chiefly on *A. Grayi*, which may best serve as the type of the genus. We shall find that, throughout this family, our knowledge is for the most part derived from petrified specimens, so that while the anatomical data are full and fairly satisfactory, the evidence as to external habit is comparatively scanty.

The stem of *Ankyropteris Grayi* reached 22 mm. in diameter, and no doubt attained a considerable length. In fact, Stenzel regarded his closely similar form as a climbing plant, and hence named it *A. scandens*, for he always found the stems and petioles of his specimens intermixed with the crowded roots of a *Psaronius*, among

---

[1] In his important memoir, " Études sur la fronde des Zygoptéri-dées," *Texte et Atlas*, Lille, 1909.

[2] Renault, *Cours de botanique fossile*, vol. iii. chap. viii. 1883 ; for his original memoirs see *Ann. des sci. nat.* (*Bot.*), ser. vi. vols. i. and iii. 1875–76.

[3] Stenzel, " Die Gattung *Tubicaulis*, Cotta," *Bibliotheca Botanica*, Cassel, 1889.

[4] Williamson, " Organisation of Fossil Plants of Coal-measures," Part xv. *Phil. Trans.* 1889, B.

[5] Williamson, *op. cit.* Part viii. *Phil. Trans.* vol. 167, 1877.

which he believes it to have scrambled, much in the same way as a *Tmesipteris* lives among the aërial roots of the New Zealand Tree-ferns at the present day. From the stem large petioles (little inferior to the stem in diameter) were given off, at considerable intervals ; the phyllotaxis was a spiral one, and in all cases observed the arrangement was clearly on the $\frac{2}{5}$ system (see Figs. 130 and 131).

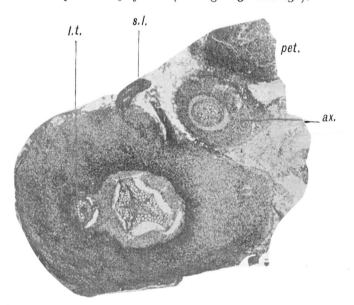

FIG. 130.—*Ankyropteris Grayi.* Transverse section of stem, with axillary shoot and part of petiole. In the middle of the stem the five-angled stele is seen (cf. Fig. **131**). *l.t.*, leaf-trace, about to give off the axillary strand ; *s.l.*, " scale-leaf " ; *ax*, axillary shoot of next node below ; *pet*, part of petiole of the subtending leaf. The small strand in the cortex to the right belongs to a scale-leaf. × about **4**. From a photograph by Mr. L. A. Boodle. Will. Coll. 1919 A.

In all the known Botryopteridaceae the stem was traversed by a single vascular cylinder ; this monostelic structure, exceptional among recent Ferns, appears to have been more widely prevalent among those of Palaeozoic age.

In our *Ankyropteris* the stele has a very characteristic structure ; its general form follows that of the wood, which in section has the outline of an irregular five-rayed star (see Figs. 130 and 131). These rays are of very unequal length ; the comparison of successive transverse sections shows that the shortest are those which have just given off a leaf-trace (Fig. 131, 1), while the longest are those which are just about to do so (Fig. 131, 5). From the position of the leaf-traces and their relation to the prominent corners of the wood, as shown in succes-

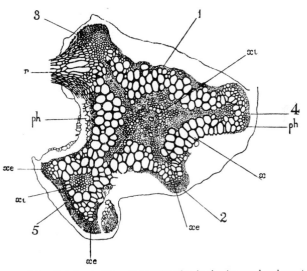

FIG. 131.—*Ankyropteris Grayi.* Transverse section of stele, showing wood and remains of phloëm. 1-5, the five angles of the wood, from which leaf-traces are given off, in order of the phyllotaxis, No. 5 belonging to the lowest leaf of the series ; *x*, principal ring of xylem ; *xi*, small tracheides of internal xylem ; *xe*, small tracheides at periphery ; *ph*, phloëm ; *r*, base of adventitious root. × 14. Will. Coll. 1919 B. (G. T. G.)

sive transverse sections, it follows that the angle of divergence between two successive leaves was in this case $\frac{2}{5}$ (Fig. 131, 1-5). A short xylem-arm from which the leaf-trace has just separated appears merely as a slight bulge (Fig. 131, 1) ; those of successively greater length assume a truncated form at the end (Fig. 131, 2, 3, and 4) ; while the longest arms of all spread out laterally, so as to be broadest at their termination, acquiring a bicornute outline (Fig. 131, 5). It is the enlarged end of the arm which, at a somewhat higher level, becomes detached, to form the xylem of a leaf-trace (Fig. 130, *l.t.*). In the wood of the stele, a central and a peripheral region may be distinguished. The peripheral tissue consists principally of large scalariform tracheides. Towards the ends of the more projecting arms, and especially at the angles of the most prominent of them, much smaller elements occur (Fig. 131, *xe*). The central tissue, like the wood as a whole, has a stellate form; the main mass, which occupies the middle of the stele, sends out prolongations into each of the arms. The central tissue used at one time to be described as a pith, but that is not its true nature, for in addition to the delicate parenchyma, it contains a system of small tracheides, quite distinct from those of the external xylem (Fig. 131, *xi*). This internal tracheal system forms a group or irregular ring about the centre of the stele, and from this central group radial bands of small tracheides extend outwards, up the middle of each arm (Fig. 131).

The internal xylem is too extensive to be regarded as wholly protoxylem; most of its elements appear to be scalariform, like the large tracheides of the peripheral zone. It is probable that the actual protoxylem was confined to the interior of the projecting arms.

It may be mentioned here that no member of any family of the Botryopteridaceae possessed a true pith, so far as is known.

Some remains of the phloëm which surrounded the wood of the stele are preserved; it includes a single or double series of large elements, which probably represent the sieve-tubes (Fig. 131, *ph*). The phloëm evidently followed the contour of the wood. The whole is surrounded by a zone of delicate tissue (which may best be regarded as an inner cortex), filling the spaces between the arms of the stele, and cylindrical in form (Fig. 130). Beyond this is the wide outer cortex, the internal layers of which are thick-walled, forming a kind of sheath to the inner cortical zone. The epidermis was provided with multicellular hairs.

The course of the leaf-trace bundles can be very clearly followed ; a single large bundle entered each petiole. To form the trace the whole distal part of one of the prominent arms (cf. Fig. 131, 5) became detached,

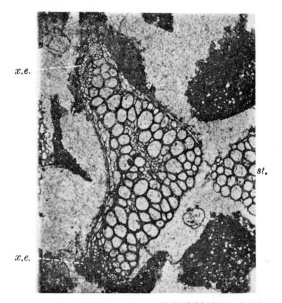

Fig. 132.—*Ankyropteris Grayi*. Shore specimen. Undivided leaf-trace, just departing from an arm of the stele (*st*). The median protoxylem group is destined for the axillary stele. *x.e.*, bands of small-celled xylem, enclosing the peripheral loops, in which are the protoxylems for the foliar bundle. × about 30. From a photograph by Mr. W. Tams. S. Coll. 2516.

forming in this case an approximately triangular concentric bundle, with the base directed outwards.

The process of the emission of the leaf-trace is best shown in a specimen from Shore, Littleborough,[1] in which the trace, on leaving the stele, has a somewhat crescentic transverse section, with the concave side directed outwards (Fig. 132). There are three groups of protoxylem,

[1] See Scott, " On a Palaeozoic Fern, the *Zygopteris Grayi* of William-son," *Ann. of Bot.* vol. xxvi. 1912, p. 39.

all internal to the wood, and each accompanied by a little parenchyma. One group is median ; the other two are lateral and lie close to the truncated ends, enclosed on the outside by a narrow band of small tracheides, forming a loop. At the level figured each lateral group has divided into two. If the trace is followed downwards to its junction with the stele, all the protoxylem groups are found to be continuous with the small internal tracheides of the corresponding arm of the stellate xylem.

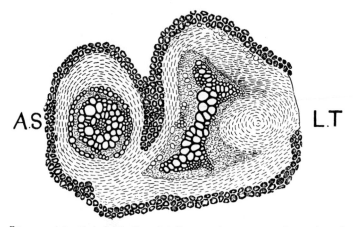

A.S   L.T

FIG. 133.—*Ankyropteris Grayi.* Somewhat diagrammatic transverse section, to show the separation of the axillary stele, A.S., from the leaf-trace, L.T. Simplified from a detailed drawing. The phloëm of the axillary stele is well preserved. × about 18. Will. Coll. 1919 B. (G. T. G.)

The bundle, as it departs from the stele, is a compound structure and may be called the undivided trace. As we follow the trace outwards through the cortex, we find that it divides into two strands, of very different form, both lying on the same radius (see Fig. 130, *l.t.*, where this division is just beginning, and Fig. 133). The outer of the two strands is the foliar bundle, which is continuous with the external side of the original undivided trace, while the inner strand is destined for the axillary shoot. We will first follow the course of the foliar bundle, which, as it separates from the inner strand and passes out into the petiole, gradually assumes a somewhat complex form. At first the bundle consists simply of a tangential, somewhat bent, plate of wood, surrounded by phloëm, and spreading out a little at either extremity (Fig. 133, L.T.), but in its outward progress these lateral expansions increase in importance, so that the ultimate form, in transverse section, is that of the letter " H," the cross-stroke of the H being placed tangentially with reference to the parent stem (cf. Fig. 135, from another species). The details of structure are described below, in connection with the petiole. The phloëm surrounds the xylem and follows its contour. This H-shaped petiolar bundle is common, with various modifications, to many Zygopterideae, and constituted the character on which the old genus *Zygopteris* was founded.

The other bundle, which is given off on the inner side of the leaf-trace, between the latter and the stele of the stem, is of special interest (Fig. 133, A.S.). It is continuous with the adaxial part of the original leaf-trace, and as it separates, assumes a circular or elliptical form in transverse section (see Fig. 130, *ax*), with the long axis in the latter case placed tangentially. It consists of a ring of xylem, with large tracheides, surrounded by a zone of phloëm, and at the centre is a group of small tracheides accompanied by parenchyma. This central group is continuous with the median protoxylem of the undivided trace. In fact, the structure of this bundle is that of the stele of the main stem, in an extremely simplified form. The *axillary stele*, as it is best termed, passed out into a cylindrical appendage, placed exactly in the axil between stem and leaf, and hence appropriately named by Stenzel the *axillary shoot* (Fig. 130, *ax*). This curious organ occurs in three out of the four forms of *Ankyropteris* in which the stem is known,[1] but has not,

---

[1] The bundle marked *r* in Renault's figure (*Flore fossile d'Autun et d'Épinac*, Part ii. Plate xxxi. Fig. 2) of *A. Brongniarti*, from its form and position, manifestly belongs, as Stenzel detected, to the axillary shoot, though interpreted by the author as an adventitious root.

so far as I am aware, been found in any other genus of fossil Ferns. There is, however, a close analogy with the axillary branches of the recent Hymenophyllaceae, a family with which, in various other respects also, the Botryopteridaceae have something in common. Stenzel, the discoverer of the axillary shoot of *Ankyropteris*, at first suggested another possible view of its nature, namely, that it might represent the fertile ventral lobe of the leaf, as in the Ophioglosseae. This was, at the time, a sufficiently probable interpretation, but was subsequently withdrawn by the author, on the ground that transitional forms occur, which are intermediate in structure between the axillary shoot and the normal stem of *Ankyropteris* ; this fact, which is also shown in the English specimens, is quite conclusive in favour of the cauline nature of the axillary organ.

Besides the foliage-leaves, *Ankyropteris* possessed rudimentary leaf-like organs, of small size, termed scale-leaves by Renault and Stenzel, who discovered them in *A. Brongniarti* and *A. scandens* respectively. They are now well known in the British species *A. Grayi* (Fig. 130) and *A. corrugata* (Fig. 134) ; the name *aphlebiae* is adopted for them. A curious feature of these appendages, which have a simple, scale-like form, is that they occur on the petiole-bases as well as on the stem. Their vascular strands are given off from the sides of the leaf-trace both below and above its separation from the stele of the stem. A single bundle enters each appendage, and then divides into two, three, or four strands. An example from *A. corrugata* is shown, in transverse section, in Fig. 134 ; it has just detached itself from the base of a petiole, and contains two bundles. The morphology of these curious organs, which may be compared with the aphlebiae of other Palaeozoic Ferns and Pteridosperms, requires further elucidation. They have been supposed to be of the nature of modified basal pinnae.

The stem also bore adventitious roots ; the vascular

strands supplying them can be distinguished from those of the aphlebiae by their more horizontal course ; they arise laterally on the arms of the stele. The roots are diarch.

The most characteristic features of the Zygopterideae are found in the structure and mode of ramification of the frond. As the lamina is usually unknown, it is only the petiole and rachis with which we are concerned. The anatomy of these parts has been elucidated with the

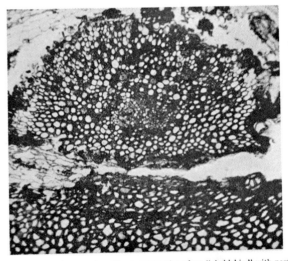

FIG. 134.—*Ankyropteris corrugata.* Transverse section of an "Aphlebia" with part of the outer cortex of the leaf-base to which it belongs. The appendage contains two vascular bundles. From a photograph by Mr. L. A. Boodle. × 36. Will. Coll. 264.

utmost accuracy by Dr. Paul Bertrand in his fine memoir "Études sur la fronde des Zygoptéridées," already referred to.

The structure of a typical *Ankyropteris* petiole is shown in Fig. 135, from an English Lower Coal-measure species, *A. westphaliensis,* P. B., which Williamson identified with a closely similar Permian form, *A. bibractensis,* described by Renault.[1] The stem is unknown ;

[1] The British form was originally named *A. bibractensis, var. westphaliensis* by Dr. Bertrand, but the difference of age renders it probable that the species are distinct.

Dr. Bertrand's suggestion that it might be identical with
A. Grayi is hardly borne out by what we know of the
petioles of the latter plant.

In *A. westphaliensis* the lateral portions of the
petiole bundle are so strongly incurved as to give the
section the shape of a double anchor, from which the
generic name *Ankyropteris* is taken. The middle band

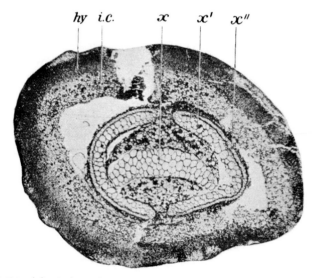

Fig. 135.—*Ankyropteris westphaliensis.* Transverse section of a petiole, showing the double-anchor form of stele. x, middle band of xylem ("apolar"); x', the main lateral bands ("antennae"); x'', the small-celled external arcs of xylem ("filaments"); the protoxylem lies between x' and x''; *i.c.*, inner cortex; *hy*, sclerenchymatous hypoderma. × 7. From a photograph by Mr. L. A. Boodle. S. Coll. 914.

(the "apolar" of Dr. Bertrand, from the absence of
protoxylem) is curved, the concavity being no doubt
directed away from the parent stem. The lateral pieces
are regarded as made up of four "antennae" (Bertrand);
the two adaxial antennae are considerably longer than
the abaxial pair. The peculiar feature, characteristic of
the genus *Ankyropteris*, consists in the presence of an
external band of small-celled xylem (x'') on the outer
side of the antennae, separated from them by a delicate

parenchyma except at the ends, where the large- and small-celled bands unite. The latter are called the " filaments " by Dr. Bertrand. As Williamson said : " It is the loop-like continuity of the parallel bands of large and small vessels at each of their extremities that constitutes the characteristic feature of this plant." [1] In *Ankyropteris* these peripheral loops are permanent, not opening at any level. The protoxylem is found inside the loops, at the four points where the filaments join the antennae (cf. Fig. 140, D), but other groups may probably have been present also. We have seen that in *A. Grayi* the peripheral loops already appear low down in the course of the leaf-trace ; they begin to be differentiated even before the trace departs from the stele.

The whole foliar bundle is concentric, the phloëm surrounding the xylem, and following its outline ; the phloëm, however, is better preserved in petioles of other species. The inner cortex is composed of short-celled parenchyma, while the outer zone is strongly constructed of narrow, thick-walled fibres. Externally, the petiole and rachis are studded with stout spines.

The main petiole bears alternate pinnae at somewhat long intervals. They are in two rows only, one row at each side, an arrangement universal in ordinary compound leaves, but somewhat exceptional in those of Zygopterideae.

To supply a pinna, a strand is given off from one of the peripheral loops of the main petiole bundle. The pinna-trace has at first the form, in transverse section, of a simple loop, with its axis nearly at right angles to that of the petiolar bundle (see diagram, Fig. 140, D, p. 313). Only the adaxial antennae are concerned in the emission of the pinna-traces ; the pinna-loop is formed without the continuity of the filament of the main strand ever being interrupted.

[1] Williamson, " Organisation of Fossil Plants of Coal-measures," Part vi., Ferns, *Phil. Trans. Royal Soc.* 1874, p. 698.

The pinna-trace bends outward and enters a branch of the rachis. It assumes a more complex form with two loops instead of one,[1] but we need not follow these changes in detail. The orientation of the pinna-trace at right angles to that of the main rachis is peculiar to the Zygopterideae ; in other plants parallel orientation is the rule. It is also characteristic of the family we are describing that the bundle of the pinna has a very different form from that of the main petiolar strand, though, as Dr. Bertrand has· shown, the one may be interpreted in terms of the other. It may also be mentioned that the pinna-trace, as it passes out, is accompanied on either side by minute strands, destined for aphlebiae (Fig. 140, D). The further branching of the pinna-strand has been observed ; the frond must, therefore, have been at least bipinnate. Nothing, however, is known of the lamina, nor even whether any such organ existed. In the Zygopterideae generally the evidence as to the presence of an expanded leaf-blade, as distinguished from the branched rachis, is extremely meagre.

In connection with the petiole just described, a few words may be said about A. corrugata (Will.),[2] a species in which all the vegetative organs are known. The petiole (once called Rachiopteris insignis, but already identified by Williamson) has the complex type of structure just described, but with shorter antennae. The stele of the stem has an almost cylindrical form, except where it is affected by the emission of a leaf-trace, which is preceded by the formation of a bilobed projection, quite comparable to a bicornute arm of the stele in A. Grayi. The system of internal tracheides is the same as in that

---

[1] The secondary rachis of A. westphaliensis was described and figured by Williamson under the name Rachiopteris inaequalis.

[2] The Rachiopteris corrugata of Williamson, " Organisation of Fossil Plants of Coal-measures," Part viii. Phil. Trans. Roy. Soc. vol. 167, 1876, p. 213, Figs. 1-24. The plant has proved to be a typical Ankyropteris, as shown by Dr. Bertrand.

plant, but in *A. corrugata* some of them may be short and globular, suggesting a partial transition to the function of water-storage. The protoxylem is internal ; narrow spiral tracheides occur on the outer border of the central xylem, where it joins the peripheral zone. The leaf-trace, on first departing from the stele, has a simple, somewhat curved transverse section, with the concavity outwards ; there is an imbedded protoxylem group near each end, and usually a third group, which, however, soon dies out, in a median position. The H-like form of the bundle is only assumed very gradually, as it passes out into the petiole. The aphlebiae, which in this species are most often found in connection with the petiole, have already been noticed (see Fig. 134). When completely developed they are winged structures, and may contain as many as five bundles. The young leaves bear, in addition to the aphlebiae, a copious growth of ramenta, and hairs are also present.

The pinna-traces are given off, as in *A. westphaliensis*, from the adaxial antennae. Here also they are loop-like in form, but on a small scale, and consequently difficult to distinguish from the strands destined for aphlebiae ; it has even been suggested that no true pinnae existed in this species.

The great peculiarity of *A. corrugata*, as compared with the other three species in which the stem is known, consists in its mode of branching, which is not axillary, but rather of the nature of a dichotomy, the stem forking into two nearly equal branches without obvious relation to the leaf-insertion (Fig. 136). This fact raises the question whether, as has been suggested, the apparent axillary branching of other species and of recent Hymeno-phyllaceae may not be a modified dichotomy, in which case the " undivided leaf-trace " would really include the stele of the smaller branch, as well as the bundle of the " subtending " leaf. This view seems highly probable ; it accords well with the anatomical relations in the *A.*

Grayi type (see above, p. 294), and dichotomy is known to occur elsewhere in the family.[1] The presence of a transitory median protoxylem in the lower part of the leaf-trace of *A. corrugata* is, however, unexplained, and might be interpreted as the last indication of a former axillary branching.

The adventitious roots of *A. corrugata* are of considerable interest. They attained a rather large size and are

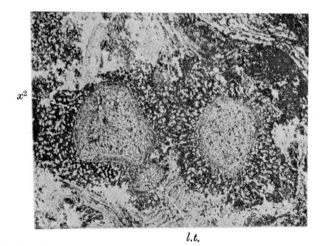

FIG. 136.—*Ankyropteris corrugata.* Transverse section of a dichotomous stem, showing the two steles. The stele on the left has a band of secondary wood at x^2. *l.t.*, leaf-trace. × about 8. From a photograph by Mr. W. Tams. S. Coll. 2715.

exceptionally well preserved. The stele is diarch, with a thick xylem-plate ; the inner cortex is generally lacunar, suggesting a watery habitat ; in the dense outer cortex an extensive periderm was developed ; an external periderm, though somewhat unusual in roots, is well known in those of *Cycas,* as well as of some Angiosperms. At the base of the root a secondary formation of xylem has been observed.

[1] See B. Sahni, " Observations on the Evolution of Branching in the Filicales," *New Phytologist,* vol. xvi. 1917, p. 1.

Secondary wood was occasionally formed in the stem also, as in the specimen shown in Fig. 136; its occurrence, however, is only local, though of interest from the analogy of *Botrychioxylem*, to be described below.

Ankyropteris corrugata is thus a very distinct species of the genus, less differentiated as regards the primary stelar structure than the *A. Grayi* group.

Before leaving *Ankyropteris*, we may refer to a small petiole, named *A. Williamsoni* by Dr. Bertrand, who regards it as representing a distinct species; it may, however, belong to the distal part of a frond of *A. westphaliensis*. However that may be, the specimen is of interest from the comparative simplicity of the foliar bundle (see diagram, Fig. 140, C.). The median band (apolar) is practically straight, and the antennae not sharply marked off from it. Peripheral loops are present, as usual. The pinna-trace (identical in structure with that of *A. westphaliensis*) is of relatively large size, and, as Dr. Bertrand has shown, must have been given off from the whole extent of a peripheral loop, and not merely from an adaxial antenna as in the forms already described. This little petiole is significant from its showing some approach to the simple foliar structure of the genus *Clepsydropsis*, to which we will now pass on.

2. *Clepsydropsis.*—This is an old genus, founded by Unger in 1854, on petioles from the Lower Carboniferous (or possibly Upper Devonian) of Thuringia, in Central Germany. The only European species which need be considered is *C. antiqua*, Unger; our knowledge of this plant is limited to the petiole and rachis, for it is only quite recently that the stem has been identified in an Australian species.

We will begin with the petiole, which has an extremely simple structure, usually regarded as the most primitive in the family. The cortex presents the ordinary features, an outer mechanical zone, and an inner region of thin-walled tissue. The concentric vascular bundle has a narrow, elongated transverse section ; it is often some-what constricted in the middle, giving the hour-glass shape from which the name of the genus is taken (see Fig. 140, B). No antennae are differentiated, but there is a peripheral loop near each end, its long axis coinciding with that of the bundle, contrary to the arrangement in *Ankyropteris*. It appears that the protoxylem lined the inside of the loops. The outer enclosure of each loop is formed of several layers of tracheides somewhat smaller than the rest ; this band answers to the " filament " of *Ankyropteris*, in a very simple form.

Pinna-traces are given off in two rows, one on each side. The pinna-trace is a simple loop, derived from a peripheral loop of the main bundle ; it is at first circular ; as it passes out into the pinna the cavity becomes elon-gated and the outer border thicker than the inner ; the orientation of the pinna-loop is at right angles to that of the main bundle (Fig. 140, B), as in *Ankyropteris*. Secondary pinnules or aphlebiae are given off from the pinnae.[1]

A certain relationship between *Ankyropteris* and *Clepsydropsis* was recognised by Dr. Bertrand ; the former appeared to be an advanced, the latter a primitive member of the series. A recent discovery, however, has proved that the stem of *Clepsydropsis* was by no means simple, but rather of the most elaborate *Ankyropteris* type. This has been shown by Mrs. Osborn, in a species named *C. australis* ; the original specimens were found near Barraba in New South Wales, in rocks considered to be of Upper Devonian age. Another specimen was found near Mount Tangorin, about 150 miles from the former locality ; the horizon is believed to be Carbonifer-ous, but it is said to be impossible as yet to draw a sharp line of distinction between the two series of rocks ;[2] there

[1] P. Bertrand, " Nouvelles Remarques sur la fronde des Zygop-téridées," *Mem. Soc. Hist. Nat. Autun.* t. xxv. 1911.

[2] See Mrs. E. M. Osborn, " Preliminary Observations on an

seems to be no doubt that the species is identical. The salient points from Mrs. Osborn's preliminary description may be quoted : " The stem stele is of a five-rayed star-shape with blunt points, the pith, which contains tracheids, being also star-shaped. The structure is in the main of the *Ankyropteris Grayi* type with less acute points, but with no axillary branches. Leaf-traces leave the stele in the same order and manner as described for *A. Grayi*. As each departs it is of a triangular shape with rounded angles, the apex of the triangle being the point of attachment to the stem. This bundle soon becomes flattened tangentially, so that before it leaves the cortex it has the appearance of a flattened ring, slightly curved, with the convexity of the curve on the adaxial side. As the trace passes outwards it becomes still more flattened and tangentially elongate, until when a little above the base of the petiole it appears as a long band-shaped xylem mass, without curvature, rather constricted in the middle, and with a peripheral loop containing parenchyma and small tracheids at each end. Thus the petiolar structure is of the Clepsydropsoid type." Aphlebia-traces are present, as in *A. Grayi*.

The Mt. Tangorin specimen, investigated by Mr. B. Sahni, shows numerous crowded petioles, though the stele is missing. The petiolar bundle only differs from that of *C. antiqua* in its somewhat more slender form and more fusiform peripheral loops. Mr. Sahni has observed the emission of the pinna-trace, which takes place exactly as in *C. antiqua*. The roots are diarch, as in other Zygopterideae.

It thus appears that the simple form of petiole long known as *Clepsydropsis* was borne on a stem with the highly differentiated stele characteristic of the *A. Grayi* type of *Ankyropteris*. On this ground Mr. Sahni has

---

Australian *Zygopteris*," *British Association Report*, 1915, p. 727; B. Sahni, " On an Australian specimen of *Clepsydropsis*," *Ann. of Bot.* vol. xxxiii. 1919, p. 81.

united the two genera, merging the more modern genus *Ankyropteris* in the older *Clepsydropsis*. On account of the marked difference in petiolar structure we here prefer to keep up both genera, but there can be no doubt that the affinity is very close, and *Clepsydropsis* can no longer be regarded as a specially primitive genus, though it has retained a simple structure of the foliar bundle.

The Australian species is further of interest from showing something of the habit of the plant, previously unknown in *Clepsydropsis*. The plant was of considerable size ; the Mt. Tangorin specimen is 11 cm. in diameter, including the leaf-bases. The latter are numerous, surrounding the stem in several cycles. The growth was no doubt upright, and the habit probably that of " a fair-sized Tree fern, resembling the fossil Osmundaceae " (Sahni).

3. *Asterochlaena.*—This genus, founded by Corda in 1845, on specimens discovered by Cotta in 1832, bears some resemblance to *Clepsydropsis* in the simple form of the foliar bundle and in the stellate stele of the stem, but in other respects is very distinct. The two species known are both of Permian age ; the genus is thus one of the latest in the family ; it is also in some ways the most complex in structure. In spite of the investigations of Stenzel (1889), who included *Clepsydropsis* in the same genus, *Asterochlaena* remained imperfectly known down to 1911, when Dr. P. Bertrand published a fine monograph on the species *A. laxa*, Stenzel, of which several specimens from the Permian of Chemnitz in Saxony were available. Our present, very complete knowledge of the structure is due to Dr. Bertrand's researches.[1]

The type specimen, including the numerous leaf-bases which closely invest the stem (Fig. 137), is 8.5 × 7 cm. in diameter, the stem itself measuring about 5 × 4 cm. The plant was thus a fairly large one ; the axis seems to have

[1] P. Bertrand, " Structure des stipes d'*Asterochlaena laxa*, Stenzel," *Mém. de la Soc. Géol. du Nord*, t. vii. 1, Lille, 1911.

been vertical; many adventitious roots are present among the leaf-bases.

The stele, as seen in transverse section, is of very complex, stellate form, with long slender arms, variously forked, and only united quite at the centre (Fig. 137). The star-shaped stele here shows its most extreme and even fantastic development. It differs essentially from

Fig. 137.—*Asterochlaena laxa.* General transverse section, showing the stellate stele with bilobed or trilobed arms, and the leaf-traces, but only the inner petioles. The Roman numerals indicate the leaves of two successive whorls. *R*, roots; *S*, pinna-traces. Slightly magnified. After Dr. Bertrand.

the stele of the *Ankyropteris Grayi* or *Clepsydropsis* type, in the fact that the number of arms bears no constant relation to that of the leaf-traces, for each arm is bilobed or trilobed at its extremity, giving rise to two or three vertical series of leaf-traces; a single-lobed arm rarely occurs.

Broadly speaking, the anatomical structure of the stele is comparable to that in *Ankyropteris Grayi* or *Clepsydropsis,* though the proportions of the parts are very different. At the centre of the star is a small, angular " mixed pith " ; the tracheides which it contains are mostly wide and short. From each angle of the mixed pith a narrow radial band of small-celled internal xylem (the protoxylem of Dr. Bertrand) extends up the middle of each arm, branching where the arm branches. At the point of branching there is usually a little triangular island, which may contain cellular tissue as well as tracheides, forming a sort of repetition of the central mixed pith on a smaller scale. Outside the protoxylem-bands the wood is made up of large scalariform tracheides. The phloëm, which contains large sieve-tubes, follows the outline of the stellate xylem, and the bays are filled by cortical ground-tissue.

Each arm of the stele divides at its extremity into two or three blunt lobes, the lobes corresponding to the points of emission of the leaf-traces. Thus the number of the latter is dependent on that of the lobes, not of the arms. Each lobe has, in the first instance, a single embedded protoxylem, no doubt originally continuous with the median band of the arm. Before the trace is detached, the protoxylem divides into two groups. When the trace becomes free from the stele it assumes a shortly elliptical or almost rectangular section, with a peripheral loop, containing the protoxylem, at each end. It becomes very similar to the leaf-trace of *Clepsydropsis*, but whereas the latter is straight and perfectly symmetrical, that of *Asterochlaena* is only symmetrical with reference to the radial plane, for the peripheral loops are displaced towards the abaxial surface (Fig. 138). As the trace passes out into the leaf-base it becomes slender and curved, with the convex side outwards.

The loop-like pinna-traces, in two series only, are given off somewhat obliquely, in the direction of the abaxial face, as follows from the position of the peripheral loops of the main bundle. It will be noticed that their position is the reverse of that usual in *Ankyropteris*. The lower pinna-traces, which begin to be given off as soon as the main trace leaves the stele, may be compared to the aphlebia-strands of *Ankyropteris*. The diarch roots arise both from the leaf-traces and from the arms of the stele.

While *Asterochlaena* possesses the most complex form of stele known in the Zygopterideae, the leaf-trace is almost as simple as that of *Clepsydropsis*, only differing from it in symmetry. Considering its late geological age, *Asterochlaena* may represent the final phase of the *Clepsydropsis* type, along a certain line of development, while *Ankyropteris* belongs to another line in which the vascular system of the leaf is the part most elaborated.

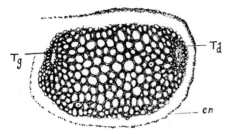

Fig. 138.—*Asterochlaena laxa.* Leaf-trace after its departure from the stele. *Tg, Td,* the two peripheral loops; *en,* endodermis. × about 40. After Dr. Bertrand.

Probably the most remarkable feature in the organisation of *Asterochlaena* is the plurality of the leaf-traces corresponding to each arm of the stele; while in *Ankyropteris* and *Clepsydropsis* the phyllotaxis and the form of the stele are closely related, in *Asterochlaena* they have come to be largely independent of each other. From this point of view one might speak of this genus as a multiple *Clepsydropsis*. But we are not justified in assuming a direct relation between the two genera; the fossil next to be described has an important bearing on the question.

4. *Asteropteris.* — While *Asterochlaena* is one of the youngest of the known Zygopterideae, *Asteropteris* is probably the oldest, for it appears to be the only genus with undisputed claims to Devonian age. Yet the two

genera were united by Stenzel, and have a good deal in common. *Asteropteris noveboracensis*, the only species, was described in 1881 by Sir J. W. Dawson,[1] who gave an excellent account of its structure ; we owe a more modern investigation of the specimen to Dr. P. Bertrand.[2] The plant is derived from the Portage Beds of the Upper Devonian of the State of New York.

Asteropteris was described by the discoverer, Dawson, as " a small tree-fern . . . of the group of Palaeozoic Ferns allied to the genus *Zygopteris* of Schimper." The diameter of the stem was 2.5 cm., or more in places. In

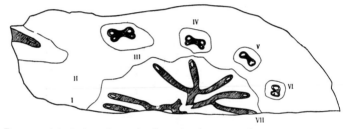

Fig. 139.—*Asteropteris noveboracensis*. Incomplete transverse section of stem, showing part of the star-shaped stele and several leaf-traces. The fracture at the middle of the stele is accidental. × nearly 3. From Dr. Bertrand.

general form the stele is much like that of *Asterochlaena* ; it has a complex, stellate section, with long, branched arms, united at the centre (Fig. 139). The total number of arms at the periphery is about twelve. At the end of each arm is a single peripheral loop, in which no doubt the protoxylem was situated. The structure, however, is much simpler than in *Asterochlaena,* for in *Asteropteris* the xylem is homogeneous throughout ; there is no mixed pith and no internal system of tracheides, apart from the peripheral loops.

In the cortex, a single leaf-trace lies opposite each

[1] J. W. Dawson, " Notes on new Erian (Devonian) Plants," *Quarterly Journal of the Geol. Soc. London,* vol. 37, 1881, p. 299.
[2] P. Bertrand, " L'Étude anatomique des fougères anciennes," *Progressus Rei Botanicae,* vol. 4, 1911, p. 255.

xylem-arm (Fig. 139) ; the traces are not multiple, as in *Asterochlaena*. The trace passes through a *Clepsydropsis* stage, but at a higher level appears to possess two peripheral loops at each end ; it remains therefore doubtful whether the pinnae were in two or four series. Dr. Bertrand finds that the fronds were in whorls, with the successive verticils superposed, another point of distinction from *Asterochlaena*.

Asteropteris shows that the stellate stele is an extremely ancient feature in the Zygopterideae, and warns us, as Dr. Bertrand has pointed out, against making the assumption that in this family the simplest form of stele was necessarily the most primitive. *Asterochlaena*, with its highly differentiated vascular system, may well have been derived from a stock resembling *Asteropteris* ; the relation to *Clepsydropsis* would then be less direct. The structure of the leaf-trace in *Asteropteris* suggests, however, that this ancient plant was itself not altogether of a primitive type.

Under the provisional name of *Zygopteris Kidstoni*, an imperfectly known fossil, found by Dr. Kidston in the Lower Carboniferous of Berwickshire, is described by Dr. Bertrand as resembling *Asteropteris* in the solid, homogeneous xylem of the stele and in the conspicuous peripheral loops, while in the form of the stele, with five short arms, and in the $\frac{2}{5}$ phyllotaxis, it approaches an *Ankyropteris*. The frond is unknown.

We now come to the series of Zygopterideae with four rows of pinnae, two rows on each side of the rachis, a remarkable arrangement, without precedent in any other family of Ferns.

5. *Dineuron.*—This genus shows the quadriseriate type in its simplest form. Only the frond is known. There are two very similar species, *D. pteroides*, Ren., from Esnost, near Autun, in France, and *D. ellipticum*, Kidston, from Pettycur, Fife, both of Lower Carboniferous age.

The mode of emission of the pinna-traces was first made out by Dr. P. Bertrand in 1909.[1]

In form the foliar bundle is as simple as that of *Clepsydropsis* (Fig. 140, I). It has an elliptical transverse section, with a peripheral loop, containing the protoxylem, at each end. In *Dineuron*, however, the loops are not permanent, for they open out as each pinna-trace is given off. To form the latter the outer border of the loop becomes detached, and soon after leaving the main bundle, divides into two small strands, as shown in the diagram. Thus the pair of pinna-traces on each side arises from the early division of the original trace ; it is a case of precocious dichotomy ; as has been pointed out both by Dr. P. Bertrand[2] and Mr. Sahni.[3] The latter author therefore speaks of the quadriseriate pinnae as pinnules or tertiary rachises, which is correct, though the term pinnae is more generally used for them. The relations are shown much more clearly in the next genus.

6. *Metaclepsydropsis.*—This genus, founded on the *Rachiopteris duplex* of Williamson,[4] is now one of the best known of the Zygopterideae. The petioles of the type species from the Lower Carboniferous of Pettycur were well described by Williamson in 1874, and their structure was further elucidated by Dr. Bertrand in 1909. Our knowledge of the stem is due to Dr. Gordon, who published in 1911 a complete investigation of the whole vegetative structure of the plant.[5]

The stem was of great length, with long internodes ; no doubt it was a creeping rhizome. A portion of stem

---

[1] *L.c.*, 1909, p. 191. For *D. ellipticum* see Kidston, " On a new Species of *Dineuron* and of *Botryopteris*, etc.," *Trans. Roy. Soc. Edinburgh*, vol. xlvi. 1908, p. 361.

[2] " L'Étude anatomique des fougères anciennes," 1911, p. 218.

[3] " On the Branching of the Zygopteridean Leaf, etc.," *Ann. of Bot.* vol. xxxii. 1918, p. 369.

[4] Williamson, " On the Organisation of the Fossil Plants of the Coal-measures," Part vi., Ferns, *Phil. Trans. Roy. Soc.* 1874, p. 687.

[5] W. T. Gordon, " On the Structure and Affinities of *Metaclepsydropsis duplex*," *Trans. Roy. Soc. Edinburgh*, vol. xlviii. 1911, p. 163.

observed by Dr. Margaret Benson was no less than 22

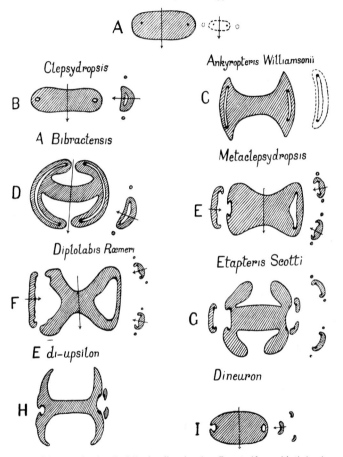

Fig. 140.—Diagrams showing the foliar bundles of various Zygopterideae, with their pinna-traces. In A-D the pinna-traces are given off in two rows (Clepsydroid type); in E-I in four rows (Dineuroid type). The arrows indicate the principal plane of symmetry of the bundle and its appendages. The black dots or lines represent the protoxylem. The small strands accompanying the pinna-traces are aphlebia-traces. A (" assumed primitive type ") is based on *Thamnopteris* (cf. Fig. 129). After Kidston and Gwynne-Vaughan.

inches long, and in this distance, as she informs me, only five nodes were present. This implies a very different habit from that of the Zygopterids already described, with their more or less crowded leaves.

The structure of the stem in *Metaclepsydropsis* is simple ; there is no sclerotic tissue in the cortex, or on the bases of the petioles ; one would not expect it in a rhizome. The stele is approximately cylindrical ; the xylem is made up of two zones, an outer, continuous zone of large reticulate tracheides, and a central region in which smaller tracheides, reticulate or scalariform, are intermixed with cellular tissue, constituting a " mixed pith " ; the structure is thus much like that in *Ankyropteris corrugata*. As in that plant, the branching of the stem was by equal dichotomy ; it is interesting to find that the forking occurs immediately above the insertion of a leaf. In one case an unusually small stele was observed, in which the outer layers of wood showed a radial arrangement of the tracheides. This indication of secondary growth is of interest for comparison with similar occurrences in *Ankyropteris corrugata* and with the normal condition in *Botrychioxylon* (see p. 319). The reticulate tracheides recur in some other Zygopterideae. Adventitious roots, of the usual diarch structure, are borne on the stem.

When a leaf-trace is given off it receives two protoxylem-groups from extensions of the central xylem of the stele ; in other words, the protoxylem of the stem is decurrent from the leaves. In connection with the two groups, an island or peripheral loop is soon formed at each end of the elliptical xylem of the trace. The lower part of the leaf-trace in *Metaclepsydropsis* is in fact precisely similar to the fully developed foliar bundle of *Dineuron*. Higher up in the petiole the more complex form characteristic of the genus is gradually assumed. The transverse section then shows a distinct waist, or median constriction, with bulky enlarged ends (Fig. 140, E). In Dr. Bertrand's terminology the central constricted part is the " apolar," while the enlarged ends are composed of four " receptive pieces." The organisation of the rachis is well known, for primary, secondary, and tertiary pinnae are found in connection.

The main bundle gives off the paired pinna-traces alternately. Hence, in any transverse section, the two ends are always in different phases. The process of emission has been fully worked out by Dr. Bertrand and Dr. Gordon ; the changes are somewhat complicated, and need only be given in outline here. In the diagram (Fig. 140, E) the right-hand end is about to give off a pinna-trace ; at this level the peripheral loop is very large. To form the trace the whole of the pinna-bar (Dr. Gordon's term, here more appropriate than " filament ") becomes detached, as shown on the left of the figure. This opens the loop, and only a small groove (the beginning of a new peripheral loop) is left on the main bundle. The detached pinna-bar then divides into two crescentic strands, as shown on the extreme right of the figure. The protoxylem-groups lie in the peripheral loops of the main bundle ; four pass out with the pinna-trace, and each half receives two, lying on the concave side, at the bends. An aphlebia-strand, which divides into two, is given off on either side of the double pinna-trace (Fig. 141).

The pair of pinna-traces enters the common base of the double pinna, which then divides into the two branches. A stage such as that shown in Fig. 141 clearly demonstrates that the two pinnae of a pair are the result of an early dichotomy of a single pinna ; thus the quadriseriate Zygopterids are brought into line with the more ordinary biseriate forms, such as *Ankyropteris*, which conform more nearly to the usual plan of leaf-construction.

The dichotomy is confined to the primary pinnae ; the secondary and tertiary ramifications are given off singly and alternately. The pinnule-trace is cut off from the hooked end of the pinna-bundle, of which it repeats the structure. It will be noticed that while the vascular structure of a primary pinna is totally different from that of the main rachis, the further subdivisions all retain the same crescentic form of strand. Nothing is known of a lamina.

Metaclepsydropsis duplex forms an excellent type of the quadriseriate group of Zygopterids. A second species, *M. paradoxa*, occurs in the Saalfeld beds of Thuringia ; it appears to differ from the better known Burntisland

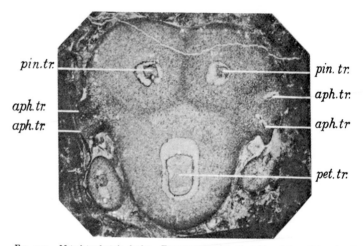

pin.tr. pin. tr.

aph.tr. aph.tr.

aph.tr. aph.tr

pet.tr.

Fig. 141.—*Metaclepsydropsis duplex*. Transverse section of rachis, giving off a pair of pinnae which are still united. *pin. tr.*, the two pinna-traces. *aph. tr.*, the aphlebia-strands, two on each side. *pet. tr.*, main bundle of the rachis. A detached pinnule is seen on the left. × 3.2. From Gordon.

species, chiefly in the more marked constriction of the foliar bundle, accompanied by the separation of the xylem into two masses, by a narrow band of thin-walled cells.[1]

7. *Diplolabis.*—This genus was founded by Renault in 1896 ;[2] he distinguished two species, under the names *D. esnostensis* and *D. forensis* ; the former, from Esnost,

---

[1] See P. Bertrand, *Nouvelles Remarques sur la fronde des Zygo-ptéridées*, 1911, p. 18.

[2] Renault, *Bassin houiller et permien d'Autun et d'Épinac, Flore fossile*, Part 2, 1896, p. 11.

near Autun, is certainly of Lower Carboniferous age ; the latter, from Forez in the Department of the Loire, was found at an Upper Carboniferous horizon, but among rolled pebbles, and is therefore of doubtful age. The two species, which are almost identical in structure, have been reduced to one by Dr. Gordon ; *D. esnostensis,* Ren., at any rate, proves to be identical with the *Zygopteris Römeri* of Solms - Laubach,[1] described in 1892 from Falkenberg in Silesia. The plant is now known as *Diplolabis Römeri.* It was first discovered in Britain by Dr. Gordon, at Pettycur ; he was also the first to find the stem, and was thus enabled to give a connected account of the whole organisation of the plant.[2]

Diplolabis is closely allied to *Metaclepsydropsis,* from which it differs in the structure of the stele of the stem and in the form of the foliar bundle. In habit the two plants seem to have been alike ; in *Diplolabis,* as in the former genus, the stem was a long, creeping rhizome. The cylindrical stele has the simplest structure known in the family ; the xylem is solid, consisting of two zones, a broad outer zone of large reticulate tracheides, and a central mass composed entirely of small, short tracheides, without any admixture of cellular tissue. Thus the stelar structure is much like that of *Thamnopteris* and *Zalesskya* among the Permian Osmundaceae. The branching, as in *Metaclepsydropsis,* was dichotomous ; the roots also are quite similar in the two genera.

The protoxylem of the stem, decurrent from the leaves, lies on the outer border of the central region of the xylem. The leaf-trace, on departing from the stele, has the same simple structure as in the corresponding part of *Metaclepsydropsis* ; it passes through similar

---

[1] Solms-Laubach, " Über die in den Kalksteinen des Kulm von Glätzisch-Falkenberg in Schlesien erhaltenen structurbietenden Pflanzenreste," i. *Bot. Zeitung,* 1892, p. 93.

[2] W. T. Gordon, " On the Structure and Affinities of *Diplolabis Römeri* (Solms)," *Trans. Roy. Soc. Edinburgh,* vol. xlvii. 1911, p. 711.

stages, but as its definitive form is more complex, the process is slow, and the typical structure is only attained at a distance of 6.5-7 inches up the petiole. The fully developed foliar bundle is shown in transverse section in the diagram (Fig. 140, F). The generic name, meaning " double forceps," well describes the form. There is a short median band or " apolar " and two long arms at each end. The arms are described by Dr. Bertrand as " antennae," while their hooked ends represent the " receptive pieces." Thus the distinction from the bundle of *Metaclepsydropsis* depends on the intercalation of the long antennae. The protoxylem lies in the bend of the hooks. The ends or receptive pieces meet and fuse to form the pinna-bar, which becomes detached and then divides into two, just as in the preceding genus, thus providing the traces for the paired pinnae. Aphlebia-traces are here also given off on either side. Except that the peripheral loops of the main bundle are larger, every-thing proceeds as in *Metaclepsydropsis*, the pinna- and pinnule-traces having much the same form and structure as in that genus. Once more there is no evidence of a lamina ; it is possible that the frond may have been a fertile one.

Renault found certain fructifications in constant association, though not in connection with both his forms of *Diplolabis*. The sporangia are in definite groups of three to six members, each group surrounding and attached to a common pedicel. It was therefore termed a synangium by the discoverer, though the sporangia are not united. There is no annulus, but the cells of the sporangial wall diminish rapidly in size towards the inner face, where dehiscence took place. The sporangia con-tain numerous small spores. It seems probable, though not yet demonstrated, that these fructifications really belonged to *Diplolabis*.

8. *Zygopteris*.—This old and once extensive genus of Corda's is now reduced by Dr. Bertrand to the single

species *Z. primaria.* This retains the generic name on grounds of priority, the species having been described by Cotta, under the name *Tubicaulis primarius,* as long ago as 1832,[1] and placed in *Zygopteris* by Corda in 1845. It is represented by a single silicified specimen from the Permian of Chemnitz. The habit of the plant, well shown in Stenzel's figures,[2] is totally different from that of *Diplolabis* or *Metaclepsydropsis,* for the petioles are closely crowded round what was doubtless a vertical stem, though the stem itself is lost. On the other hand the structure of the petiolar bundle is of the same type as that of *Diplolabis,* from which it differs only in the greater length of the apolar or median band, and the relatively smaller development of the antennae. Dr. Bertrand[3] has been able to prove that the pinnae were in four series, but the exact way in which the pinna-traces were given off could not be determined. The precise affinities of the plant, therefore, remain somewhat doubtful. Dr. Gordon has shown that the leaf-trace of *Diplolabis,* in traversing the lower part of the petiole, passes through a stage closely similar to the foliar bundle of *Z. primaria.*

9. *Botrychioxylon.*—We have seen that in *Ankyropteris corrugata* and *Metaclepsydropsis duplex* a certain amount of secondary wood was formed, in exceptional cases. The interest of *Botrychioxylon*[4] lies chiefly in the fact that here the secondary development was normal and apparently constant ; indeed the whole of the broad outer zone of xylem in the stem is radially arranged, and has all the appearance of a secondary tissue (Fig. 142).

The type-specimen was found by Mr. Lomax in a coal-ball from Moorside, Oldham, of Lower Coal-measure age ;

[1] C. B. Cotta, *Die Dendrolithen in Beziehung auf ihren inneren Bau,* Dresden and Leipzig, 1832.
 . [2] G. Stenzel, " Die Gattung *Tubicaulis,* Cotta," Cassel, 1889, p. 26, Pl. v. and vi. [3] *L.c.* 1909, p. 136.
[4] D. H. Scott, " On *Botrychioxylon paradoxum,* sp. nov., a Palaeozoic Fern with secondary Wood," *Trans. Linnean Soc. London,* 2nd ser., *Botany,* vol. vii. 1912, p. 373.

the plant was thus contemporary with *A. corrugata,* and later than the *Metaclepsydropsis.* Another specimen was known to Williamson, who rightly thought it allied to his *Rachiopteris* (now *Ankyropteris*) *corrugata.*

The Moorside specimen shows an equal dichotomy of

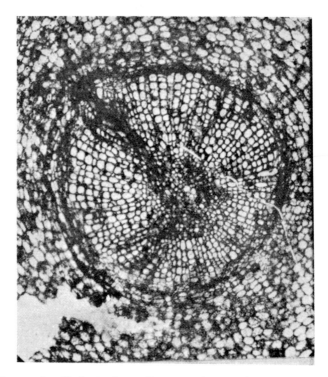

FIG. 142.—*Botrychioxylon paradoxum.* Transverse section of stele and inner cortex. The mixed pith is seen in the middle, surrounded by a zone of secondary wood, of unequal thickness. A root-strand is passing out through the wood. × 35. From a photograph by Mr. L. A. Boodle, F.L.S. S. Coll. 2464.

the stem ; the transverse section figured (Fig. 142) is from one of the two branches. The stem bore, in addition to the scattered leaves, characteristic forked spines or aphlebiae, and adventitious roots. The cortex is very thick and uniform, and the stem has the character of a rhizome.

The stele has a simple, more or less cylindrical form ; the central region is occupied by a mixed pith, of mingled tracheides and parenchyma, just as in various other Zygopterids. Protoxylem-groups have been detected on the outer border of the central tissue. The whole of the outer zone of wood, which reaches a great thickness, is composed of elements arranged in regular radial rows ; on the exterior there is a cambium, followed by a rather narrow band of phloëm. The thickness of the secondary zone diminishes from below upwards, and there is no room for doubt that the cambium was functional in the normal way. The secondary tracheides are scalariform, and the sculpturing appears to have extended to their tangential walls. The presence of true medullary rays has not been demonstrated ; the protrusions of the mixed pith which occur are connected with the traces of leaves or other appendages. A periderm was formed in the outer zone of the cortex.

The leaf-trace is given off in much the same way as in *A. corrugata*, but where it passes through the cortex it retains, to a great extent, the secondary structure of the stele, a remarkable feature in the leaf-trace of a Fern. In the petiole, however, this peculiarity has disappeared, and the foliar bundle is that of an ordinary Zygopterid, with primary tissues only. Unfortunately the petiole is not very well preserved, and the exact structure of the vascular bundle remains a little doubtful. In general form it resembles that of a *Metaclepsydropsis*, but with more indication of antennae ; the sinus at each end of the xylem appears to have been open, thus agreeing with the *Metaclepsydropsis* rather than the *Ankyropteris* type. There is no evidence on the crucial point, whether the pinnae were in two or four series.

The diarch roots, like the stem, show a certain amount of secondary growth in thickness.

The whole structure of *Botrychioxylon* proves that it was one of the Zygopterideae ; its exact relationships within the family cannot be determined until we have better evidence as to the detailed structure of the rachis and its subdivisions. The prevalence of secondary xylem, and especially the complete replacement of primary by secondary tissue in the outer zone of wood in the stem, is the main feature of the genus ; there is here a manifest analogy with *Botrychium* among the Ophioglossaceae ; anatomically *Botrychioxylon* stands in the same relation to a typical Zygopterid as *Botrychium* to *Ophioglossum*. The fact that internal tracheides occasionally occur in the pith of *Botrychium* and other members of the recent family, strengthens the analogy, which probably indicates an actual affinity, now generally admitted, between the two groups.

10. *Etapteris.*—This genus, though the stem is still unknown, is of considerable importance ; the petioles, of which several species have been distinguished, are regarded by Dr. Bertrand as showing the highest differentiation attained in the family ; in the case of one species the fructification has been identified and fully described, while something is also known of the external appearance of the frond. The species in question is *E. Lacattei* from the Permian of Autun ; this is the latest member of the genus, which has a wide geological range, for one of the species is derived from the Lower Carboniferous of Falkenberg ; this early species is *E. Tubicaulis*, the *Zygopteris Tubicaulis* of Goeppert (1852). The other three species described, *E. Scotti*, P. Bertrand, *E. di-upsilon* (Williamson), and *E. shorensis*, P. Bertrand, are of intermediate age, all occurring in the Upper Carboniferous (Lower Coal-measures).

For the anatomy we will take as our type *E. Scotti* ; the commonest British species, and also recorded from Langendreer in Westphalia. It was identified by Williamson and others with the French *E. Lacattei*, but Dr. Bertrand has shown that they are distinct, though nearly allied.

The cortex usually consists of three zones, an inner delicate layer, often destroyed, a middle zone of thick-walled tissue, and an outer sheath of fibres, serving a mechanical function. The vascular bundle is as usual the important feature (see diagram, Fig. 140, G). It has, in transverse section, the typical H-form ; the long rectangular median band or apolar is straight ; the stout lateral arms are somewhat reflexed ; in Dr. Bertrand's terminology, the expanded limbs are the " receptive pieces," while the constricted portions, joining them to the median band, represent the antennae. The proto-xylem-groups are external ; there are two at each end, lying in slight depressions at the base of the receptive pieces, facing outwards. It is from these points that the strands for the pinna-traces are detached ; the process is peculiar ; two small separate strands first become free (Fig. 140, G, on right), but these are not the definitive pinna-traces, for they fuse as they pass out, to form a pinna-bar (Fig. 140, G, on left). The pinna-bar again divides into two crescentic strands, which enter the pinnae (see extreme right of figure) ; it will be noticed that there is no peripheral loop in this case, for the sinus is never closed. The separate origin of the paired lateral strands is remarkable, but is really only a slight modification of the usual process of formation of the pinna-bar, and perhaps not constant even in the genus. It does not affect the interpretation of the paired pinnae as a dichotomy. The common base of the pinnae is evident (Fig. 143).

The tracheides are reticulate, a character which varies somewhat within the genus. The phloëm is sometimes very well preserved ; it is sharply differentiated into large sieve-tubes and minute cells ; the former are best developed on the median band and the inner side of the arms (Fig. 143).

The other species need only be shortly mentioned, so far as the anatomy is concerned. The oldest, *E. Tubi-*

caulis, is remarkable for the very short apolar, and the generally thick and clumsy form of the foliar strand. *E. di-upsilon*, on the other hand, admirably described by Williamson in 1880,[1] is characterised by the great length both of the apolar and the arms (Fig. 140, H). This is one of the largest petioles of the family, exceeding 2 cm. in diameter. It was at one time wrongly regarded as

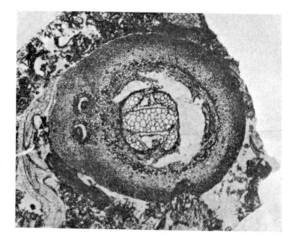

FIG. 143.—*Etapteris Scotti*. Transverse section of rachis. In the main bundle, the sieve-tubes on either side of the apolar are preserved. On the left the two traces are entering the common base of the paired pinnae. On the right a pinna-bar is seen. × 9. S. Coll. 2009. From a photograph by Mr. W. Tams.

belonging to the stem now known as *Ankyropteris Grayi*. *E. shorensis*[2] is intermediate between the last two species. In all these three forms there is a want of differentiation between the antennae and the receptive pieces.

Etapteris Lacattei (Renault), long known from Renault's classical researches, chiefly differs from *E. Scotti*, above described, in the more slender form of the bundle ; the

[1] Williamson, " On the Organisation of the Fossil Plants of the Coal-measures," Part x., *Phil. Trans. Roy. Soc.* Part ii. 1880, p. 537, Pl. 21, Figs. 90, 91.

[2] First distinguished by Dr. Bertrand in 1911 ; see his *Nouvelles Remarques sur la fronde des Zygoptéridées*.

antennae are well differentiated. The pinna-strand has a more complex form than in other species, with two long arms on the distal side. The pinnae were formerly known under the distinct name of *Zygopteris elliptica*, Ren.

We now come to the interesting subject of the *fructification* of *Etapteris*, our knowledge of which is almost entirely due to the researches of Renault, on *E. Lacattei*.[1] The evidence of identification, re-examined in recent years by Dr. Bertrand, now leaves no room for doubt. The sporangia (see Fig. 144) occur in groups, often of considerable extent. They are elongated, slightly curved sacs, thickest towards the distal end, and of relatively large size, reaching a length of 2.5 mm. and a diameter of 1.3 mm. Each sporangium is attached by its thin end to a short pedicel; the pedicels are united in little tufts, three to eight in each tuft, on a common peduncle (Fig. 144, 1 and 2). The whole mass is traversed by fragments of a branched rachis, on which the peduncles were no doubt borne. In some sections of the rachis the characteristic H-like form of the *Etapteris* bundle is clearly shown ; the finer ramifications, bearing the sporangia, can be certainly recognised, according to Dr. Bertrand, as the ultimate branches of the frond of *E. Lacattei*.

The wall of the ripe sporangium consisted of at least two layers of cells, of which the inner, more delicate layer has usually perished. The outer wall shows a marked differentiation ; on two opposite sides it consists of small elongated cells, becoming fibrous towards the base of the sporangium. But on the other two sides (alternating with the former) the cells are larger, with thicker walls, and with their maximum dimension vertical to the surface of the capsule (see Fig. 144). These larger cells thus form a vertical *annulus*, but one of a very peculiar kind, for it

[1] *Flore fossile d'Autun et d'Épinac*, Part ii. p. 43. The original discovery was made by M. Renault as early as 1876. " Vég. silicifiés d'Autun," *Ann. des sci. nat. (Bot.)*, sér. vi. vol. iii.

consists not of a single row of cells, but of a broad band, many cells in width (see Fig. 144, 2 and 3). At the summit of the sporangium the cells of the annulus thin

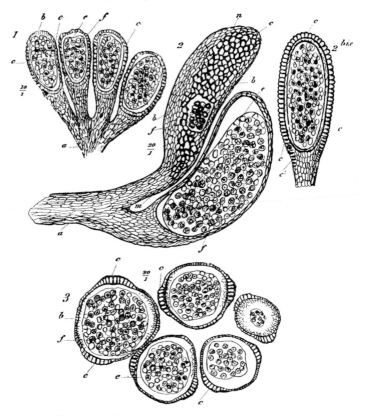

FIG. 144.—*Etapteris Lacattei.* 1. Group of four sporangia, on a common pedicel (*a*). × 10. 2. Two sporangia on pedicel. The upper shows the annulus (*c*) in surface-view, with spores exposed at *f*; the lower is in section. × 20. 2 *bis*. Sporangium, cut in plane passing through annulus. 3. Group of sporangia in transverse section. × 20. Lettering common to the figures : *a*, common peduncle ; *b*, sporangial wall ; *c*, annulus ; *e*, tapetum (?) ; *f*, spores ; *m*, pedicel of individual sporangium ; *n*, probable place of dehiscence. All after Renault.

out somewhat, so that we may regard it, if we like, as double, consisting of two distinct bands, one on each side. The pedicel is traversed, up to the base of the capsule, by a concentric vascular bundle, a condition very rare among recent Ferns, though approached in *Helmintho-stachys* and *Botrychium*. The pedicel, however, is best regarded as a branch of the rachis rather than as a sporangium-stalk.

Numerous spores are contained in the sporangia; they measure .08 mm. in diameter, which would be an ordinary size for the spores of recent Ferns. They are of the tetrahedral type, as is shown by the presence of the three radiating ridges, which are often visible on the exospore. M. Renault found other spores, of similar dimensions, in the same sporangia, which do not show the triradiate marking, but present a reticulate appearance, suggesting the presence of a group of polygonal cells within their cavity. This appearance has proved to be illusory, and the difference in the spores no doubt depends simply on their condition at the time of preservation, and is no indication of heterospory. The type of fructification is rather that of a homosporous member of the Filicineae. The leaves, or divisions of the leaf, appear to have been dimorphic; the branched rachis associated with the sporangia shows no signs of a lamina. We know, from numerous specimens preserved as impressions, that dimorphism was an exceedingly common phenomenon among the Ferns and Fern-like plants of the Carboniferous period. As to the form of the leaf, either sterile or fertile, beyond the fact that it was a compound one, we have no direct evidence from the silicified specimens.

Pear-shaped sporangia, with a very broad and extensive annulus, are commonly found associated with other Zygopterids, such as *Ankyropteris westphaliensis* and *A. corrugata* in the petrifactions of the English Lower Coal-measures, and in all probability represent the fructifications of those species.

M. Grand'Eury described, under the name of *Schizopteris*, specimens from the Coal-measures of the Loire, related to the structural specimens of *Etapteris*, which we have been considering. One of the forms described by Grand'Eury, *Schizopteris pinnata*, is a large bipinnate frond, with an apparently fleshy rachis, bearing small flabelliform and laciniate leaflets on its ultimate sub-divisions. The author also described a *fertile* frond (*Schizostachys frondosus*) very similar to the former, but bearing tufts of elongated sporangia in the place of the laciniate leaflets of the sterile *Schizopteris*.[1] The arrange-ment, form, and size of these sporangia agree very closely with the characters of those described by Renault in *Etapteris*. The structure of the *Schizostachys* sporangia is to some extent preserved, and the spores are visible in their cavities. The agreement in all points with the petrified specimens of *Etapteris* is so exact as to make it certain that, as M. Renault first suggested, they belonged to a species of that affinity. As it is also beyond doubt that *Schizopteris* and *Schizostachys* belonged together, we are enabled to form a fair idea of the external form of both the sterile and fertile leaves of *Etapteris*. These fronds were included by Zeiller[2] in the old genus *Zygopteris* under the name of *Z. pinnata*. Having inspected the fine specimens from Commentry in the collection of the École des Mines, I have no doubt that the attribution to *Etapteris* is correct ; according to Dr. Bertrand the species is very probably identical with *E. Lacattei*.

11. *Corynepteris*.—The genus *Corynepteris* of Baily appears, according to Zeiller's investigations, to have been closely allied to *Etapteris*. Several species have been described, and in some the form of the frond is well known. In certain of the species it is of the *Sphenopteris* type, resembling the frond of *Zygopteris* (*Etapteris*) *pinnata*, but Pecopteroid fronds have also been found with a

[1] Grand'Eury, *Flore carbonifère du Département de la Loire*, 1877, pp. 198-203, Plate xvii.

[2] Zeiller and Renault, *Flore fossile de Commentry*, p. 76, Plate xxxii. Figs. 5-7, St. Étienne, 1888.

similar fructification. The sori are borne on pinnules, either like those of the sterile frond or reduced and modified. The sporangia, so far as the annulus is concerned, are much like those of *Etapteris*, but in most cases they are grouped in a ring round a centre, so as to resemble the synangium of an *Asterotheca*. *Corynepteris* thus, to a certain extent, combines the characters of Marattiaceae with those of Zygopterideae ; [1] at present it is only known from impressions. Dr. Bertrand has shown that in *C. coralloides* the pinnae were in pairs and coalescent at the base, as in the quadriseriate Zygopterids. He suggests a possible identity with *Etapteris*, but some differences seem to exist.

We have still to consider a genus which at present stands a little apart from the rest of the family.

12. *Stauropteris.*—The best-known species, *S. oldhamia*, Binney,[2] is one of the commonest fossils of the Coal-measure nodules ; a very similar species, of Lower Carboniferous age, has been named *S. burntislandica* by Dr. Paul Bertrand. We will first direct our attention to the former.

The stem is unknown ; the specimens consist of fragments of the petiole and rachis of a highly compound frond, without any recognisable lamina, but bearing sporangia on its ultimate branches. In the large petioles the xylem has a characteristic cruciform section, while the whole stele is approximately square, the phloëm filling up the bays between the xylem-arms, and often extending to the centre, so as to interrupt the

---

[1] For an account of the genus *Corynepteris*, see W. H. Baily, *Journal Geol. Soc. Dublin*, vol. viii. 1860 ; Zeiller, *Flore fossile du bassin houiller de Valenciennes*, 1888, pp. 41 and 117. P. Bertrand, " Relation des empreintes de *Corynepteris* avec les *Zygopteris* à structure conservée," *Comptes Rendus*, t. 158, 1914.

[2] E. W. Binney, *Proc. Manchester Literary and Philosophical Society*, 1872. W. C. Williamson, " On the Organisation of the Fossil Plants of the Coal-measures," Part vi., *Phil. Trans. Roy. Soc.* vol. 164, p. 685, Figs. 20-27, 1874.

continuity of the wood (Fig. 145). The example figured
is tetrarch ; often, however, there is more than one
protoxylem-group at each angle, a condition which is
correlated with the branching. As Dr. P. Bertrand has
observed, the protoxylem is sunk a little below the surface
of the wood, which is therefore not strictly exarch. The
phloëm contains large sieve-tubes, and the sieve-plates
on their lateral walls are sometimes clearly shown. A

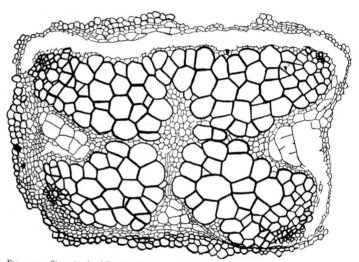

FIG. 145.—*Stauropteris oldhamia.* Transverse section of vascular bundle of main rachis,
showing the cruciform xylem with protoxylem near the four angles. Groups of large
sieve-tubes are seen in the bays of the wood, and small-celled phloëm between wood
and cortex, and in the middle. × 60. S. Coll. 2202. From Tansley, *New Phytologist.*

lax, palisade-like tissue occurs below the epidermis, and
probably had the function of assimilation. The branches
were given off in pairs, successive pairs springing from
opposite sides of the rachis, a mode of branching which
has been traced in full detail by Dr. Bertrand, in his work
of 1909, proving that the plant agrees with those Zygopterids which have four series of pinnae, given off in alternate pairs from the two sides of the rachis. In *Stauropteris* the structure comes so near radial symmetry that
it is not easy to distinguish, in transverse section, between

the lateral and the antero-posterior faces ; the maximum development of the phloëm, however, lies on the two latter, and the bundle is somewhat broader in this plane (the reverse of the usual case in Zygopterideae ; see Fig. 145 and the diagrams in Fig. 146 ; in the former figure the antero-posterior plane is horizontal).

The two pinnae of a pair are united at the base, and their vascular strands may be connected where they leave the main bundle ; it thus appears that the dichotomous theory of the pairs holds good here as well as in other Zygopterids. The paired pinna - traces are accompanied on their outer sides by strands which pass out to the lobed aphlebiae, another point of agreement with typical Zygopterideae (Fig. 146).

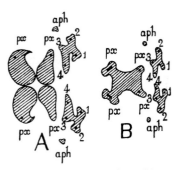

FIG. 146.—*Stauropteris oldhamia.* A. Diagram of primary rachis, transverse, showing the main quadruple bundle and the pair of pinna-traces, given off from it. *px*, the four protoxylem-groups of the main bundle ; those of the pinna-traces are numbered in the order of their appearance ; *aph*, aphlebia - traces. B. Corresponding diagram of a secondary rachis (pinna) giving off the tertiary strands. Lettering as in A. After Dr. P. Bertrand.

A great peculiarity of *Stauropteris* is that the strands of the pinnae (secondary rachises) repeat in essentials the structure of the main bundle (Fig. 146, B), whereas in all other Zygopterids they are quite different. The quadruple structure may again be repeated in the tertiary rachis, or the bundle may here assume a triangular section, with three protoxylem-groups instead of four. In any case this triarch structure appears in the quaternary rachis. The xylem of the pinnae and pinnules is more consolidated than that of the main rachis (cf. Fig. 146, A and B).

Another important point in which *Stauropteris* differs from other Zygopterideae is the persistence of the quadri-seriate ramification ; elsewhere in the family this is limited to the pinnae of the main rachis ; all the higher orders of branching are biseriate. In *Stauropteris* the quadriseriate arrangement is repeated again and again, in the successive orders of ramification, and it is only the finest branches of the rachis that are restricted to two series.

The frond of *S. oldhamia* was extremely complex, with branches of many orders ; the excessively fine terminal ramifications of the naked rachis have a correspondingly

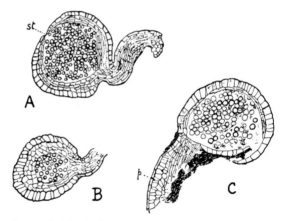

FIG. 147.—*Stauropteris oldhamia.* Three sporangia inserted terminally on ultimate branches of the rachis. In A the stomium, *st*, is shown. B is cut tangentially. In C, *p* is the palisade-tissue of the rachis. The relatively large spores in C are probably beginning to germinate. Cf. Fig. 148. × about 35. S. Coll. ; A, 2213 ; B, 2207 ; C, 2219. (R. S.)

simple vascular structure ; the little cylindrical strand has no definite protoxylem.

It was on the delicate ultimate branches of the rachis that the terminal sporangia were borne (Fig. 147). The fronds at present known appear to be all fertile ; whether other vegetative leaves also occurred, or the foliage was of an extreme xerophytic type, with the laminae wholly suppressed, cannot yet be determined. The analogy of *Etapteris* and *Botryopteris*, however, is favourable to the former hypothesis.

The sporangia are nearly spherical sacs, about .7 mm.

in diameter, with a wall several cells thick and the outer-most layer strongly differentiated. There is no annulus, but a well-marked stomium at the end opposite the stalk (Fig. 147, A) served for dehiscence. Numerous spores of the tetrahedral type, 32 to 40 μ in diameter, fill the cavity.

At the time when these sporangia were first discovered,[1] the question was left open whether the plant was a Fern or a Pteridosperm, for there was nothing to show for certain whether the fructification represented homo-sporous sporangia or microsporangia. A year previously a case had been observed in which spores were found germinating inside an isolated sporangium, the stages agreeing with those found in recent Ferns.[2] Subsequently, similar stages of germination were detected in typical sporangia of *Stauropteris oldhamia*, establishing a strong presumption that this plant also was a true homosporous Fern.[3] Some of the germinating spores are shown in Fig. 148. All four have sent out rhizoids, cut off by a wall from the body of the spore, and in C another cell has been cut off above the rhizoid. In the light of these observa-tions there is no longer any reason to doubt that *Stauro-pteris* was really a Fern, while the analogies with other Zygopterideae are sufficiently close to justify us in classing the whole family with the Ferns.

The older species, *S. burntislandica*, P. B., from the Lower Carboniferous of Pettycur, Fife, differs from the Coal-measure form in the more consolidated xylem of the main rachis and in the less frequent branching. In other respects the two species agree ; in the Lower Carboni-ferous plant, as in *S. oldhamia*, the ultimate branches of the frond are slender cylindrical stalks, with no trace of a

---

[1] Scott, " The Sporangia of *Stauropteris oldhamia*," *New Phytolo-gist*, vol. iv. 1905.

[2] Scott, " Germinating Spores in a Fossil Fern-Sporangium," *New Phytologist*, vol. iii. 1904.

[3] Scott, " The Occurrence of Germinating Spores in *Stauropteris oldhamia*," *New Phytologist*, vol. v. 1906. I am indebted to my wife, Mrs. D. H. Scott, F.L.S., for much help in these observations.

lamina. Sporangia, closely resembling those of the Oldham species, are commonly associated with the frond, but have not yet been found in actual connection.

Remarkable spindle-shaped bodies, about 1.3 mm. in length, originally observed by Dr. Margaret Benson, F.L.S., and described by Mrs. D. H. Scott, F.L.S., under the name *Bensonites fusiformis*, frequently accompany the specimens of the Burntisland *Stauropteris*, and may probably have been borne on branches of the rachis.[1] The multi-

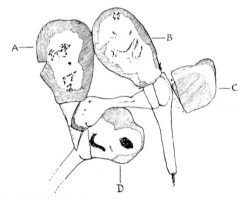

FIG. 148.—*Stauropteris oldhamia.* Four germinating spores from the interior of a sporangium. All four are putting out rhizoids. In C (lying horizontally) an additional cell has been cut off between rhizoid and spore. × 335. S. Coll. 2215. Drawn by Mr. L. A. Boodle.

cellular body is stalked, contains a delicate vascular strand, and terminates in a well-marked head, surmounted by a long beak.   From the appearance of the head, which resembles that of a gland of *Lyginopteris oldhamia* (see below, Chapter XI.), it is supposed that the organ may have been of a glandular nature.

We have so far assumed that *Stauropteris* was a member of the family Zygopterideae, a view which has been powerfully advocated by Dr. P. Bertrand, who regards the genus as a highly developed form of the Zygopterid type. Lignier, on the other hand, maintained that *Stauropteris*

[1] R. Scott, " On *Bensonites fusiformis*, sp. nov., a fossil associated with *Stauropteris burntislandica*, and on the sporangia of the latter," *Ann. of Bot.* vol. xxii. 1908, p. 683.

was much more primitive than the Zygopterideae, though related to them, and that it cannot be included in the same family.[1] As he pointed out, the frond of *Stauropteris*, with its almost radial symmetry and often-repeated quadriseriate branching, is much more unlike a normal leaf than that of any of the typical Zygopterids. Lignier compared the habit of the *Stauropteris* frond to a *bush*, that of the quadriseriate Zygopterid frond to a *hedge*, and the normal biseriate type of leaf to a *palisade*.

Like some other modern writers, notably Potonié and Tansley, Lignier interpreted the leaf as a modified branch-system of a thallus or stem, such as that of *Psilophyton* (see Chap. X.). Consequently, on this view the most stem-like leaves are likely to be the most primitive, and *Stauropteris* fulfils this condition, for here the dorsiventral organisation typical of the true leaf is shown at most in the ultimate ramifications only. Among the Zygopterideae proper, Lignier considered the quadriseriate forms as the more primitive, for they retain something of a radial organisation in the main rachis ; the biseriate type (*e.g. Ankyropteris*) was held to be the most advanced, the two pinnae of each pair having here fused into one— exactly the converse of the dichotomous interpretation of the paired pinnae maintained by P. Bertrand and Sahni and adopted here.

Lignier also laid stress on the very simple, exannulate structure of the *Stauropteris* sporangia, so different from those of *Etapteris* or even *Botryopteris* (see p. 332).

It would take us too far to enter here on any full discussion of the two views ; the true position of *Stauropteris* can hardly be settled while the structure of the stem remains unknown ; Lignier even doubted whether it ever possessed a true stem, sharply delimited from the frond. We have provisionally included *Stauropteris* in the Zygopterideae, with which it admittedly has important

---

[1] O. Lignier, " Le *Stauropteris oldhamia* et les Cœnoptéridées, etc.," *Bull. de la Soc. Bot. de France*, sér. 4, t. xii. 1912.

characters in common. While the primitive nature of the genus, as maintained by Lignier, requires further corroboration, *Stauropteris* may fairly be regarded as representing a line of descent which separated far back from that of the other Zygopterideae, and as thus retaining some early characters of the race (such as the simple sporangia). The possible relation of the *Stauropteris* type to the newly recognised class of Psilophytales will be further considered in the next chapter.

Relationships of the Genera.—The Zygopterideae may be conveniently ranged in two groups, the Clepsydroideae, with biseriate pinnae, and the Dineuroideae [1] with quadriseriate pinnae. We have not adopted these sub-families as headings, because at present the division cannot be consistently carried through, for in the case of the genera *Botrychioxylon* and *Asteropteris* we do not yet know for certain which arrangement existed.

As regards antiquity, there is nothing to choose between the two groups ; *Dineuron* and *Metaclepsydropsis*, with four series, are about as old as *Clepsydropsis* with two, while *Asteropteris*, probably the oldest of all, is doubtful. The considerable age (going back to the Lower Carboniferous) of the extreme quadriseriate type *Stauropteris*, indicates that this condition was of very early origin. Evidently we do not possess the data for attempting to trace the evolution of the family. The interpretation of the paired pinnae of the Dineuroideae as a precocious dichotomy of the primary pinna suggests that the simpler, biseriate arrangement preceded the quadriseriate. There seems to be better evidence for the dichotomy than for the opposite theory of Lignier, who derived the biseriate from the quadriseriate condition by fusion.[2] Mr. Sahni, in agreement with the view expressed in 1910 by Kidston

---

[1] These useful names are due to Mr. B. Sahni, " On the Branching of the Zygopteridean Leaf," *Ann. of Bot.* vol. xxxii. 1918.

[2] Or, as in the special case of the higher orders of ramification in the *Stauropteris* frond, by the abortion of the proximal pinna of each pair.

and Gwynne-Vaughan, holds that the Clepsydroideae were more primitive than the Dineuroideae. We have adopted the same hypothesis, but with some reserve, for the question is still an open one ; it is remarkable that the more complex types of stem-structure have so far been found among the biseriate Zygopterids ; this may perhaps be correlated with their more crowded leaves, but in any case it shows that the Clepsydroideae were an advanced group.

The orientation of the pinnae at right angles to that of the main rachis, instead of their lying in the same plane, as in normal leaves, is difficult to explain in the case of the Clepsydroideae, and might be used as an argument in favour of Lignier's theory of fusion. At any rate it shows that the organisation, even of the simpler type of Zygopterid frond, was by no means that of an ordinary leaf. Kidston and Gwynne-Vaughan [1] discussed this question, and suggested that the frond must have grown " rigidly erect," like a vertical axis.

While it seems premature to discuss lines of evolution among the Zygopterideae, it may be pointed out that certain genera show a manifest affinity among themselves : ·e.g. *Clepsydropsis* and *Ankyropteris* (merged by Mr. Sahni) ; *Asteropteris* and *Asterochlaena* (Clepsydroideae) ; *Metaclepsydropsis, Diplolabis,* and perhaps *Dineuron* (in Dineuroideae) ; *Etapteris* and the restricted *Zygopteris* seem to stand a little apart. *Stauropteris* is the most isolated genus of the family.

Some more general considerations may best be deferred to the end of the chapter and to the next one.

B. Botryopterideae

Botryopteris.—We will first consider *Botryopteris,* the type-genus of the family, and very distinct from the *Zygopterideae.* Our knowledge of this genus was, in

[1] Part iv. 1910, p. 473.

the first instance, based on M. Renault's species, *B. forensis*, which that author described very thoroughly, though he had only a single specimen of the stem to work with.[1] Subsequently, however, it turned out that certain English Carboniferous fossils, which fortunately occur in considerable abundance, may be placed in the

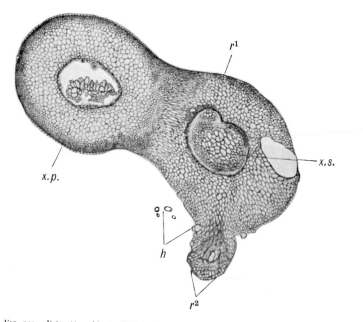

FIG. 149.—*Botryopteris hirsuta* (Will.).   Transverse section of stem at its junction with the petiole ; *x.s.*, xylem of stem ; *x.p.*, xylem of petiole ; *r¹*, *r²*, diarch roots, springing from the stem ; *h*, hairs.   × about 15.   (G. T. G.)   S. Coll. 569.

same genus ; four British species have now been described. Hence we are able to supplement the descriptions of the original discoverer by observations on our own, specifically distinct, examples.   Anatomically, *Botryopteris* shows a decidedly simpler structure than the former group. Here, as in the Order generally, the stem is monostelic ; the stele, however, is of a rather rudimentary type, con-

---

[1] *Cours de bot. foss.* vol. iii. chap. viii. ; *Ann. des sci. nat.* (*Bot.*), sér. vi. vol. i. 1875 ; *Flore fossile d'Autun et d'Épinac*, Part ii. p. 33.

sisting of a more or less cylindrical strand of solid wood, surrounded by phloëm, in which, in the Coal-measure species (*B. ramosa, B. hirsuta*,[1] and *B. cylindrica*), the large sieve-tubes are sometimes preserved. The two former are very similar, and not always easy to distinguish, though it is possible that more than two species are concerned. *B. hirsuta* (Will.) had a small stem, about 2-3

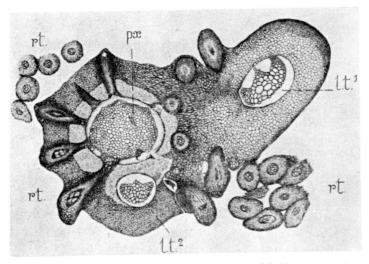

FIG. 150.—*Botryopteris ramosa.* Transverse section of stem and leaf-bases. *px*, proto-xylem-group in stele; *l.t.*[1], leaf-trace in attached petiole; *l.t.*[2], leaf-trace in cortex; *rt*, roots, some in connection with stem, and others free. × about 8. S. Coll. 2314. (G. T. G.)

mm. in diameter, and bore spirally arranged, somewhat crowded leaves, the petioles of which were at least equal to the stem in diameter (Fig. 149). In *B. ramosa* (Fig. 150), where the petioles, as a rule, are relatively smaller, the stem is often larger than in *B. hirsuta*, sometimes reaching a diameter of 5-6 mm., while in the French species, *B. forensis*, it attains a diameter of 7.5 mm., in M. Renault's specimen. In all the species, the surface of the stem, and of the leaves also to some extent, was

---

[1] *Rachiopteris ramosa* and *hirsuta* of Williamson.

clothed by filamentous multicellular hairs, which, in the case of the French species, had a very peculiar structure, for each cell bore a ring of teeth at its distal end, giving the hair the appearance of a miniature *Equisetum*. This peculiarity proved of some importance in identifying the various organs of the plant.

The wood of the stem consists entirely of tracheides, mostly pitted, with a transition to scalariform structure,

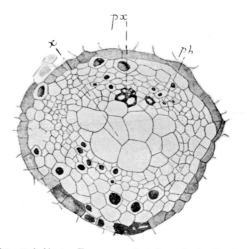

Fig. 151.—*Botryopteris hirsuta.* Transverse section of vascular bundle of young petiole, showing the xylem in course of differentiation. *px*, lignified protoxylem ; *x*, thin-walled xylem not yet lignified ; *ph*, phloëm-zone. The dark external layer may be the endodermis. × 150. S. Coll. 564. (R. S.)

especially in the smaller elements. The proportion of the two kinds of tracheides is very variable in different specimens, and may prove to afford specific distinctions. The protoxylem is not always well marked ; its position in the stem will be considered in connection with that in the petiole.

In *B. hirsuta* and *ramosa* a $\frac{2}{5}$ phyllotaxis appears to have prevailed. The petiolar bundle is often actually larger than the stele of the stem, and contains larger tracheides (see Fig. 149). Its form, as seen in transverse section, is very characteristic. The elliptical band of xylem has three prominent points, all projecting on the same side, and directed towards the upper and inner face of the petiole. Hence the specific name *tridentata*, given to this petiole by Felix, before its connection with *B. hirsuta* was known. The three prominent points (occasionally reduced to two) mark the position of the spiral protoxylem-elements. In some specimens the phloëm encircling the wood is exquisitely preserved.

Where the leaf-trace departs from the vascular cylinder of the stem, its spiral tracheae are directed inwards (Fig. 150, *l.t.*²). As, however, the bundle left the stem, it swung round, as it were (as often happens in recent Ferns also), taking up the position shown in Figs. 149 and 150, *l.t.*¹. In M. Renault's type the form of the petiolar bundle is comparable to that in the English species, but the structure is far less simple, the three xylem-points are much longer, so that he compares the sectional form of the wood with that of the Greek omega (ω) and the proto-xylem-groups more numerous (Fig. 152).

The structure of the cortex of the stem shows no striking differentiation; in the petiole the outer cortical layers constitute a continuous sclerotic zone (Fig. 149). In *B. ramosa* the cortical tissues are denser and more uniform than in *B. hirsuta*.

The stem, in all the species, gave rise to very numerous diarch adventitious roots (Fig. 149, *r*¹, *r*²; Fig. 150, *rt*), resembling those of many living Ferns.

In the petiolar bundle the position of the protoxylem is shown, not only by the presence of spiral tracheides at the prominent points, but also by direct developmental evidence, such as is rarely to be found in a fossil plant. In several cases a petiole or rachis has fortunately been preserved when still young, with its xylem only partially lignified, so that the small, thick-walled elements of the protoxylem, already differentiated, contrast sharply with the rest of the wood, in which the walls are still unthickened (see Fig. 151).

As the leaf-trace approached the stele its three adaxial protoxylem-groups commonly united into one, and as fusion with the stele took place, this group necessarily took up an internal position in the stelar wood ; every stage of the fusion is shown in serial sections of *B. hirsuta* or *ramosa*. Thus the xylem of the stele was endarch (Fig. 150, *px*) ; spiral elements are not often to be found in the stem, which was a comparatively short and

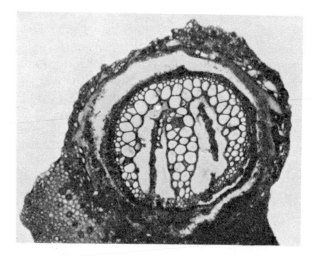

FIG. 152.—*Botryopteris forensis.* Transverse section of vascular bundle of petiole, showing the inverted ω form. The protoxylem-groups are at and near the ends of the three xylem-arms. × about 20. From an Autun specimen. S. Coll. 1639. Photographed by Mr. W. Tams.

presumably rather slow-growing rhizome. The small tracheides sometimes found at the periphery of the wood were probably in connection with the adventitious roots. In *B. forensis* the wood is described as exarch, but the single transverse section is insufficient to settle the point.

The rachis of the English species often shows branching, its branches being given off singly, and not in pairs as in some Zygopterideae, but such knowledge as we have of the form and structure of the lamina is entirely derived from M. Renault's observations on the French species. The fine branches of the rachis had a simpler anatomical structure than the main petiole ; they bore broad, lobed pinnules, with prominent veins, which branched repeatedly by dichotomy. The tissue of the lamina appears to have been fleshy ; on the one surface numerous stomata were present, while the other bore the characteristic equisetiform hairs ; it is on the latter feature that the identification of the leaf is based. Renault regarded the

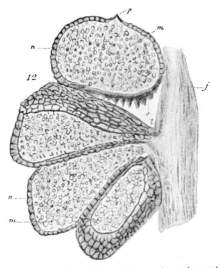

FIG. 153.—*Botryopteris forensis*. Group of sporangia, *m, m*, inserted on rachis, *j* ; *l*, pedicel of sporangium ; *n*, wall of sporangia ; *o*, multiseriate annulus. The uppermost sporangium is in nearly transverse section ; *p*, stomium, or place of dehiscence. × 35. From Renault.

stomatiferous surface of the leaf as the upper one, and supposed that the leaves of *Botryopteris* floated on the surface of the water, while other aërial leaves were borne by the same plant. These conclusions must be considered as highly hypothetical.

In one case M. Renault described a young frond in beautiful preservation, which was still circinately coiled, and bore numerous equisetiform hairs on its outer surface.

The *fructifications* of *Botryopteris forensis* bear a

general resemblance to those of *Etapteris*, but differ in detail. The sporangia occur associated in large masses, and crowded together, representing, no doubt, the collective output of a compound fertile frond. The pyriform sporangia are shortly stalked and grouped in tufts, on the branches of the fertile rachis (see Fig. 153). The latter shows in section the characteristic ω-shaped

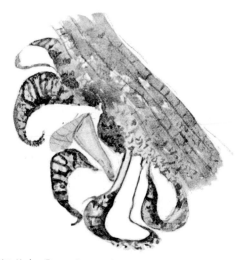

Fig. 154.—*Botryopteris*. Group of sporangia attached laterally to an axis, probably part of rachis. The sporangia show the multiseriate annulus; they have already dehisced. Associated with *B. ramosa*. Cf. Fig. 153. × 66. S. Coll. 776. (R. S.)

vascular bundle of the species, thus placing the identification beyond doubt.

The size of the individual sporangia is somewhat smaller than in the French *Etapteris*, their length ranging from 1.5 to 2 mm., and their maximum diameter from .7 to 1 mm. The essential difference, however, from the sporangia of *Etapteris* is in the annulus, which in *Botryopteris* was limited to one side of the capsule, where it formed a broad, oblique band of thick-walled cells (Fig. 153). The spores, except for their somewhat smaller size, agree exactly with those of *Etapteris*, and, curiously enough, the same two states of the spore, already discussed in the case of that genus, recur here.

In one case a group of sporangia was found to be associated with a very curious envelope or indusium, of complicated structure, which M. Renault regarded as derived from a zone of sterile and highly modified sporangia.

It may be mentioned that the English specimens of *B. hirsuta* and *ramosa* are found associated with numerous sporangia, which appear to have essentially the same structure as those of the French species, but are of much smaller size. It is extremely probable that they represent the fructification of the English representatives of the genus. The association is close and practically constant, and as these species are among the commoner coal-ball fossils, this fact is of great weight. In one case the sporangia, which appear to have already dehisced, are found grouped on a rachis, as in Renault's specimens (see Fig. 154). They are, in the common form, of roundish shape, 350-400 μ in dia-

FIG. 155.—*Botryopteris.* Sporangium in transverse section, showing the multiseriate annulus, and containing some spores. Associated with *B. ramosa.* × about 100. S. Coll. 933. (R. S.)

meter, with a broad band of enlarged cells on one side (see Fig. 155), comparable to the false annulus of Osmundaceae. The somewhat triangular spores are characteristic.

Botryopteris cylindrica (Will.) [1] is another species from the Lower Coal-measures, occurring most frequently in the Halifax coal-balls ; it was thus a contemporary of *B. hirsuta* and *ramosa.* In the second edition of this

[1] Williamson, " Organisation of Fossil Plants of Coal-measures," Part ix., *Phil. Trans. Roy. Soc.* ii. 1878, p. 350, Figs. 80-88 (including roots and rachis) ; Hick, " On *Rachiopteris cylindrica*," *Mem. and Proc. Manchester Lit. and Phil. Soc.* vol. xli. 1896 ; Bancroft, " A Contribution to our Knowledge of *Rachiopteris cylindrica*," *Ann. of Bot.* vol. xxix. 1915.

book Williamson's name, *Rachiopteris cylindrica*, was used, and it was suggested that the plant might ultimately

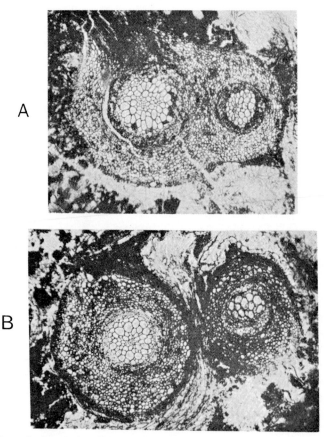

FIG. 156.—*Botryopteris cylindrica.* a form. A. Transverse section, showing unequal dichotomy. In the smaller branch the double protoxylem is still very eccentric; in the larger branch there are three protoxylems. A root is being given off from this branch. B. Transverse section of stem and petiole. In the stem there are either two or three internal protoxylems. In the petiole there are two, almost confluent, on the lower (originally adaxial) side of the bundle. In both specimens the delicate outer cortex is almost lost. × about 24. S. Coll. 1906. From photographs by Mr. W. Tams.

require a new genus. At present, however, the simplest course is to include it under *Botryopteris*; it differs from the other British species chiefly in habit. The plant has

recently been fully investigated by Miss N. Bancroft,
D.Sc.   The preservation is remarkably good.

The stem, unlike that of other species, was long and
slender (about 2-2.5 mm. in diameter), bearing leaves at
long intervals, of perhaps 1 or $1\frac{1}{2}$ inches, and branching
dichotomously.   There are two forms of stem, dis-
tinguished as α and β by Dr. Bancroft.   In the α type

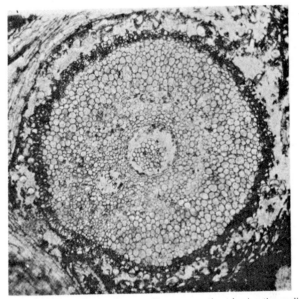

Fig. 157.—*Botryopteris cylindrica.* β form. Transverse section, showing the small stele
and wide, little-differentiated cortex, bounded by a hairy epidermis. On the left a
small leaf-trace is passing through the cortex. × about 30. S. Coll. 195. From a
photograph by Mr. W. Tams.

the cylindrical stele is relatively large, and the highly
differentiated cortex has a strong mechanical construction (Fig. 156).   In the β form the stele is smaller, and
the cortex wider and very uniform, without mechanical
tissues (Fig. 157).   Both forms, but especially β, bear
numerous hairs.

The stele of the α stem may occasionally have a single,
central protoxylem, but more usually there are from two

to five such groups around the centre ; the more central tracheides, accompanying the protoxylems, are distinctly smaller than those further to the outside (Fig. 156). In the β form a single, central protoxylem is constant, except where branching is about to occur.

The dichotomy of the stem may give rise to equal or unequal branches (Fig. 156, A). The emission of a leaf-trace, especially in the case of the α stem, somewhat resembles an unequal dichotomy, but while the proto-xylem of the branches is always internal (Fig. 156, A) the leaf-trace is endarch at the start (Fig. 156, B), though one or two transitory centripetal elements may appear a little higher up. The leaf-trace of the α form is relatively large, and often has two protoxylems on the adaxial side ; in the β stem it is small and always monarch (Fig. 157).

A zone of phloëm, in which a layer of large elements, no doubt the sieve-tubes, can be distinguished, surrounds the xylem and is often well preserved.

As regards the two types of stem, it is suggested by Dr. Bancroft that the β form may represent the aquatic condition of an amphibious plant ; another possibility is that it may have been a rhizome. The absence of mechanical tissue and the reduction of the xylem would agree with either interpretation ; the abundance of hairs is perhaps more suggestive of a rhizome, though not inconsistent with aquatic habit. The α stem was no doubt aërial ; as roots are borne on this stem also, it may probably have been creeping or decumbent.

The rachis of the leaf was repeatedly branched ; the thin stalks, which appear to represent its terminal branch-lets, are compared by Dr. Bancroft to those of *Stauro-pteris*. No lamina has been observed. Sporangia, of the type of those associated with *B. hirsuta* and *ramosa*, accompany the specimens. The tetrahedral spores have been found united in tetrads.

The well-preserved diarch roots resemble those of living Ferns. The elongated stem, with distant leaves ;

and the differentiation (slight as it is) of central and peripheral regions in the wood, suggest a comparison with such a Zygopterid as *Diplolabis*, but the leaf-traces and petioles are those of a simple *Botryopteris*.

The most ancient and in some respects the most primitive species of the genus is *B. antiqua*, Kidston,[1] from the Calciferous Sandstones of Pettycur and the Culm of Esnost in France. In habit this Lower Carboniferous species most nearly resembles *B. hirsuta*, for the petioles are usually larger than the stem and are given off at frequent intervals. The stele has one or more internal protoxylems, decurrent from the leaf-traces, as in *B. hirsuta* or *ramosa*. The trace, where it leaves the stele, is slightly mesarch, but in traversing the cortex the few centripetal elements disappear ; the protoxylem, however, is somewhat sunk, between two small cusps on the adaxial side.

Dr. Benson finds that the leaf-traces are of two kinds, monarch or diarch ; the former but not the latter are accompanied by aphlebia-strands, given off from the stele. It thus appears that the plant was heterophyllous. Sporangia, with a multiseriate annulus or areola, are closely associated with the petioles, in both the Scottish and French specimens ; they resemble those attributed to the Coal-measure species, but are usually smaller, about 260 μ in average diameter.[2]

In petiolar structure *B. antiqua* and *B. cylindrica* are about on a level, but the stele of the latter is somewhat the more differentiated. All the four species from the Lower Carboniferous and Lower Coal-measures have relatively simple foliar bundles, while the Permo

[1] Kidston, " On a new Species of *Dineuron* and of *Botryopteris* from Pettycur, Fife," *Trans. Roy. Soc. Edinburgh*, vol. xlvi., Part ii. 1908. Pelourde, " Observations sur quelques végétaux fossiles de l'Autunois," *Ann. Sci. Nat. (Bot.)* sér. 9, t. xi. 1910. Benson, " New Observations on *Botryopteris antiqua*, Kidston," *Ann. of Bot.* vol. xxv. 1911.

[2] Scott, " Sporangia attributed to *Botryopteris antiqua*, Kidston," *Ann. of Botany*, vol. xxiv. 1910.

Carboniferous *B. forensis* is much more complicated in this respect, as well as in the structure of the sporangia. There seems to be no reason to doubt that this latest of the species represents the highest known development of the genus.

As regards the stele, the structure is very simple throughout ; the somewhat greater differentiation in the case of *B. cylindrica* is no doubt correlated with the very different habit of the plant.

A genus closely allied to *Botryopteris*, and perhaps forming the simplest type of the family, is Renault's *Grammatopteris*, founded on a species, *G. Rigolloti*,[1] from the Permo-Carboniferous of Autun. The habit represents the opposite extreme to that of *Botryopteris cylindrica*, for the crowded petioles here form a dense envelope round the stem. The stele has a solid cylinder of xylem, as in *Botryopteris* ; the spiral elements are stated to be at the periphery, but this requires further investigation. The leaf-traces and petiolar bundles have the form of a straight tangential band, described as having the spiral elements at the two ends. The genus is imperfectly known. Small sporangia of the *Zygopteris* type were found by Renault in association with the plant, but there is no proof of connection.

The genus *Tubicaulis*, as now limited, has a remarkable history. Only three specimens referable to it have been described ; one was found in the Permian of Saxony in 1815, and recorded by Cotta in 1832 ; [2] another was found by Mr. Lomax ninety years later in a roof-nodule from the Lower Coal-measures of Shore, Lancashire, and described by Dr. Stopes in 1906.[3] The two specimens are, of course, specifically distinct. The Permian species is *T. Solenites*,

---

[1] *Flore fossile d'Autun et d'Épinac*, p. 45, Plate xxx. Figs. 9-11, Plate xxxi. Fig. 1.

[2] *Die Dendrolithen in Beziehung auf ihren inneren Bau*, p. 21, Taf. ii. Stenzel, " Die Gattung *Tabicaulis*, Cotta," Cassel, 1889.

[3] " A New Fern from the Coal-measures : *Tubicaulis Sutcliffii*, spec. nov.," *Mem. and Proc. Manchester Lit. and Phil. Soc.* vol. l.

Cotta ; that from the Coal-measures is named *T. Sutcliffii*, Stopes. Both were large plants ; the specimen of *T. Solenites* was, when found, a yard long, and from 5 to 8 inches in diameter, most of this thickness being made up of the crowded leaf-bases and petioles, while the fragment representing *T. Sutcliffii* had a diameter of $2 \times 4\frac{1}{2}$ inches. The structure of the stem is excessively simple, the stele having a solid cylindrical strand of xylem, which Dr. Stopes believes to have been wholly or chiefly centripetal in development. The petioles, which increased rapidly in diameter after leaving the stem, contain a horse-shoe bundle, with the concavity outwards ; the protoxylem groups clearly lie on the convex, adaxial side. The numerous adventitious roots are diarch. Small sporangia, much like those attributed to the British species of *Botryopteris* (Fig. 155), are associated with the specimen, and as no other plant is present in the nodule, this association has some significance.

A third specimen, derived from the Permo-Carboniferous of Autun and previously confused with *Grammatopteris Rigolloti*, has been recognised by the late Prof. Bertrand and his son as a new species of *Tubicaulis*, and named *T. Berthieri*.[1] This is the best-preserved specimen for the anatomy of the stem, and confirms the statement that the protoxylem of the stele was external, while that of the leaf-trace was in two groups towards the margins, on the adaxial side.

Tubicaulis is placed by Dr. P. Bertrand in the Zygopterideae, on the ground that the orientation of the pinna-trace was at right angles to that of the main rachis. The genus is here retained among the Botryopterideae, on account of the undifferentiated structure of the stelar wood ; if we could accept the sporangia associated with *T. Sutcliffii* as belonging to the plant, the position of the genus in the family would be confirmed. At present its

[1] C. E. and P. Bertrand, " Le *Tubicaulis Berthieri* (sp. nov.)," *Mém. de la Soc. d'Hist. Nat. d'Autun*, t. xxiv. 1911.

true affinities are open to question, though in any case it must be regarded as one of the simpler representatives of the Order Botryopteridaceae in the wide sense.

It will be seen that the three genera here included in the family Botryopterideae, *Botryopteris*, *Grammatopteris* and *Tubicaulis*, agree chiefly in the simple structure of the stele. This is not a strong basis for a systematic group ; there is no reason why a Zygopterid, for instance, should not also have had an undifferentiated form of stele. Renault pointed out that the foliar bundle of *Grammatopteris* resembled that of a Zygopterid with the vertical bars omitted ; Dr. Bertrand has suggested that this genus may be a primitive or reduced form of the *Anachoropteris* type (see next Section). The doubt as to the position of *Tubicaulis* has already been referred to ; we cannot therefore say that the Botryopterideae constitute a natural family, like the Zygopterideae. They are kept together, on grounds of convenience, until we are better informed.

In the meantime there can be no doubt that the type-genus, *Botryopteris*, at all events, is quite distinct from the Zygopterideae as shown (apart from sporangial characters) by the very different structure of the foliar bundle, with its adaxial protoxylem, and, according to Dr. Bertrand, by the parallel orientation of the pinnae with reference to the principal rachis.

C. *Anachoropterideae*

The genus *Anachoropteris*, Corda, as now known, stands apart both from Zygopterideae and Botryopterideae, and must form the type of a separate family. The stem has not been observed ; Dr. Bertrand has shown that a stem attributed by Renault to *Anachoropteris Decaisnei* is merely an axis of *Ankyropteris*, accidentally associated with a petiole of the other genus. So far as the vegetative structure is concerned, we are therefore

limited in the case of *Anachoropteris* to the characters of
the frond. The structure, however, of the petiole and
main rachis is very characteristic, and does not admit of
confusion with any other genus.

The concentric vascular bundle, as seen in transverse
section, is extremely incurved, with the margins revolute
(see Fig. 158). From the shape of the petiole it appears

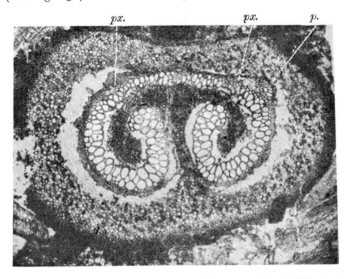

FIG. 158.—*Anachoropteris rotundata* (= *A. pulchra*). Transverse section of petiole, showing
the incurved form of the vascular bundle, and the forked strand of sclerenchyma filling
up the concavity. *px*, protoxylems ; *p*, pinna-strand. × about 12. From a Westphalian specimen. S. Coll. 2828. Photographed by Mr. W. Tams.

that the convex side of the bundle was turned towards
the stem, an unusual feature, paralleled in *Tubicaulis*.
The space enclosed by the curvature of the bundle is
occupied by a mass of sclerenchyma, of correspondingly
complex form (Fig. 158). The species illustrated is
A. rotundata, with which, according to Bertrand and
Kubart, *A. pulchra* is identical. The protoxylem-groups,
which may be four in number, lie on the convex side of
the xylem, each somewhat sunk in a " cupule," to use
Dr. Bertrand's phrase. We may compare this with

the condition in *Botryopteris antiqua*. The pinna-strands too are given off from the convex side ; each is connected with a protoxylem-group; on entering the pinna the strand is curved in the same sense as the main rachis-bundle, but to a much less extent ; aphlebia-strands are also present in the base of the pinna. The orientation of the vascular system of the pinnae, as pointed out by Dr. Bertrand, is parallel to that of the main rachis, not rectangular to it as in Zygopterideae.

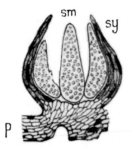

FIG. 159.—*Chorionopteris gleichenioides*, the fructification of *Anachoropteris pulchra*. Synangium in longitudinal section, showing three of the sporangia. *sy*, outer synangium-wall ; *sm*, sporangia containing spores ; *p*, supporting pinnule. × about 25. After Corda.

The genus *Anachoropteris* has recently gained much in interest from Dr. Kubart's important discovery of the fructification. The reproductive organs in question, from Bohemian coal-balls of Middle Coal-measure age, were described and figured by Corda as long ago as 1845 under the name *Chorionopteris gleichenioides*.[1] Dr. Kubart has now shown that the frond on which these fructifications are borne is identical with Corda's *Calopteris dubia*, and has further proved that the rachis of this frond has the structure of *Anachoropteris pulchra*. He has also re-investigated the structure of the fructification and its mode of attachment to the frond.[2]

Chorionopteris is a small synangium (Fig. 159) comparable in some respects to that of *Ptychocarpus* (p. 252), but containing four sporangia only, as in *Scolecopteris* (p. 256). There is a thick outer wall, common to the whole synangium, and within this are the four sporangia,

[1] Corda, *Beiträge zur Flora der Vorwelt*, p. 90, Taf. liv. Figs. 10-16.

[2] B. Kubart, " Ein Beitrag zur Kenntnis von *Anachoropteris pulchra*, Corda," *Denkschriften der K. Akad. der Wiss. in Wien*, Band 93, 1916.

with walls only one cell thick and without an annulus. They are seated on a basal receptacle in which is a mass of tracheides, forming the end of a vascular strand. As in *Ptychocarpus*, a delicate tissue can be recognised between the sporangia. Each sporangium contained a very large number (probably at least 2000, according to Dr. Kubart's calculations) of small spores, about 22 μ in diameter. The synangium opened at the top, owing perhaps, as suggested by Dr. Kubart, to the springing apart of the sporangia—how they individually dehisced is unknown.

The synangium, in general proportions and in the basal mass of tracheides, shows some agreement with Mr. Watson's *Cyathotrachus altus* (see p. 254).

As regards the insertion of the synangia, Dr. Kubart finds that they were borne on the incurved margins of small pinnules, a position frequent among recent Ferns, and not on the ultimate branches of a naked rachis, as in *Botryopteris*. Thus the fertile frond of *Anachoropteris* had an expanded lamina ; the minute lobed leaflets figured by Dr. Kubart have something the appearance of *Sphenopteris* pinnules.

It is clear from the new data that *Anachoropteris* was far apart from the other genera placed in Botryopteridaceae. The complex synangia are unlike any form of fructification known either in Botryopterideae or Zygopterideae. The simple synangia attributed to *Diplolabis*, or those of the problematic genus *Corynepteris* make but a small approach towards the highly organised spore-fruits of *Chorionopteris* (*Anachoropteris*) which are on the highest level of synangial development as found in some Marattiaceae. The difference from the free sporangia of *Botryopteris* is even more complete. If we judge by the fructification, the Anachoropterideae must be ranked as the most advanced group of the whole Order. The petiolar structure is also fairly complex and peculiar, though a certain affinity to the family Botryopterideae may perhaps be indicated here. We shall not be in a position to determine the true relationships of *Anachoropteris* until the structure of the stem is known, but the characters of the fructification, as determined by Dr. Kubart, fully establish its claim to constitute a distinct family.

The genus had a wide range in the Upper Carboniferous ; *A. rotundata* is not uncommon in the Coal-balls of our Lower Coal-measures.

Affinities of the Order.—The habit, anatomy, and sporangial characters all point to the Botryopteridaceae having been true Ferns. The germinating spores of *Stauropteris*, agreeing so closely with the corresponding stages in recent homosporous Ferns, raise this presumption almost to a certainty, and there is at present no countervailing evidence to be weighed.

The division of the Order into three families makes it difficult to say anything definite as to the general characters, for in Anachoropterideae the stem is unknown, and the complex synangial fructification is quite different from anything occurring elsewhere in the Order. At the same time the petiolar structure, especially the inverse curvature of the bundle, establishes a certain affinity with the other constituent families. At present, however, the Anachoropterideae are best left on one side, as a highly differentiated side-line, showing in the fructification a convergence with the Marattiaceae. It is quite possible that there was an actual affinity, but this question cannot be profitably pursued until we know the structure of the stem.

The other two families are better known, especially the Zygopterideae, owing to the recent investigations of Dr. Paul Bertrand and Dr. W. T. Gordon. The characters which the two groups have in common are the protostelic stem, the monodesmic petiole, and, in the case of certain members of each, the multiseriate annulus of the sporangium. The relation between the families is not, however, very clear, for the petiolar structure is not readily comparable. In the Zygopterids the protoxylem-groups lie to right and left in the leaf-trace and are as a rule immersed at one stage or another, In the Botryo-pterids the protoxylem (in one or more groups) is adaxial and the structure endarch ; in certain cases the proto-xylem may be slightly and temporarily immersed, just after the trace leaves the stele. Dr. Bertrand has, it is true, found analogies between the foliar strand of *Botryo-pteris forensis* and that of a Zygopterid, but *B. forensis* is the latest and most advanced species, and the com-parison can at best only indicate a certain parallelism of development.

Possibly the genera *Grammatopteris* and *Tubicaulis*, *incertae sedis*, may help to bridge the gap between the two families. They are not, however, so old as other types, such as *Clepsydropsis* and *Metaclepsydropsis* on the one hand, and *Botryopteris antiqua* on the other, in which the distinctive characters of the families are already perfectly well marked. Nor must it be forgotten that in *Asteropteris*, the oldest of all (Upper Devonian), we have an apparently typical Zygopterid, with a stellate stele and immersed protoxylems. In fact, while an affinity between Botryopterideae and Zygopterideae cannot be denied, we are at present without any clear indication of their supposed common ancestry.

We have now to consider, very briefly, the question of the probable affinities of the group with other Filicales.

The fructification, on which one would naturally lay the chief stress, appears to remove the Order from any of the more typical groups of Leptosporangiate Ferns. The size and form of the sporangia are too variable to be characters of any importance, but the annulus, when present, has definite peculiarities. In the genera *Etapteris* and *Botryopteris* it forms a well-defined longitudinal or oblique *multiseriate* band of cells, occurring on both sides of the sporangium in *Etapteris*, on one side only in *Botryopteris*. The nearest analogy among recent Ferns is perhaps to be found in Osmundaceae, where the annulus is represented by a unilateral group of thickened cells, the areola, resembling the *Botryopteris* arrangement in a reduced form.

On the other hand, no annulus is differentiated in the sporangia referred to *Diplolabis* or in *Stauropteris*. The annulus evidently afforded less constant characters among Palaeozoic Ferns than is now the case.

The position of the sporangia in *Etapteris*, *Botryopteris*, and *Stauropteris*, where they are borne on ultimate branches of the rachis, is not very closely paralleled among recent Ferns, but finds its nearest analogy in *Helminthostachys* and *Botrychium* among the Ophioglossaceae,[1] the comparison being closest with the case of *Botryopteris* (Fig. 153).

The question of the morphology of the frond presents some difficulty. In most Zygopterideae there is no evidence for the existence of an expanded lamina, even in cases where the material is abundant, as in *Ankyropteris westphaliensis* and *corrugata*, *Metaclepsydropsis duplex* and *Stauropteris oldhamia* and *burntislandica*. In *Stauropteris*, the presence of palisade-tissue on the naked rachis suggests that no lamina may have been developed.

Among the Botryopterideae, the numerous specimens of the four British species, *B. hirsuta, ramosa, cylindrica*, and *antiqua*, again show no sign of any laminar expansion.

On the other hand, in *Etapteris Lacattei*, if *Zygopteris pinnata* is rightly identified with that species, the frond was dimorphic, the sterile form having small laciniate leaflets, while in the fertile examples the rachis bore nothing but sporangia. In *Botryopteris forensis*, if we

[1] See Bower, "Spore-producing Members. II. Ophioglossaceae," Plate v. Fig. 81.

accept Renault's conclusions, the case was the same, and here the sterile lamina was better developed. There is thus a certain presumption in favour of dimorphism [1] in the Order, though it must be admitted that in certain cases the negative evidence is strong. Nor would the absence of a lamina be without analogy among supposed fossil Ferns, at least those of earlier date. As Halle says : " On the whole, the present evidence seems to indicate that the Lower Devonian flora is characterised by the absence of flattened fern-pinnules or foliar laminae generally." [2] It is possible that some such naked forms of frond may have come down to Carboniferous times (see Chap. X.).

We cannot therefore feel certain whether all Botryopteridaceae were dimorphic (only the fertile fronds, in many cases, being known to us), or whether, in some of them, the frond was constantly a mere rachis, destitute of expanded leaflets. It will be remembered that in some forms of *Corynepteris* (which has now been proved to be a Zygopterid), and in the isolated genus *Anachoropteris*, the fructifications were borne on the leaflets of a normal fern-frond. It thus appears that in the present state of our knowledge we are not in a position to make much use of the habit of the frond in discussing the affinities of the Order as a whole.

The peculiar quadriseriate arrangement of the pinnae, which forms so striking a feature in many of the Zygopterideae, has already been considered (pp. 335-337).

In anatomical characters certain analogies between the Botryopteridaceae and recent families of Ferns may be traced. In previous editions of this book stress was

[1] The word dimorphism is used to include both the differentiation of sterile leaves, and that of sterile and fertile parts of the same leaf. In the case of fossil Ferns it is usually impossible to say which was the case, and among recent Ferns the distinction is not always constant, even in the same species.

[2] T. G. Halle, *Lower Devonian Plants from Röragen in Norway*, 1916, p. 38.

laid on a comparison (already drawn by Renault) with the structure of the Hymenophyllaceae. We now know that the axillary branching, which formed one of the chief points of agreement, was only a special case in Botryopteridaceae, limited, so far as we know, to three closely allied species of *Ankyropteris*. Dichotomy seems to have been the prevalent mode of branching in the Order, where any branching has been observed. From the dichotomy it is probable that the occasional axillary arrangement was derived. Most likely it arose quite independently in the Hymenophyllaceae, though in some species the parallelism is remarkably close ; the leaf-trace appears to give off the stele of the axillary shoot just in the same manner as in *Ankyropteris Grayi*, the resemblance extending even to details.

In certain cases the stelar structure is also very similar. The stele of *Trichomanes reniforme*, for example, agrees very nearly with the simplified form of stele found at the base of the axillary shoot of *A. Grayi*, etc. There is the same bilateral structure in both, the internal protoxylem forming two groups, accompanied by parenchyma. In other species, however, the protoxylem may be peripheral (*e.g. T. scandens*) or scattered (*e.g. T. spicatum*).

These analogies between the recent family and certain highly specialised Zygopterideae are interesting, but can hardly be regarded as indicating any special affinity. With the simpler type, *Botryopteris*, there is also a certain analogy, though a much less close one. Mr. Boodle says, in his paper on Hymenophyllaceae : [1] " The solid stele of *Botryopteris*, as the wood consists of tracheides only, resembles the stele found in the lower part of the seedling-stem of *Trichomanes*, rather than the solid stele of *T. spicatum*, etc."

---

[1] L. A. Boodle, "Comparative Anatomy of the Hymenophyllaceae, Schizaeaceae, and Gleicheniaceae. I. Hymenophyllaceae," *Ann. of Bot.* vol. xiv. 1900, p. 489.

Another, very different family, with which the Botryo-pteridaceae have been compared, is that of the Ophio-glossaceae. An analogy with this group was already pointed out by Renault, in his early work, especially as regards the fructification, a point already alluded to. It was with *Helminthostachys* that he specially compared the Botryopteridaceae ; he then suggested that the fossil Order might be intermediate between Ophioglossaceae and Hymenophyllaceae. Of late years some interest-ing points of anatomical comparison between the recent Adder's-tongues and the family Zygopterideae have been noticed. The presence of internal or centripetal xylem has now been recognised in the stem of all three genera of Ophioglossaceae. In *Helminthostachys* the wood is regu-larly mesarch, thus possessing normally an inner, centri-petal zone. In *Botrychium Lunaria* " the central (or centripetal) primary xylem is usually only represented by a few tracheides at the periphery of the pith " (Lang) ; occasionally they may extend to the centre. In *Ophio-glossum* internal xylem appears to occur only exception-ally. The anatomy of the recent family has been carefully studied by Professor Lang [1] who finds many points of agreement with the Zygopterideae. The comparison between *Botrychium* and *Botrychioxylon* is especially interesting, for in both the recent and the fossil genus we have not only a strongly developed secondary zone, but a system of internal tracheides also.[2] The other genera of Ophioglossaceae correspond rather to the more typical Zygopterideae in which the external as well as the internal

[1] W. H. Lang, On the Interpretation of the Vascular Anatomy of the Ophioglossaceae," *Mem. and Proc. Manchester Lit. and Phil. Soc.* vol. 56, Part ii. 1912. " Studies in the Morphology and Anatomy of the Ophioglossaceae. I. *Botrychium Lunaria*," *Ann. of Bot.* vol. xxvii. 1913; II. " Helminthostachys Zeylanica," *ibid.* vol. xxix. 1915. See also D. H. Campbell, " The Eusporangiatae," Carnegie Institution, Washington, 1911; Bower, "On the Primary Xylem, etc., in the Ophio-glossaceae," *Ann. of Bot.* vol. xxv. 1911, p. 537.

[2] See Scott, " On *Botrychioxylon paradoxum*," 1912, for a fuller comparison.

xylem is wholly or chiefly primary. Professor Lang has further shown that axillary branching takes place in the genera *Botrychium* and *Helminthostachys*, though as a rule the axillary buds remain dormant. When they develop into branches, the vascular connection, in the case of *Botrychium*, is with the subtending leaf-trace, as in *Ankyropteris Grayi* and its allies, but in *Helminthostachys* the stele of the branch abuts directly on that of the main axis, a condition which Professor Lang brings into relation with the " dichotomy " of other Zygopterideae.

Unfortunately nothing is known of the geological history of the Ophioglossaceae ; we are therefore driven to compare directly a recent with a Palaeozoic group of plants, a procedure which is apt to be misleading. Still, the points of agreement (though there are important points of difference also, *e.g.* the polydesmic petioles of the recent family) seem sufficient to justify the opinion that the Ophioglossaceae have more in common with the Botryopteridaceae (especially the family Zygopterideae) than with any other known group of plants. The affinity, however, must be a somewhat remote one. For a full statement of the evidence, Professor Lang's papers should be consulted.

The case is very different with the Osmundaceae, for here the recent family has been traced back as far as the Permian, and shows in its oldest members a marked approach to the Botryopteridaceae in the structure of the stem. The stele of the earliest known genera, *Thamnopteris* and *Zalesskya*, with the solid wood differentiated into two zones, corresponds very closely with that of the Zygopterid *Diplolabis*. No doubt the structure of the leaf-trace is very different ; in fact no one would derive the Osmundaceae from the Zygopterideae, but the evidence is strongly suggestive of a common origin, as advocated by Kidston and Gwynne-Vaughan. These authors have suggested an hypothesis by which the very divergent leaf-traces of the two families may be derived from a common primitive type. The theory is based on the changes observed in the leaf-trace of *Thamnopteris*, which, it will be remembered, is mesarch on leaving the stele and becomes endarch and C-shaped higher up in its course (see above, p. 285). On this view the primitive dorsiventral and probably concentric leaf-trace contained a solid, elliptic, central mass of xylem, in which the proto-xylems were immersed (mesarch) ; at a still earlier stage it may be assumed that they were derived from a single median strand.

From this simple leaf-trace it is possible to derive the various Zygopterid forms of foliar bundle on the one hand and the C-shaped strand of the Osmundaceae, etc., on the other.[1]

The evidence from the sporangia has been already referred to. On the whole, the case for attributing a common origin to the Botryopteridaceae and Osmundaceae seems to be exceptionally strong. Recent comparisons have chiefly been drawn between the latter family and the Zygopterideae, but it is evident that *Botryopteris* also deserves consideration, for this genus, at least in its simpler and earlier forms, seems to be anatomically more primitive than any known Zygopterid. There is no very essential difference between an Osmundaceous leaf-trace in the lower part of its course and that of a simple *Botryopteris*. Kidston and Gwynne-Vaughan, in their first memoir on the Fossil Osmundaceae, have stated that they " regard the Osmundaceae as directly descended from an ancestral stock from which at least two other types of structure arose—that of *Botryopteris* and that of *Zygopteris* " (in the wide sense).

The Botryopterideae may fairly be called a synthetic

[1] See, in addition to the memoirs cited above under Osmundaceae, a posthumous paper by Gwynne-Vaughan, " Observations on the Anatomy of the Leaf in the Osmundaceae," *Ann. of Bot.* vol. xxx. 1916.

group, in so far as they show analogies with a number of later families of Ferns. While their connection with the Osmundaceae is the best established, the points of resemblance with the Hymenophyllaceae and Ophioglossaceae are also significant. They have further been compared with the Schizaeaceae, on account of the multiseriate annulus sometimes observed in that family, though its position is different ; anatomically a basis of comparison may be found in the internal tracheides occurring in the stele of some species of *Schizaea*.[1] Attention has already been drawn to a possible relation to the Marattiaceae, materially supported by the recent discovery of the synangia of *Anachoropteris*.

The Botryopteridaceae, though retaining some primitive characters, are in various directions a specialised group, too much so to have themselves been the ancestors of modern Ferns, but the analogies which they present with so many families suggest that they may well represent an offshoot (or rather offshoots) from the same main line of descent.

The late Dr. Arber, in 1906,[2] traced back the Leptosporangiate Ferns to an ancient Palaeozoic race, which he named the Primofilices (*i.e.* Ferns characteristic of the Primary Rocks), of which the Botryopteridaceae formed but one group. He further suggested that possibly the origin of the Eusporangiatae was also to be sought among the Primofilices. This view of Dr. Arber's still holds good, as the best hypothesis available, in the present state of our knowledge of the early Ferns.

[1] Tansley and Chick, " Structure of *Schizaea malaccana*," *Ann. of Bot.* vol. xvii. 1903 ; Boodle, " Comp. Anat. of Hymenophyllaceae, Schizaeaceae, and Gleicheniaceae. IV. Further Observations on *Schizaea*," *ibid.*

[2] E. A. N. Arber, " On the Past History of the Ferns," *Ann. of Bot.* vol. xx. 1906.

Prof. Seward has employed the name " Coenopterideae " (generalised Ferns) in the same sense as Dr. Arber's Primofilices, but its application has sometimes been restricted to the Botryopteridaceae.

II. Summary

The general conclusion to which we are led by a consideration of the evidence bearing on the existence of Ferns in the Palaeozoic period is that this class was then fairly well represented, though by no means holding the dominant position formerly assigned to it. On the one hand we have, as a characteristic group, the remarkable group of the Botryopteridaceae, very different from any of the more modern families of Ferns, though presenting analogies with them in various directions. On the other hand, we have the Marattiaceous type, much more complex in anatomical structure, and with clear affinities to the recent Ferns of that group. The doubts that were at one time cast on the authenticity of Palaeozoic Marattiaceae were suggested by the similarity between supposed Marattiaceous fructifications and the pollen-bearing organs of certain Pteridosperms and Cycadophyta. In the absence of anatomical evidence we are doubtless often left in uncertainty whether a given fructification is to be referred to the one category or the other. The structure of the *Psaronius* stems, however, appears conclusive as to the existence of a considerable group of true Palaeozoic Marattiales (in a wide sense) to which, no doubt, many of the fronds bearing synangia belonged.

Dr. Arber's proposed group, the Primofilices, embracing all the more primitive Palaeozoic Ferns, with the Botryopteridaceae as at present the best-known family, has already been referred to, and the idea has proved to be a fertile one. We are not, as yet, in a position to fill in the features of this ancient race, for outside the Botryopteridaceae themselves, in the widest sense, our knowledge of such Ferns is scanty. But, as Dr. Arber pointed out, many of the Fern sporangia of the petrifactions will doubtless find their place here, and so, perhaps, will some of the fructifications, such as *Oligocarpia* or *Senftenbergia*, which have been provisionally referred to definite recent families. *Pteridotheca William-sonii* (Figs. 121 and 122, p. 265) is a good example of a Palaeozoic Fern with annulate sporangia borne on leaflets of an ordinary vegetative type, and there are several similar cases. Various families of Ferns are known to have been well developed in the Mesozoic Period, and their ancestors must have been present in Palaeozoic times. For reasons already given, we cannot regard the Botryopteridaceae as lying on the direct line, but some of the forms of " Primofilices " with non-specialised sporophylls may well have been nearer the progenitors of Ferns as we know them.

Various facts, already mentioned, suggest a possible connection between the Primofilices and the Marattiales, an hypothesis which, indeed, is almost inevitable on general grounds. The Ferns grouped under Primofilices, as this name is intended to imply, are of great antiquity, occurring commonly in the Lower Carboniferous (various Botryopteridaceae) and extending back to the Devonian (*Asteropteris*), while the Marattiales are not known to be older than the Upper Carboniferous (Lower Coal-measures).

It is doubtful if the distinction between Eusporangiate and Leptosporangiate Ferns existed in Palaeozoic times— in other words, whether the development of the sporangium from a single cell had yet been arrived at. In the Botryopteridaceae, at any rate, it is improbable that this was the case, the mode of insertion of the sporangia, and their large size in many cases, pointing to a multicellular origin.

The conclusions of Professors Campbell and Bower, as to the relative antiquity of the Eusporangiate type, are thus amply justified by palaeontological evidence. On the other hand, it may be doubted whether this evidence justifies the view that the confluent synangium was the primitive type of Fern-fructification. The fossil data suggest, on the whole, that free sporangia represent the original form of Filicinean fructification, and that their cohesion to form synangia was a secondary modification, though one which, in certain groups, took place at a very early period.[1]

From an anatomical point of view, two main types of stem are sharply distinguished among the Palaeozoic Ferns. On the one hand, we have the large, highly complex, polystelic stems represented by *Psaronius*, and belonging, no doubt, to Tree-ferns allied to the Marattiaceae. On the other, we have the herbaceous monostelic forms, such as the Botryopteridaceae.

The monostelic group is generally further characterised by having only a single vascular bundle in the petiole, and it is remarkable that this peculiarity also extended to many of the polystelic forms (species of *Psaronius*), which, in the simplicity of their petiolar structure, differed widely from Marattiaceae, while agreeing with them in the anatomy of the stem. On the evidence now available, it appears that monostelic structure of the stem was more common among Palaeozoic than among recent Ferns, while monodesmic structure of the petiole was the rule,[2] though not, of course, without exceptions. Summing up the results, we may say that the Palaeozoic, or at least the Carboniferous Ferns, group themselves anatomically into two main cycles—the Palaeo-Marattiales on the one hand, and on the other that great synthetic group of Ferns (Primofilices) with a simple anatomical structure, of which we may take the Botryopteridaceae as the best-known examples.

Space forbids us to extend our studies to the Ferns

---

[1] Stur came to a similar conclusion, "Culm- und Carbonfarne," p. 161. See, however, F. O. Bower, " Studies in the Morphology of Spore-producing Members," iii. Marattiaceae, *Phil. Trans. Roy. Soc.* 1897, B, p. 35, for an able statement of the opposite view ; also his *Origin of a Land-Flora*, p. 523, 1908.

[2] See L. A. Boodle, " On the Comp. Anatomy of Hymenophyllaceae, Schizaeaceae, and Gleicheniaceae," *Ann. of Bot.* vol. xiv. 1900, vol. xv. 1901, vol. xvii. 1903.

of later epochs. It may be interesting, however, to point out that during the Mesozoic period nearly all the different groups of recent Ferns made their appearance.

Among the Marattiaceae, the Palaeozoic genus *Asterotheca* has been found to persist in the Triassic and even Rhaetic beds. On the other hand, specimens from the Rhaetic and the Lias have been referred to the recent genera *Marattia* and *Danaea*.

Gleicheniaceae have been identified as far back as the Lias, and perhaps the Trias.

One of the most curious features of the Fern-vegetation throughout the Secondary period is the prominence of the family Matonineae, now represented by a single genus, with two species, *Matonia pectinata* and *M. sarmentosa*, plants of limited distribution in the Malayan region. This group, which combines the characters of Cyatheaceae and Gleicheniaceae, can be traced back, on evidence derived from the fructifications as well as from foliar characters, at least as far as the Rhaetic beds.[1]

Cyatheaceae can be identified as far back as the Lias, and Schizaeaceae are found in the Jurassic.

Osmundaceae have been recognised by their fructifications in the Rhaetic and Trias, and fossils from these rocks have even been referred to the recent genera *Osmunda* and *Todea*.

The fossil history of the Osmundaceae from an anatomical point of view, investigated by Kidston and Gwynne-Vaughan, has already been fully considered (p. 278).

There appears to be little satisfactory evidence as yet as to Mesozoic Hymenophyllaceae.

The family Dipteridineae, formerly included under Polypodiaceae, appears to have a long geological record, Ferns referred to this group having been found in the Lias, Rhaetic, and Trias.[2]

---

[1] See Seward, " On the Structure and Affinities of *Matonia pectinata*, with Notes on the Geological History of the Matonineae," *Phil. Trans. Roy. Soc.* vol. 191, B, 1899.

[2] Seward and Dale, " On the Structure and Affinities of *Dipteris*,

True Polypodiaceae have not been traced further back at present than the Jurassic rocks.[1]

The palaeontological data just cited may be compared with the arrangement of the families of Ferns, proposed by Professor F. O. Bower,[2] on the basis of an exhaustive investigation of the development of the sorus, and the output of spores. The main lines of his classification are exhibited in the following table :—

FILICES—Isosporeae

SIMPLICES	Botryopteridaceae. Ophioglossaceae. Marattiaceae.	EUSPORANGIATE.
	Osmundaceae. Schizaeaceae. Gleicheniaceae. Matonineae.	
GRADATAE	Loxsomaceae. Hymenophyllaceae. Cyatheaceae. Dicksonieae (with some exceptions). Dennstaedtiinae.	LEPTOSPORANGIATE.
MIXTAE	Davallieae (with some exceptions). Lindsayeae. Pterideae and other Polypodiaceae.	

with Remarks on the Geological History of the Dipteridineae," *Phil. Trans. Roy. Soc.* B, vol. 194, 1901.

[1] For a fuller summary, see Zeiller, " Les Progrès de la Paléo-botanique de l'Ère des Gymnospermes," *Progressus Rei Botanicae,* vol. ii., 1907.

[2] " Studies in the Morphology of Spore-producing Members," iv. The Leptosporangiate Ferns, *Phil. Trans.* vol. 192, B, 1899. For a more recent statement, see his *Origin of a Land-Flora,* 1908, especially the scheme on p. 653 ; also " Farne im weitesten Sinne (Pteridophyta)" in *Handwörterbuch der Naturwissenschaften,* Jena, 1913, Bd. iii.

The Simplices are those Ferns in which all the sporangia of a sorus are produced simultaneously, the Gradatae those in which there is a definite succession in time and space, the Mixtae those in which there is a succession in time, but no regular succession in space.

Other characters of importance coincide more or less with the above ; for example, the sporangia tend to become smaller, with fewer spores in each, as we advance from the Simplices to the Mixtae.

It will be seen that the geological evidence, so far as it goes, harmonises well, on the whole, with the main divisions in Professor Bower's system. The old distinction between Eusporangiatae and Leptosporangiatae takes a secondary place, and to this the palaeobotanist can make no objection, for on existing evidence it is doubtful whether the distinction existed among Palaeozoic Ferns.

In Professor Bower's later work the old heterosporous Order, the Rhizocarps, is broken up into two groups, the Marsiliaceae being associated with the Schizaeaceae, and the Salviniaceae with the Cyatheaceae.

A remarkable lacuna in our knowledge of the older fossil Filicales is the entire absence, so far as is yet ascertained, of any satisfactory evidence for the existence of heterosporous forms. Fossil Rhizocarps have often been described, but, so far as the earlier strata are concerned, on the most questionable evidence.

There are strong reasons for supposing that heterospory must have appeared among Fern-like plants in Palaeozoic times, but this question will be considered in the last chapter of the book.

CHAPTER X

Early Devonian Pteridophytes

DURING the last few years our knowledge of the Lower and Middle Devonian Flora has greatly increased, owing to remarkable discoveries in Norway and in Scotland. So far the great result attained is the definite recognition of a class of early vascular plants, quite distinct from any of the phyla hitherto known. The new class is called the Psilophytales, taking its name from *Psilophyton*, a genus, established as long ago as 1859 by Sir William Dawson, which had remained obscure until the investigation of new material confirmed, in essentials, the statements of the original discoverer, and established the group on a broader basis.

It will be most profitable to concentrate our attention at once on the Scottish discoveries, which relate to fossils with excellently preserved structure, and thus give, for the first time, a perfectly clear idea of the vegetative and reproductive characters of the Psilophytales. Reference will then be made to observations on allied plants less favourably preserved, but also of importance.

RHYNIA, Kidston and Lang [1]

The name *Rhynia* is used by Kidston and Lang for their specimens, allied to *Psilophyton*, with structure

[1] R. Kidston and W. H. Lang, " On Old Red Sandstone Plants, showing structure, from the Rhynie Chert Bed, Aberdeenshire, Part I. *Rhynia Gwynne-Vaughani*," *Trans. Royal Soc.*, Edinburgh, vol. li. Part III., 1917 ; Part II. " Additional Notes on *Rhynia Gwynne-*

preserved. The relationship to Dawson's genus is clear, as will be seen later. The fossil plants now placed in the genus *Rhynia*, as well as others, are derived from the chert of the Muir of Rhynie in Aberdeenshire. This plant-bearing deposit was first discovered in 1913 by Dr. W. Mackie, who figured sections of two of the specimens. The full investigation of the structure, at the hands of Drs. Kidston and Lang, has made these most ancient land plants among the best known of fossil remains. The precise age of the bed has not been determined, but it is known to be not later than the Middle Old Red Sandstone. The plants which it contains are thus the oldest known land plants with structure preserved.

The chert is formed of a series of old peat-beds, which were no doubt subject to periodic inundations, for each bed has a thin layer of sand on the top.

In some cases the *Rhynia* plants are found upright as they grew, the vertical stems rising six inches above the old surface of the peat, which was mostly composed of the débris of the plant. Fossilisation was probably due to water, containing silica in solution, discharged from geysers or hot springs. The plants grew gregariously, their stems densely tufted, like a growth of heather on a modern moor.

The morphology of *Rhynia* was extremely simple ; the plant had no roots and no leaves. The underground part consisted of the creeping rhizomes, from which sprang vertical branches, to form the upright aerial stems. Kidston and Lang, in their second paper, distinguish two species of *Rhynia*, *R. Gwynne-Vaughani* and *R. major* ; at first all were included under the former name. Though the two species are much alike, there are some important distinctions between them as regards

---

Vaughani, with descriptions of *Rhynia major* and *Hornea Lignieri,*" *ibid.* vol. lii., Part III., 1920 ; Part III. " *Asteroxylon Mackiei,*" *ibid.* 1920.

I am indebted to the authors for an opportunity of reading Parts II. and III. in MS., and consulting the Figures, before publication.

the aerial parts of the plants ; their rhizomes are quite similar. In both species they are dichotomously branched, creeping stems, bearing numerous non-septate rhizoids. Large hemispherical bulges occur on the rhizomes, formed by the localised growth of the peripheral tissues, and these outgrowths produce abundant rhizoids. The rhizome has a slender stele, an outer and inner cortex and a thin-walled epidermis, without stomata. Except for this last point and the special delicacy of the tissues, there is no essential difference between the structure of the

Fig. 160.—*Rhynia Gwynne-Vaughani*. External view of a portion of stem, exposed on a fractured surface of the chert, showing the epidermal cells and several of the hemispherical projections or bulges. × 14. After Kidston and Lang (I. iii. 7).[1]

rhizome and that of the aerial stem, in which the anatomy is best exhibited.

The upright aerial stems are somewhat sparingly branched by dichotomy. It is necessary at this point to distinguish between the two species, for *R. Gwynne-Vaughani* presents some important morphological features which are absent in the other species. In the former, the aerial stems are studded at irregular intervals with hemispherical bulges or outgrowths (Fig. 160), similar to but smaller than those of the rhizome. They were formed from the more superficial tissues and had

[1] These references are to the Part, Plate, and Figure in Kidston and Lang's Memoirs.

no vascular supply. In some cases, probably near the base of the stem, these swellings bear rhizoids (Fig. 167).

The most interesting point about the hemispherical bulges is that many of them became the seat of a new development; they grew out into adventitious branches (Fig. 168). These branches sometimes, though not always,

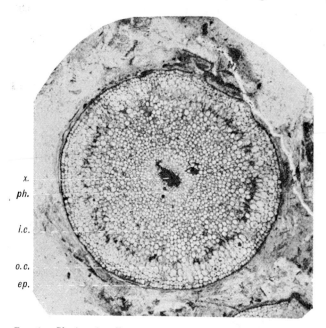

Fig. 161.—*Rhynia major.* Transverse section of aerial stem. *x*, xylem; *ph*, phloem; *i.c.*, inner, *o.c.*, outer cortex; *ep*, epidermis. × 14. After Kidston and Lang (l. v. 21).

possessed a stele of their own, but if so it was entirely unconnected with the vascular system of the main stem. The adventitious shoots were attached by a more or less narrow base, and appear to have easily become separated; they are often found loose in the peat, and probably formed a ready means of vegetative propagation. It is remarkable that the smaller branches were sometimes wholly destitute of any vascular system; no doubt they developed one in cases where they grew up into new plants.

The whole of this curious apparatus is absent from the aerial stems of *R. major*, in which neither hemispherical swellings nor adventitious branches have been observed. It thus appears that *R. Gwynne-Vaughani*

Fig. 162.—*Rhynia Gwynne-Vaughani*. Longitudinal section of stem. *pr*, a hemispherical bulge. Other lettering as in Fig. 161. × 20. After Kidston and Lang (I. v. 26).

possessed a method of vegetative increase, which the larger species dispensed with.

Otherwise the differences between the two species are mainly a matter of size. The dimensions of course vary, in each case, in different parts of the stem, but for the main axis the diameter is commonly about 2 mm. in *R. Gwynne-Vaughani*, and about 5 mm. in *R. major*. There was also, as we shall see later, a great difference in the dimensions of the sporangia and spores.

We now come to the anatomy of the aerial stem, which is practically the same in both species of *Rhynia*.

Except in the slenderest twigs of *R. Gwynne-Vaughani*, which may be destitute of any vascular system, the stem is traversed by a central stele, of the simplest structure (Fig. 161). It consists of a strand of xylem surrounded by a tissue which there is reason to regard as phloem. In the smallest steles the xylem (which may be reduced

FIG. 163.—*R. Gwynne-Vaughani.* Transverse section of aerial stem, showing the stele dividing preparatory to dichotomous branching. × 20. After Kidston and Lang (I. v. 30).

to one or two tracheides in the transverse section) shows no differentiation. In the larger steles of *R. Gwynne-Vaughani*, however, and in all those of the more robust *R. major*, the central tracheides are distinguished by their small size from the wider elements of the outer zone of xylem ; there is thus some indication of centrarch structure (Fig. 165). It is only in the case of *R. Gwynne-Vaughani* that the sculpturing of the tracheides is preserved ; they are annular elements, with the rings occasionally connected (Fig. 166).

The phloem, commonly four or five cells thick, forms a zone round the xylem (Figs. 162, 165). It consists of rather large, thin-walled, much elongated elements, with oblique end-walls ; though sieve-plates have not been observed, the whole character of the tissue indicates that it is of the nature of phloem. It contrasts sharply enough with the shorter, square-ended cells of the inner cortex, but there is no sign of any pericycle or endodermis to mark the boundary.

It may be pointed out that though the adventitious branches, occurring in *R. Gwynne-Vaughani*, have no

FIG. 164.—*R. Gwynne-Vaughani*. Part of epidermis in surface view, showing the fusiform epidermal cells and one stoma. × 160. After Kidston and Lang (I. vi. 32).

vascular connection with the stele, in the normal dichotomous branching of the plant the stele divides, as in a Lycopod, to supply the two branches, and vascular continuity is maintained (Fig. 163). Otherwise there are no complications ; the plant has no leaves, and neither are there any leaf-traces.

The broad zone of the inner cortex consists, as seen in transverse section, of rounded cells, often ranged in radial rows, and with intercellular spaces between them (Figs. 161, 165) ; this was no doubt the assimilatory tissue of the plant. The thinner outer cortex, or hypoderma, one to four layers in thickness, is composed of larger, clear cells.

The epidermis is well preserved ; it consists of fusiform cells (Fig. 164) with a thick cuticle on the outer wall. The most interesting point is the presence of scattered stomata ; their structure is in all respects that of the typical stomata of a vascular plant (Fig. 164), but they are very sparingly distributed. This fact is of course suggestive of a xerophytic habit ; on the other

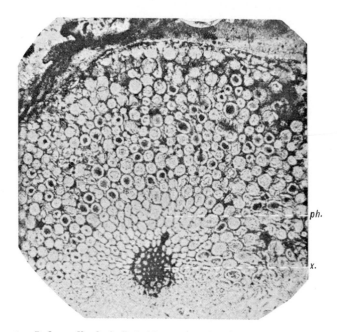

FIG. 165.—*R. Gwynne-Vaughani.* Part of transverse section of aerial stem, including the well-preserved stele. *x*, xylem, with the smallest elements about the centre ; *ph*, the broad zone of phloem. × 60. After Kidston and Lang (I. vii. 41).

hand, the stomata are not depressed below the level of the epidermal surface. Beneath each stoma there is an interruption of the hypoderma ; thus the stomata were in direct communication with the intercellular spaces of the inner cortex, which at these p ints reached the superficial layer.

In one or two cases the apex of the stem has been observed in a fair state of preservation ; there is no evidence, from the sections available, for the presence of a special apical cell.

We have now completed our survey of the simple vegetative organisation of the *Rhynia* plants. Happily, however, we are not restricted to a knowledge of the soma ; the work of Kidston and Lang has also made known the structure of the sporangia in both species. It is true that these organs have not yet been found *in situ* on the vertical stems ; the specimens are detached,

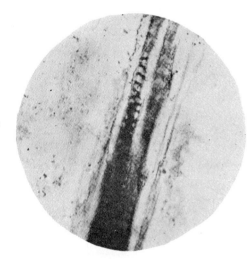

Fig. 166.—*R. Gwynne-Vaughani.* Tracheides in longitudinal section, showing the annular thickening of the walls. × 250. After Kidston and Lang (I. vii. 47).

but in some cases they are found in connection with portions of branches, which show the characteristic structure of *Rhynia,* so that there is no doubt as to the plants to which the reproductive organs belonged.

The sporangia are long, more or less cylindrical sacs, borne terminally on the branches of the stem (Fig. 169). Their dimensions are very different in the two species ; in *R. Gwynne-Vaughani* the sporangium is only about 3 mm. long, by 1-1.5 mm. in diameter, while in *R. major* the length reaches 12 mm. and the diameter 4 mm. The spores, with which the sporangia are sometimes filled, likewise differ in size, those of *R. Gwynne-Vaughani* averaging about 40 μ, and those of *R. major* about 65 μ in diameter.

It will be noticed that the terminal position of the sporangia on the stem is quite peculiar among Pteridophyta, only finding a doubtful analogy in Psilotales, according to some interpretations. The sporangia of *Rhynia* are sometimes found in pairs, and may possibly have been so borne on the plant, but this is uncertain.

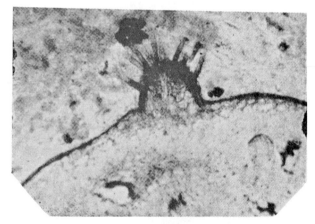

Fig. 167.—*R. Gwynne-Vaughani.* Superficial tissues of aerial stem, showing a hemispherical bulge, bearing rhizoids. × 60. After Kidston and Lang (I. viii. 53).

In structure, apart from dimensions, the sporangia of the two species appear to agree. The cylindrical sac is somewhat pointed at the distal end ; at the base, as we have seen, it passes over into the stout stalk, which has the structure of a small stem. The sporangium is strongly constructed ; the wall is several layers of cells thick and shows considerable differentiation (Fig. 170). The superficial layer consists of thick-walled cells, much elongated vertically, with a strong cuticle ; in transverse sections of the sporangium this layer resembles the well-known palisade or columnar wall of a *Lepidostrobus* sporangium.

Superficial sections, however, show that the cells are fusiform as seen from the surface, thus resembling those of the vegetative epidermis, though on a smaller scale, a fact which is of some significance. Beneath the epidermis there are several layers of intermediate cells, often badly preserved, while lining the sporangial cavity

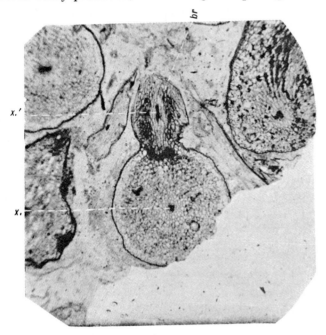

Fig. 168.—*R. Gwynne-Vaughani.* Transverse section of aerial stem, bearing an adventitious branch, *br*, attached by a fairly narrow base. *x*, xylem of stem ; *x'*, xylem of branch Other stems also shown. × 20. After Kidston and Lang (I. viii. 57).

is a more definite inner layer of persistent cells, originally interpreted as a tapetum. The cells, however, appear to have been too rigid to be of this nature, and the authors now suggest a comparison with the tracheidal sheath of Oliver's *Tracheotheca* (see Vol. II.). No indication of any mechanism for dehiscence has been detected.

While the normal sporangia of *Rhynia* are well-differentiated organs, comparable to those of advanced

Pteridophyta, it is worth noting that in two cases (in *R. Gwynne-Vaughani*) somewhat ill-defined sporangia, containing normal spores, were observed ; this, as Kidston and Lang point out, may be suggestive of a less differentiated condition, in which spores were formed within the end of a stem instead of in a definite sporangium. The structure of the next genus, *Hornea*, gives weight to this suggestion.

The spores, often filling the sporangia, are sometimes found united in tetrads, sometimes free (Fig. 171). They

Fig. 169.—*Rhynia major*. Slightly tangential longitudinal section of a sporangium, terminating a fairly stout stem. The sporangium is crowded with spores. × 4½. After Kidston and Lang (I. ix. 62).

appear to have had a cuticularised outer wall, and, so far as can be seen, are perfectly typical Pteridophytic spores. Spores are also found loose, scattered through the peat.

RELATION OF RHYNIA TO PSILOPHYTON

As already mentioned, the genus *Psilophyton* was founded by Sir William Dawson in 1859. It was based on specimens from the Lower Devonian of Gaspé in the Province of Quebec, Canada. *Psilophyton princeps* [1] is

---

[1] See Dawson, " Fossil Plants of Devonian and Upper Silurian Formations of Canada," *Report Geol. Survey*, Canada, 1871 ; also his *Geological History of Plants*, New York, 1888.

the most important species ; others have been described, but their relation to the type seems somewhat doubtful. *P. princeps* has been found in other localities, as for example in the Lower Devonian of Röragen, Norway, from which some comparatively good specimens have recently been described by Halle.[1] The plant has

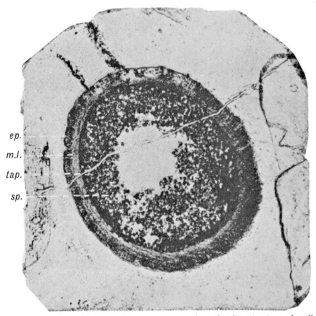

ep.
m.l.
tap.
sp.

FIG. 170.—*R. major.* Transverse section of sporangium, showing structure of wall. *ep.,* thickened epidermis ; *m.l.,* middle layers of wall ; *tap,* " tapetum " ; *sp,* spores. × 14. After Kidston and Lang (II. iii. 24).

usually been regarded with some suspicion by palaeo-botanists, the fragmentary specimens admitting of much doubt as to their correlation, but the recent observations on *Rhynia* have gone a long way to confirm Dawson's account. (See his restoration reproduced in Fig. 172.)

Psilophyton princeps, according to Dawson, consisted

---

[1] " Lower Devonian Plants from Röragen in Norway," *Kungl. Svenska Vetenskaps-akad. Handlingar,* Bd. 57. 1, 1916.

of somewhat slender upright stems, on the same scale as those of *Rhynia major*, or sometimes larger, springing from a creeping rhizome. The upright stems were frequently branched by dichotomy, in places forming a sympodium, and their tips were circinately coiled, a curious point, which is well established. The lower parts, especially, of the stems bore numerous spines, not

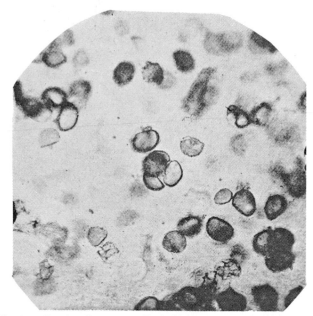

FIG. 171.—*R. major.* Spores, some still united in tetrads. × 160. After Kidston and Lang (I. x. 70).

exceeding the diameter of the stem in length ; sometimes only their scars are found. The fructification consisted of oval sporangia, often in pairs, borne terminally on the ultimate branches of the stem (Fig. 172).

Various points have been disputed by critics ; the connection of the aerial stems with the rhizomes appears not to have been demonstrated, but is highly probable. The fertile branches are usually without spines, and their connection with the plant has therefore been doubted—Halle, in fact, described them under another name, *Dawsonites arcuatus*.

Although most of the specimens are preserved merely as impressions, in some cases the structure of stems referred to *Psilophyton princeps* is very fairly preserved, and was well figured by Dawson from what he termed a "rhizoma." Kidston and Lang reproduce his Figures, and demonstrate an almost exact agreement with the structure of *Rhynia*, extending even to the annular tracheides of the central cylinder, which are practically identical in the two plants. There can be no question that Dawson's specimens with structure preserved belonged to a plant of the same type of structure as *Rhynia*. The late Dr. Arber further compared the superficial features of the stem in *Rhynia*, and in a specimen of *Psilophyton*, and came to the conclusion that the two were identical.[1]

If, as appears from these observations, the superficial and anatomical characters of

Fig. 172.—*Psilophyton princeps*. Dawson's original restoration. The rhizome, with root-like branches, is shown below. In the aerial stem one side is represented in vernation, with circinate apices, the other in fruit. *a*, branch with sporangia, enlarged; *b*, part of stem enlarged, to show the spines; *c*, "scalariform tissue of the axis," highly magnified. From Dawson, 1888.

[1] The passage is in a posthumous work of Dr. Arber's on the Devonian Floras, shortly to be published. Kidston and Lang's Figures 6 and 7, of *Rhynia*, may be compared with Halle's Figures, Pl. 2, Figs. 3 and 5, of *Psilophyton*.

Psilophyton and *Rhynia* were so closely similar, it becomes extremely probable that the agreement extended to the general morphology, and that the rhizome and the fructification attributed by Dawson to *Psilophyton* really belonged to that plant ; as regards the fructification, in particular, the agreement with the sporangia of *Rhynia* is quite as near as can be expected from specimens in a different state of preservation.

Kidston and Lang, after comparing the structural features of the two plants, say : " If this interpretation be correct, there would be a substantial agreement in structure between *Psilophyton princeps* and *Rhynia Gwynne-Vaughani*. The two plants further agree in bearing large oval sporangia on the ends of ultimate branches of the stem. *Psilophyton princeps* differs from *Rhynia*, however, in the presence of spines, in the more profuse dichotomous branching, in the subordination of some of the branches to a sympodial main axis, and in the absence, so far as we know, of lateral adventitious branches." [1]

Since this was written the authors have found that the adventitious branches are likewise absent from *Rhynia major*, so this point disappears as a generic distinction. The spines of *Psilophyton* have been compared with the hemispherical bulges of *Rhynia Gwynne-Vaughani*. Dawson regarded the former as rudimentary leaves, but this interpretation is doubtful. On the whole, there is no doubt that *Psilophyton* and *Rhynia* were related plants, and only further observations can decide how close the relation was. The question is further discussed below, p. 410.

For *Rhynia* and *Psilophyton* Kidston and Lang in 1917 established the new class Psilophytales, " characterised by the sporangia being borne at the ends of certain branches of the stem without any relation to leaves or leaf-like organs." This class has since been

[1] *L.c.*, Part I. p. 779.

enriched by the discovery of a new genus, which we have now shortly to describe, and still more recently a third genus, *Asteroxylon*, has been included in the group.

HORNEA, Kidston and Lang

The one species, *Hornea Lignieri*, Kidston and Lang, is another of the Rhynie plants.   Its remains sometimes

FIG. 173.—*Hornea Lignieri.* Large protocormous rhizome in vertical section, with three lobes, a stem arising from each lobe.   × about 10.   After Kidston and Lang (II. iv. 27).

formed an almost pure peat, while elsewhere they were mixed with those of other plants.   This remarkable genus, even more peculiar than *Rhynia* itself, is fully described in the second part of Kidston and Lang's memoir on the Rhynie fossils.

The general habit of *Hornea Lignieri* resembled that of *Rhynia*, so far at least as the aerial stems are concerned, but it was a smaller plant.   It consisted of a peculiar lobed rhizome, from which sprang dichotomously branched aerial stems, on the ends of which the sporangia were borne. Like *Rhynia*, it was both leafless and rootless. The preservation of the specimens is not quite equal to that of *Rhynia*, but all the essential points could be made out.

Whereas the rhizome of *Rhynia* is stem-like, the basal part of the *Hornea* plant is made up of thick, lobed masses, which are compared by Kidston and Lang to

Fig. 174.—*H. Lignieri.* Flat, broad rhizome, showing rhizoids springing from the lower surface. *b.t.*, termination of stele. × about 10. After Kidston and Lang (II. v. 29).

the protocorms of certain species of *Lycopodium* (Fig. 173). This protocormous rhizome has no vascular system of its own—it is entirely cellular ; from the superficial layer very numerous rhizoids grew out, sometimes one from every cell, burrowing into the peat (Fig. 174). As regards dimensions, in one case a flat, cake-like rhizome measured 8 × 2 mm. Fungal hyphae are frequent in the intercellular spaces of the rhizome.

The steles of the aerial stems end blindly in the tissue of the rhizome, the xylem terminating below in the form

of an inverted cup (Fig. 174, *b.t.*) ; this expansion does
not consist of tracheides, but merely of thick-walled cells.
The aerial stems themselves are cylindrical and branch
by dichotomy, most frequently in the more slender
upper region. They have no protrusions or adventitious shoots, agreeing in this respect with *Rhynia major*
and not with *R. Gwynne-Vaughani*. The structure of
the aerial stem is on the same simple lines as that of
Rhynia.

No stomata have been observed in the epidermis, but
this may be due merely
to imperfect preserva-
tion. The cortex shows
little differentiation.
The central stele is relatively well developed, *x.o.*
and consists of a solid *x.i.*
strand of xylem, sur-
rounded by a zone of
delicate tissue, com-
posed of narrower and
more elongated cells
than those of the cor-
tex, and no doubt re-
presenting the phloem.
The xylem shows a
constant differentiation.

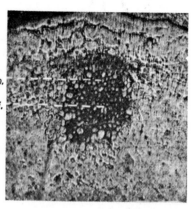

FIG. 175.—*H. Lignieri.* Stele of stem, in transverse section, close to the rhizome. *x.o.*,
outer xylem ; *x.i.*, central xylem. × 60.
After Kidston and Lang (II. vii. 47).

for the more central tracheides are decidedly smaller than
those towards the outside (Fig. 175). Longitudinal sections
show that the central elements become broken up into
short lengths, while those at the periphery remain continuous (Fig. 176) ; the former may perhaps be regarded
as·a somewhat diffuse protoxylem. The tracheides have
annular or locally spiral thickenings, and do not differ
very essentially from those of *Rhynia*.

So much for the vegetative structure ; the sporangia,
however, constitute the really distinctive feature of the

genus *Hornea*. They are terminal on branches of the stem, as in *Rhynia*, but are less sharply differentiated, and may be described simply as the modified ends of branches (Fig. 177). The size of the sporangium varies with that of the stem bearing it, the diameter ranging from 1 mm. to 2 mm. with a length of about 2 mm. The top is often broad and flat (Fig. 177), and the outline may be irregular.

The sporangial wall is thick, and differs little from the outer layers of the stem ; the epidermis may have some-

FIG. 176.—*H. Lignieri.* Stele in longitudinal section, showing the continuous outer xylem (*x.o.*) and the central xylem (*x.i.*) interrupted by breaks. × 60. After Kidston and Lang (II. vii. 49).

what thicker cell-walls and cuticle than in the vegetative region. Beneath the epidermis there are half a dozen layers of intermediate cells, and then comes a more resistant " tapetum," lining the whole cavity. No provision for dehiscence has been observed.

The most remarkable feature of the sporangium is the form of the spore-containing cavity. It is dome-shaped, overarching a central column of sterile tissue ; in fact the arrangement is just the same as in the sporogonium of the moss *Sphagnum,* and the sterile tissue is best called by the same name as in Mosses—the columella

(Figs. 177 and 178). The presence of a definite and highly developed columella is a character previously unknown among Pteridophyta,[1] though certain analogies are presented by the sub-archesporial pad of *Mazocarpon* or some species of the recent *Lycopodium*, and by the

sm^1 $s.m^2$

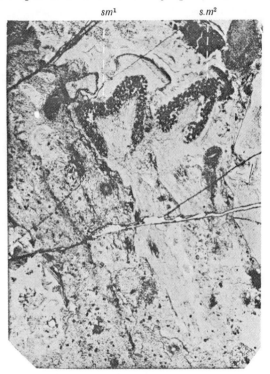

Fig. 177.—*Hornea Lignieri.* Two well-preserved sporangia ($s.m^1$ and $s.m^2$), cut in accurate longitudinal section, terminating two slender stems. The sporangium to the left is bifurcate, that to the right simple. Note the columella in each, overarched by the spore-bearing layer. × 12. After Kidston and Lang (II. ix. 58).

sterile tracts met with in the sporangia of some *Lepidostrobi*.

The details of the columella are shown in Fig. 178. It " is composed of narrow, elongated, thin-walled cells which give the tissue, as usually preserved, a peculiar

---

[1] Unless *Sporogonites* is a Pteridophyte. See below, p. 395.

fibrous appearance " (Kidston and Lang). The columella, as well as the outer wall, is lined by the " tapetum." The columella corresponds in position to the stele of the stem, and is directly continuous with the phloem, which it resembles in structure.

A very remarkable feature in the morphology of the

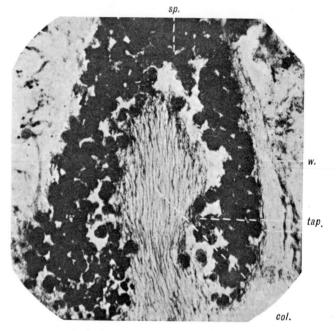

Fig. 178.—*H. Lignieri.* Portion of the right-hand sporangium in the last figure, enlarged, showing the columella (*col.*) in longitudinal section. *w*, wall; *sp*, spores in the dome-shaped cavity, lined by the tapetum (*tap.*). × 60. After Kidston and Lang (II. x. 69).

sporangium remains to be mentioned. Where the sporangium terminates a simple branch, it is itself simple, as described. But in some cases the modified branch was in the act of dichotomy, and then the sporangium also is forked, with a forked or lobed columella (see the left-hand sporangium in Fig. 177). This fact, in connection with the anatomical structure, appears to demonstrate clearly that the spore-bearing organ is nothing but a terminal part of the stem, modified for reproductive purposes. There is no special stalk—the sporangium is always perfectly continuous with the vegetative stem.

On the other hand, the spores themselves are those of a typical Pteridophyte. They fill the dome-shaped cavity, and are excellently preserved. Often they are still

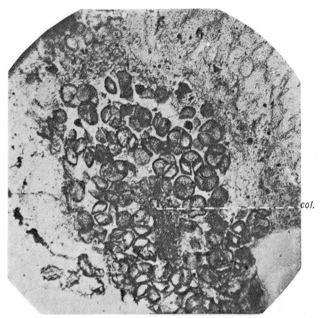

FIG. 179.—*H. Lignieri.* Spores in tetrads, around the columella (*col.*). × 105. After Kidston and Lang (II. x. 71).

associated in tetrads (Fig. 179) ; in other cases they have already become isolated ; their diameter is about 50 μ.

The genus *Hornea* is of special interest in several directions, and its discovery must be reckoned as among the most striking results of palaeobotanical research. The rhizome, as we have seen, presents close analogies with the protocorm, which forms an early stage in the development of various recent Lycopodiaceae ; the rhizome of *Hornea* is, of course, a more primitive structure, for it bears no protophylls, the whole plant being leafless ; it represents the protocorm in an early condition, when it was still a permanent organ of a plant far simpler than any of the Lycopods.[1]

The sporangia are of the utmost interest from two points of view.. In the first place they are quite clearly modified branches, containing spores. It thus appears that the dictum which has been accepted by most botanists for the last forty years, that the sporangium is an organ *sui generis*, must be given up. It is rather a modified part of the ordinary vegetative structure ; the spores, the true reproductive organs, are in this early type, produced in the tissue of branch-endings, only beginning to be specially adapted to their function of carrying the asexual reproductive cells.

It must be remembered that *Hornea* does not stand absolutely alone in this respect ; in some specimens of *Rhynia* the sporangia show but little differentiation, though as a rule they are fairly specialised organs. These facts seem to indicate that the modification of particular branches for reproductive purposes was a change which took place rapidly, soon leading to the formation of true sporangia, wholly adapted to their new functions.

The other point of primary morphological significance in the sporangium of *Hornea* is the presence of a columella, a central axis of sterile tissue surrounded by the spore-containing cavity. This character, so well known among the Bryophytes, has never before been observed in so definite a form in a vascular plant, though, as already pointed out, sterile tissue in the sporangium may occur. In *Hornea* the columella does not pierce the spore-bearing layer, but is overarched by it, the fertile region thus having a dome-like form. In this respect the sporangium of *Hornea* agrees with the sporogonium of the Anthocerotales among Liverworts and of *Sphagnum* and

---

[1] The question of the protocorm is more fully discussed by Kidston and Lang in their second memoir.

Andreaea among the true Mosses, while differing from that of the Bryales. But such comparisons are at best remote, for *Hornea* is not one of the Bryophyta, as is known from the fact that the vegetative plant is itself the sporophyte.

It is important to bear in mind the relation of the columella and spore-bearing layer to the tissues of the stem. The columella, as we have seen, is continuous with the phloem of the stele, and apparently of similar structure. Where the sporiferous end of the stem is forked, the columella is forked also, as though the stele were entering on dichotomy. The spore-bearing layer is of corresponding form, for it belongs anatomically to the inner cortex. Thus, as we have already seen, the spores are formed in the terminal part of a stem ; the sporogonium-like structure is to a great extent dependent on this relation. The significance of the apparently Bryophytic features of *Hornea* remains an open question. As Kidston and Lang point out, the true sporogonium of the Moss may either be a simpler parallel development, or a reduction from a higher type of sporophyte such as that of *Hornea*.

SPOROGONITES, Halle

A couple of years before the discovery of *Hornea*, Halle had described, from the Lower Devonian rocks of Röragen in Norway, a fossil with the characters of a sporogonium, to which he gave the name of *Sporogonites exuberans*.[1] The specimens are numerous ; they are not petrified, but in some the structure is partly preserved in a carbonaceous form. The external appearance of the fossil is strikingly like that of the fruit of a large moss, consisting of a simple stalk and a terminal capsule. The stalk may be at least 50 mm. in length, with a diameter of 0.5 mm. ; the obovate capsule is 6-9 mm. long and

[1] Halle, *l.c.* 1916, pp. 27 and 40, Pl. 3, Figs. 10-32.

2-4 mm. in diameter, with a rounded apex and a tapering base, passing over into the stalk. Thus the dimensions are on the scale of the largest Moss-fructifications. The slender seta, contrasting with the massive capsule, gives the whole much more the character of a true sporogonium than the clumsy form of the *Hornea* fruit.

By the examination of the carbonaceous specimens Dr. Halle was able to make out the structure. He found that while the basal part of the capsule is sterile, the upper part contains a dome-shaped spore-bearing region, surrounding and overarching a central, sterile columella. The tetrahedral or globular spores are 20-25 μ in diameter.

Owing to the mode of preservation the internal structure of *Sporogonites* could only be determined with difficulty; the discoverer's conclusions have, however, been strikingly confirmed by the subsequent demonstration of the presence of a similar columellate fructification in *Hornea*.

It is not known how the spores were dispersed; there is no trace of an operculum, though there is a thickening of the wall in the apical part of the capsule. Dr. Halle points out that *Sporogonites* must be regarded as a sporogonium comparable to that of the Bryophyta, but that it does not fall within the limits of any of the existing groups of that phylum. It may be a generalised Bryophytic type, but, as Dr. Halle says, " the possibility must be faced that it may represent only the upper part of a more highly developed sporophyte, perhaps on the line of descent of the Pteridophytes." [1] The discovery of *Hornea* lends a certain probability to the latter interpretation.

The genera *Rhynia* and *Hornea* are associated by Kidston and Lang in the family Rhyniaceae, " characterised by the plants being rootless and leafless and composed of rhizomes which bear rhizoids, branched aerial stems and terminal sporangia. The vascular

[1] *L.c.* p. 40.

system is correspondingly simple, the central stele having a cylindrical strand of xylem either composed of similar tracheides or with a distinction of central and peripheral xylem."

The relation of Halle's *Sporogonites* to this family remains uncertain, until we have a more complete knowledge of the sporophyte.

We have next to consider a more complex type of plant, included by Kidston and Lang in the class Psilophytales, but quite distinct in its characters from the family Rhyniaceae.

ASTEROXYLON, Kidston and Lang

This is another of the Rhynie discoveries. The one species, *Asteroxylon Mackiei*, is named after Dr. Mackie, the discoverer of the plant-bearing chert, who figured a section in his original report.[1] The plant occurs in the lower beds of the chert, and has also been found in loose blocks. The remains are more fragmentary than those of the other Rhynie fossils, but the preservation is often good. The plant was of considerable dimensions, exceeding those of *Rhynia* or *Hornea*.

The material consists of the following parts :

1. The main aerial stems, which were leafy.

2. The leafless rhizomes.

3. Transitional regions. The connection of these three parts is certain. In addition there are found in association, but without connection :

4. Axes of peculiar type, perhaps sporangiophores.

5. Dehiscent sporangia.

The cylindrical rhizomes, about 5-1 mm. in diameter, usually branched dichotomously ; there are no true roots, but the finer branches behaved in a remarkably root-like manner, burrowing into the tissues of other plants, or of their own kind, like Stigmarian rootlets.

---

[1] W. Mackie, "The Rock Series of Craigbeg and Ord Hill, Rhynie, Aberdeenshire," *Trans. Edinburgh Geol. Soc.* vol. x. 1913.

The rhizomes bear a general resemblance to those of *Rhynia*, but are entirely destitute of rhizoids.

The anatomy of the rhizome is quite of the *Rhynia* type (Fig. 180) ; the inner zone of the cortex was inhabited by an endophytic Fungus. The stele consists of a wide layer of phloem surrounding a more or less cylindrical xylem, in which no protoxylem can be distinguished ; the tracheides are spirally thickened.

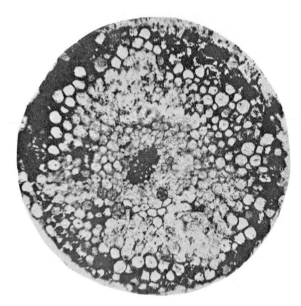

FIG. 180.—*Asteroxylon Mackiei*. Transverse section of rhizome, showing small concentric stele and wide cortex. Cf. stem of *Rhynia*, Fig. 161. × 45. From a photograph, after Kidston and Lang (III. iv. 29).

The transitional region is that in which the simple structure of the rhizome gradually passes over into the more complex organisation of the leafy aerial stem. The chief changes are that the originally cylindrical xylem gradually assumes a stellate form, while externally scale-leaves appear on the stem ; in this region they may be with or without leaf-traces. The epidermis shows a well-marked cuticle, and stomata are present. It is in this region that the phloem is best preserved ; it consists simply of delicate, elongated tubes, with pointed or

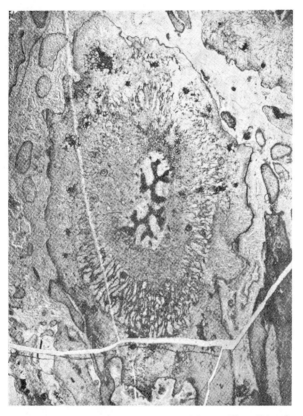

FIG. 181.—*Asteroxylon*. Transverse section of large aerial stem. The stellate xylem of the stele is double, as if in preparation for dichotomy. The trabecular middle cortex is well shown. There are numerous sections of leaves, some attached, others surrounding the stem. × 7. After Kidston and Lang (III. xiii. 96).

transverse ends. The arms of the xylem, as it becomes stellate, encroach on the phloem-zone.

We now reach the leafy shoots, the most characteristic region of the plant, differing widely from anything we have met with in the simple organisation of the Rhyniaceae. The aerial shoots range from over a centimetre to under a millimetre in diameter, the differences no doubt depending on the position of the shoot in the branch-system. In this region the branching was usually lateral and exogenous; cases of dichotomy were also

Fig. 182.—*Asteroxylon.* Longitudinal section of aerial stem, with leaves, two of which are attached. The dark bodies in the inner cortex are Fungi. × about 12. After Kidston and Lang (III. iv. 31).

observed (Fig. 181), and in one instance an endogenous branch was found.

The leaves clothe the shoots somewhat thickly, and appear to be spirally arranged. They are small, simple leaves, about 5 mm. in length, with an oval transverse section, and recall the foliage of a *Lycopodium* (Figs. 181, 182). In one respect, however, there is a remarkable difference from typical leaves, for although a leaf-trace enters the base of each leaf, it stops short of the free lamina, which was thus without any vascular supply.

The stele of the main leafy shoots no longer has the simple structure which we have hitherto met with in the Psilophytales. The xylem-strand is here of an extreme stellate form (Fig. 183), with long, sometimes forked, arms, often expanded at the ends, and attenuated towards

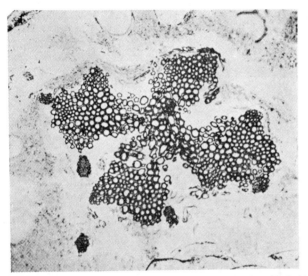

Fig. 183.—*Asteroxylon*. Transverse section of stellate xylem of stele, with leaf-traces departing from the enlarged ends of the rays.   × 33.   After Kidston and Lang (III. vii. 55).

the middle of the star, so that their continuity is sometimes interrupted. The position of the protoxylem is not always evident, but where clearly shown it forms groups of small and compressed tracheides within the ends of the rays, but close to the surface (Fig. 184). This immersed but peripheral position of the first-formed tracheides is well known among Zygopterideae, and also occurs in some Lycopods, *e.g.* in certain species of *Lycopodium*.

In young stems immature steles have been observed, with only the xylem-poles differentiated, thus proving the generally centripetal course of development of the wood. The protoxylem-elements are relatively narrow, and spiral or annular. The tracheides throughout the rest of the wood are spirally thickened, the spiral band

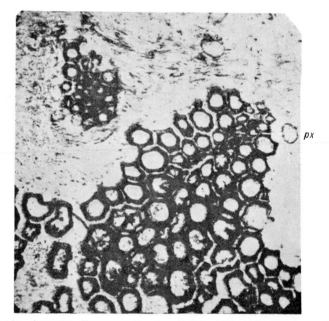

px

FIG. 184.—*Asteroxylon*. Transverse section of an arm of the stellate wood, with its immersed protoxylem (*px*). A centric leaf-trace is seen near by. × 210. After Kidston and Lang (III. x. 81).

forming a thin, flat ledge (Fig. 185).   The fact that the comparatively massive xylem-strand (reaching 2 mm. or more in diameter) contains nothing beyond spiral tracheides is a striking difference from the higher Pteridophyta and a probable indication of a primitive position.

The stele, as a whole, is cylindrical, for the phloem not only fills the bays of the stellate xylem, but extends round the ends of the arms (Fig. 181).   In this respect

the structure is that of a Lycopod rather than a Zygopterid. In the smaller aerial shoots the bays of the xylem
are shallow, and it is possible that in the ultimate branches
the slender xylem-strand may have been reduced to a
mere cylinder.

Small leaf-traces are given off from the arms of the
xylem, in more than one vertical series to each arm. The
structure of the leaf-trace is concentric, and the proto-

Fig. 185.—*Asteroxylon.* Longitudinal section of xylem, to show the spiral tracheides.
Towards the right, a narrow element of the immersed protoxylem is seen. × 210. After
Kidston and Lang (III. x. 77).

xylem is central (Fig. 184). Towards the periphery of
the stem the trace often becomes larger, and the xylem
hollow. As already mentioned, the trace extends into
the base of the leaf, but does not enter the lamina. Much
larger traces, which are sometimes found, no doubt
belong to branches of the stem, for they gradually assume
the stellate form. The steles of the lateral branches
depart from the xylem-arms, but the main stele may also
divide dichotomously.

When fully differentiated, the cortex consists of three zones, the middle one having a trabecular structure ; the trabeculae, separating the lacunae, are radiating vertical plates (Fig. 181). The tissue of the leaf, above the ending of the vascular bundle, is a uniform parenchyma. Stomata (Fig. 186) occur both on the stem and the leaves ; unlike those of *Rhynia* they are depressed below the epidermal surface. On the aerial shoots the stomata are quite normal, but in the transitional region the pore is unusually large.

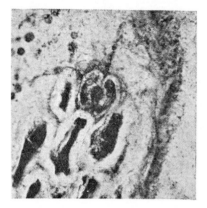

FIG. 186.—*Asteroxylon.* Stoma in surface view, and adjoining epidermal cells, with contracted dark contents. From an aerial shoot. × 210. After Kidston and Lang (III. viii. 65).

The parts of the plant so far considered, the simple, rootless, and hairless rhizome, the transitional region, and the leafy aerial stems, are demonstrably connected, and suffice to give a definite idea of the vegetative construction of *Asteroxylon*. We have now to deal with organs of a different kind, the relation of which to the plant is not certain, though very probable.

In one or two loose blocks, especially in one belonging to Dr. Gordon, lent by him for investigation, certain peculiar axes or appendages are present, in such close association with the stems of *Asteroxylon* that it is scarcely possible to doubt that they belonged to that plant. There is, however, no proof of connection, nor unfortunately does the state of preservation of the tissues admit of any convincing histological correlation. As these axes are, in their turn, closely associated with sporangia, they are termed by Kidston and Lang, " possible sporangiophores." Their structure may now be described.

The fertile axes, as we may provisionally call them, are somewhat slender, of considerable length, and dichotomously branched.   The state of preservation is usually such, that while the epidermis and stele are preserved, the intermediate cortical tissues have perished.

There is a great variety in the structure of the stele or vascular strand ; the term to be used depends on our

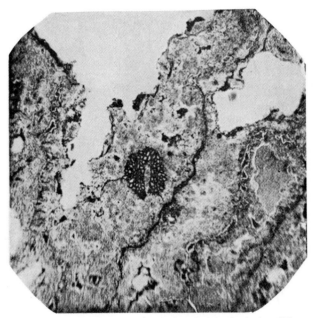

FIG. 187.—*Asteroxylon.*   Fertile axes in transverse section, showing in the middle, a stele with horse-shoe xylem.   × 60.   After Kidston and Lang (III. xvi. 111).

interpretation of the morphology of the whole organ. In the simplest case the stele consists of a simple mass of xylem surrounded by phloem ; often the xylem is double, while the phloem forms a continuous zone around it (Fig. 188) ; there may then be some resemblance to the foliar strand of a Zygopterid.   In other cases a phloem-island may appear inside the xylem, and again this island may be united to the outer phloem, giving the xylem a horse-shoe form (Fig. 187) ; or the phloem may extend right across the wood ; lastly, in the extreme case of duplication, there may be two distinct steles or strands in a common cortex. It is doubtful how far these various conditions may be connected with dichotomy of the axis.

There are no lateral appendages, nor, as a rule, are

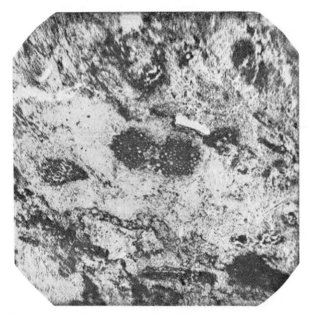

FIG. 188.—*Asteroxylon.* Other fertile axes, the middle one showing a double stele. × 60
After Kidston and Lang (III. xvi. 113).

there any lateral traces given off from the stele. In one or two cases, however, the stele had split off some smaller lateral portions, and this was observed to take place in the immediate neighbourhood of sporangia ; it is possible that the latter may have originally been connected with the axis at these points.

As regards dimensions, a good-sized double strand is about 300 μ in diameter, and thus intermediate in size between the stele and the leaf-traces of the vegetative stem. The xylem-elements are narrower than those of the stem ; their sculpturing is not preserved, so that no detailed comparison is possible. The position of the protoxylem has not been detected with certainty.

The cortex, when present, is uniformly parenchy-

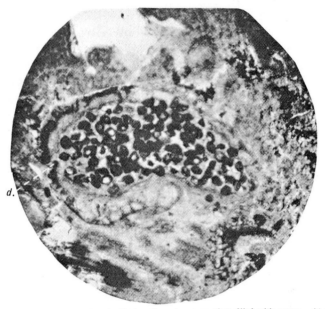

FIG. 189.—*Asteroxylon*. Longitudinal section of a sporangium filled with spores. At the larger end, on the left, the place of dehiscence (*d*) in the thickened epidermis is seen. × 50. After Kidston and Lang (III. xvii. 123).

matous ; in the epidermis well-preserved stomata of the usual form have been observed.

In Dr. Gordon's block of the Rhynie chert, sporangia are found, in close association though not in connection with the supposed fertile axes ; they are quite distinct from those of either *Rhynia* or *Hornea*. The sporangium is about 1 mm. in length and somewhat pear-shaped (Fig. 189). Unlike the sporangia of the Rhyniaceae, it was dehiscent, opening at the larger end (Fig. 189). The epidermal cells, like those of so many Fern sporangia, are thickened on the inner and lateral walls ; these cells become larger towards the distal end of the sporangium, but at the place of dehiscence they are shallow. The whole sporangial wall is of considerable thickness, owing to the presence of a layer of delicate tissue below the epidermis.

Inside some of the sporangia (Fig. 189) and also free in the surrounding matrix, spores are found, of a bright yellow colour. They are about 64 μ in diameter, show the customary triradiate marking, and are sometimes found associated in tetrads. They are thus quite ordinary Pteridophytic spores. The sporangia themselves are rather strikingly similar to those of the Fern *Stauropteris* (compare Fig. 189 with Fig. 147, p. 332).

In going on to consider the general habit of *Asteroxylon*, we must distinguish between the parts which certainly belonged to the plant, and those which are only attributed to it on the ground of association. As regards the vegetative organs, the case is clear, and the investigators are fortunate in having been able to reconstruct so much of the plant. They are fully justified in their conclusion that *Asteroxylon* was a terrestrial plant, which grew in a peaty soil, and consisted of an underground rhizome, of simple structure, without true roots and also without absorbent hairs, and giving rise to more complex, branched aerial shoots, clothed with simple leaves, while the transitional region intervened between the rhizome and the leafy shoots.

When we come to the fertile parts, the position is different, for there is no proof of their connection with the plant. There is in fact a double breach of continuity, first, between the vegetative shoots and the supposed fertile axes, and secondly between the latter and the sporangia. But in both cases the close association is highly suggestive. It is true that if we were dealing with the plants of the coal-balls, for example, such association would have little or no weight, but the plants of the Rhynie chert are by no means so varied or so mixed as the fragments in the coal-balls, and the risk of error is correspondingly diminished.

As Kidston and Lang suggest, " the fertile axes might have replaced the leaves on a distal region of the shoot, or have been ultimate subdivisions of a fertile region continuing certain vegetative shoots."

AFFINITIES OF ASTEROXYLON

In approaching this problem the first question which arises is : On what grounds is *Asteroxylon* referred to the Psilophytales ? An examination of the morphology and structure of the aerial shoots alone would hardly suggest such an affinity. The somewhat dense clothing of leaves is unlike anything in Rhyniaceae or even *Psilophyton*, and the anatomy is comparatively complex, rather recalling some higher race of Pteridophytes, such as Psilotales, Lycopods, or Zygopterids.

The arguments for including *Asteroxylon* in the Psilophytales appear to be four :

1. The structure of the rhizome.
2. The absence of roots.
3. The sole presence of spiral tracheides in the wood.
4. The general morphological comparison with *Psilophyton*, embracing the leafless rhizome, the leafy aerial stems, and the once more leafless fertile branches, bearing terminal sporangia; this comparison involves certain assumptions.

1. The simple anatomy of the *Asteroxylon* rhizome is quite on the lines of *Rhynia* (apart from the absence of rhizoids on the former). Kidston and Lang, in fact, compare the rhizome of *Asteroxylon* with the whole plant of *Rhynia*.

2. The absence of true roots, their functions being discharged by mere branches of the rhizome, is a rare

character among vascular plants, and may well be regarded as a mark of affinity with the relatively primitive phylum Psilophytales.

3. The exclusive presence of spiral tracheides in the xylem, where it is so well developed as in the aerial stems of *Asteroxylon*, certainly seems a primitive feature, allying the plant to the Rhyniaceae.

4. The general morphological analogy with *Psilophyton princeps*, as restored by Dawson, may well be used to support the other arguments ; we return to this point below.

On the whole of the evidence it seems that Kidston and Lang are justified in their statement that *Asteroxylon*, though more complex than *Rhynia* and *Hornea*, yet appears to be in some respects simpler than most Vascular Cryptogams. This greater simplicity is best recognised by including the plant in the Psilophytales, recently founded as the most ancient and primitive phylum known among Pteridophyta.

A few words may be added on the special relation of *Asteroxylon* to Dawson's *Psilophyton*. We have already compared the latter genus with *Rhynia* and found clear indications of affinity ; in fact it was on the strength of this relation that the class Psilophytales was originally established by Kidston and Lang in their first memoir. In their later work they incline to regard the affinity with *Asteroxylon* as a closer one, and propose to include *Psilophyton* in the Asteroxylaceae, as distinguished from the simpler family Rhyniaceae. First of all it may be remarked that if Dawson's figures of the anatomy of his *Psilophyton princeps* were really taken, as he states, from a rhizome, the structural agreement would be about as close with *Asteroxylon* as with *Rhynia*.

Otherwise, the question turns on Dawson's restoration of *Psilophyton* (see Fig. 172). He shows, as already explained, a leafless, branching rhizome, surmounted by branching aerial stems bearing spines ; the ultimate fertile branches are, however, spineless, and bear the terminal sporangia. It seems probable that the restoration was essentially correct, and if so, all the regions can be matched in *Asteroxylon*, if we assume that its leaves correspond to the spines of Dawson's plant. The nature of these latter organs is, however, a doubtful point. Halle says that it seems absurd to call the spines leaves ; [1] yet, as he realised, it is quite possible that they were of this nature, however rudimentary. For that matter, the leaves of *Asteroxylon* were themselves somewhat rudimentary, at least as regards the vascular supply.

On the other hand, the view may be taken that the spines of *Psilophyton* are rather comparable to the hemispherical emergences of *Rhynia Gwynne-Vaughani*, as was suggested by the late Dr. Arber in his posthumous essay on the Devonian Floras ; he could find no essential distinction between what he called macroscopic (*Psilophyton*) and microscopic (*Rhynia*) emergences.

If, as seems probable; the fertile axes and sporangia are rightly attributed to *Asteroxylon*, there is here a clear analogy with Dawson's plant, as he figured it. It has even been stated that the sporangia of *Psilophyton* dehisced longitudinally, a doubtful observation considering the state of preservation, but one which has been regarded as offering another point of comparison with such sporangia as those of *Asteroxylon*. In dimensions the *Psilophyton* sporangia agree better with those of *Rhynia*.

The question, however, of the relation of *Psilophyton* to *Asteroxylon*, turns essentially on the interpretation of the spines in the former. If we regard them as leaves, an affinity with *Asteroxylon* is undoubtedly suggested, while if we compare them with the emergences of *Rhynia Gwynne-Vaughani*, a nearer relation to the *Rhynia* type is indicated. There is a Lower Devonian genus, *Thursophyton*, believed to be akin to *Psilophyton*, in which the

[1] Halle, 1916, p. 37.

crowded scales or spines offer a somewhat better analogy with the foliage of *Asteroxylon*. The genus *Arthrostigma*, to which we shall briefly refer below, may throw some further light on the question.

Adopting the view that *Asteroxylon* may best be regarded as a somewhat advanced member of the Psilophytales, we may now consider the relations of the genus to other groups. Kidston and Lang point out the highly synthetic nature of the plant, combining certain characters of very different phyla.

In some respects *Asteroxylon* shows marked analogies with the Psilotales, as in the leafless rhizomes and leaf-bearing aerial shoots, with a gradual transition from one to the other, the first leaves appearing as mere scales. The absence of roots is a striking negative point of agreement, though the want of absorbent hairs on the rhizome of *Asteroxylon* is a difference. The anatomical features of the simple rhizome on the one hand, and the more complex aerial stem on the other, are also quite comparable. The authors consider that the analogies between Psilotales and *Asteroxylon* (and in a lesser degree other Psilophytales) favour the opinion that the recent group has preserved a primitive organisation, rather than the hypothesis that it owes its simplicity to reduction. We shall return to this question in the final chapter.

The external morphology of the leafy shoots of *Asteroxylon* is especially comparable with that of *Lycopodium*, and the same applies to the anatomical characters, the stele resembling that of such species as *L. Selago*. The immersed position of the protoxylem is not without analogy in the genus *Lycopodium*, as Sinnott has shown,[1] and the leaf-traces are very similar. There has hitherto been no evidence for the antiquity of the *Lycopodium* type of stele, and it is remarkable that something like it

---

[1] E. W. Sinnott, " On Mesarch Structure in *Lycopodium*," *Bot. Gazette*, vol. xlviii., 1909, p. 138.

should at last be detected among the oldest known land-plants.

A more remote comparison may be drawn with the stele of some Zygopterids, such as *Asteropteris* (itself a Devonian plant) and *Asterochlaena* ; but in these Primo-filices the whole stele is stellate, the phloem following the contour of the xylem, while in *Asteroxylon*, as in *Lyco-podium*, the stele is cylindrical, the phloem filling up the bays of the stellate xylem as well as extending round the arms.

Kidston and Lang dwell especially on the comparison of *Asteroxylon* with *Stauropteris* ; the resemblance of the sporangia of the latter to those attributed to the former is undoubtedly striking, as already pointed out; a more general comparison is drawn with the massed remains of *Stauropteris*, comprising the main axes, the branches of successive orders and the sporangia. A general similarity to the various organs belonging certainly or probably to *Asteroxylon* is evident, but it must be borne in mind that in such a comparison the petiole of *Stauropteris* has to do duty for the stem of the older genus.

It will be remembered that there are two views of the position of *Stauropteris* : first the view of Dr. P. Bertrand (provisionally adopted in this book) that the plant is a highly differentiated Zygopterid, and secondly the opinion of the late Prof. Lignier that it is more primi-tive than any Zygopterid, though on the same general line of descent. The question has already been dealt with (p. 334), but is reopened by the discovery of *Asteroxylon*.

On the general hypothesis of Lignier and some other writers, the plant of the Vascular Cryptogams was derived from a thalloid body, by the conversion of lateral branches of the thallus (cauloids) into leaves, a process which he termed " cladodification." *Stauropteris* is supposed to represent a stage in this process, the foliar characters still being very imperfectly realised, and an apparent radial symmetry still prevailing throughout most of the frond. *Asteroxylon* may be interpreted as an earlier link in the chain, for here, so far as is known, the radial symmetry is complete throughout. The terminal sporangia postulated by Lignier, who based his view partly on the imperfectly known *Psilophyton*, are present both in *Asteroxylon* and *Stauropteris*, and in themselves are remarkably similar in the two genera.

If we carry out this comparison, it would appear to follow that the supposed fertile axes of the Devonian plant were of the nature of leaves or at least were on the way to become leaves. On this view *Asteroxylon* would have possessed two kinds of leaves or incipient leaves—the fertile axes, no doubt modified branches, and the small leaves clothing the stem ; the latter would be comparable to the " phylloids " of Lignier, the characteristic leaves of the Lycopod phylum. Lignier regarded his phylloids as leaf-like emergences, and as quite distinct in origin from the true leaves of the megaphyllous lines (Phyllineae) derived from branches or branch-systems of the thallus. Mr. Tansley, however, has brought the two categories together, by the suggestion that leaves of the Lycopod type may have arisen " by foliar specialisation of short undivided branchlets of the thallus, instead of whole branch systems as in the Fern type." [1]

It might be possible to bring the morphology of *Asteroxylon* into line with that of the Zygopterideae by comparing the small stem-leaves of the former with the scale-leaves or aphlebiae of the latter, the fertile axes corresponding to the main, fertile fronds. The vascular strand of the fertile axis of *Asteroxylon*, in some of its Protean forms, does in fact bear a certain resemblance to the foliar bundle of the simpler Zygopterideae. As regards the stele of the stem there is the difference in

[1] A. G. Tansley, " The Evolution of the Filicinean Vascular System," *New Phytologist Reprint*, 1908, p. 9.

contour above mentioned ; the position of the protoxylem, however, is quite Zygopteridean.

With reference to the special comparison between *Asteroxylon* and *Stauropteris*, Kidston and Lang recall Lignier's suggestion that the latter may have been an independent frond, not borne on a stem ; in that case its main axis might be compared to the stem of *Asteroxylon*. This, however, seems a very improbable suggestion ; *Stauropteris*, as we know it, is after all a quadriseriate Zygopterial frond ; its radial symmetry is only apparent, the organisation being in reality bilateral (see above, p. 330). All the evidence goes to show that such fronds were borne on typical stems, with their own organisation, distinct from that of their appendages.

This, however, is a side issue ; *Asteroxylon*, at any rate, had a perfectly characteristic stem ; it is quite possible that the fertile axes, if they belonged, as we suppose, to the same plant, represent branch-systems becoming differentiated into fertile fronds, comparable to those of the Zygopterideae.

The general question was discussed by Halle, in his memoir of 1916, written, of course, before the discovery of the Rhynie petrifactions. He supports the views of Lignier, with special reference to the Lower Devonian Flora, as known at that time. In particular, he suggests, though as a " pure speculation, that megaphyllous forms may be evolved from a type like *Psilophyton Goldschmidtii*," a species described by him, in which the " lateral branches already appear to have a bilateral or dorsiventral symmetry." [1] He accepts as possible Lignier's suggestion that real fern-fronds may be derived from forms similar to the fertile branches of *Psilophyton* (*Dawsonites arcuatus* of Halle). He further remarks that, as, in the Lower Devonian, we find frond-like structures bearing sporangia, but no fronds with developed laminae, " One can hardly escape the conclusion that the

[1] Halle, 1916, p. 38.

' modified' fertile fronds may represent the primitive state in this case, and that the flattened pinnules are a later development."[1] These suggestions find some support in the organisation of *Asteroxylon* as discovered and interpreted by Kidston and Lang. The simpler morphology of the Rhyniaceae would then represent an earlier stage, in which the differentiation of the fertile frond from the stem or thallus had not even begun.

So much for the possible relation of *Asteroxylon* and its allies to the Fern-phylum, through the Zygopterideae. The points in common with the Psilotales and Lycopods have already been noticed. Halle, who only had the carbonaceous impressions of *Psilophyton* and similar Devonian fossils to work with, also laid stress on the Lycopod relation, and remarked that " from this point of view, the whole pteridophytic stock would be monophyletic, the Lycopsida and the Pteropsida being derived from a common form already vascular."[2] Kidston and Lang, on the evidence of their own plants, in which alone the structure is preserved, accept these conclusions in a general sense. They state that " *Asteroxylon* appears to agree with *Psilophyton* in possessing, in a generalised and archaic form, characters that are definitely specialised in the Psilotales, Lycopodiales, and Filicales." *Asteroxylon* is regarded as diverging from the original stock somewhat in a Lycopod direction, while a connection with the Fern-type is suggested by a comparison with *Stauropteris*.

Without necessarily committing ourselves to any definite phylogenetic conclusions, we cannot but recognise the remarkable combination of characters which such a plant as *Asteroxylon* presents.

---

[1] Halle, 1916, p. 38.   [2] Halle, *l.c.* 1916, p. 39.

ARTHROSTIGMA

This is a Lower Devonian genus, represented by a single species, *A. gracile*, first described by Sir William Dawson in 1871, from the Gaspé beds in Canada, and since found in the Lower Old Red Sandstone of Callander in Scotland, and in the Lower Devonian of Röragen, Norway. It probably occurs in other localities.

In habit, the plant is rather like an overgrown *Psilophyton*, but not branched nearly so freely. The stems, in the flattened condition, may be as much as $1\frac{1}{4}$ inch in diameter, though usually less. They are studded with peculiar appendages, which may be called leaves — short but pointed, with a very wide base, and often falcate, *i.e.* hooked downwards (Fig. 190). The leaves are, as a

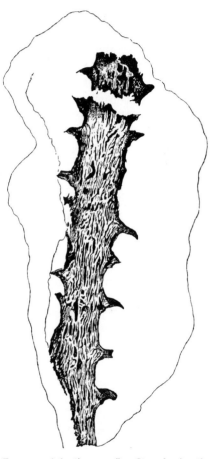

FIG. 190.—*Arthrostigma gracile.* Stem, bearing the falcate leaves. From Lower Old Red Sandstone, Callander. $\frac{3}{4}$ of natural size. After Kidston, 1893.

rule, scattered, often very sparsely, and appear to be spirally arranged, though Dawson thought they were in whorls.   Some exceptional specimens, described by Halle, in which the leaf-bases densely clothe the stem, may perhaps not really belong to the same plant.

The stem branched occasionally, sometimes forking, while in other cases the branch, though of considerable thickness, was given off almost at right angles to the main axis.

A central strand has often been observed in the stem, and Halle, in 1916, was able to make out its structure, by the treatment of carbonised material.   The strand was found to consist of a solid, pithless column of trache-ides, described as scalariform, though they might, perhaps, be equally well compared with the annular xylem-elements of the Rhyniaceae.

That the pointed appendages are really leaves, and not mere spines, is indicated by the fact that a vein can often be seen in each ; it was presumably of a vascular nature.   This observation, though it needs to be further confirmed, no doubt tends to support the interpretation of the *Psilophyton* spines also as rudimentary leaves.

Arthrostigma used to be regarded as a Lycopod, but the general resemblance to *Psilophyton* (with which small specimens of *Arthrostigma* have sometimes been confused) indicates that its right place is in the Psilophytales.

Some little strobiloid fructifications, which Dawson attributed to *Arthrostigma*, do not seem to have been found in association with the stems anywhere else but at Gaspé, and cannot at present be accepted as belonging to the plant.

Arthrostigma is of interest as a large and striking example of a Lower Devonian plant of the *Psilophyton* type.[1]

---

[1] In addition to the works of Dawson (1871 and 1882) and Halle (1916) above cited, see Kidston, " On the Occurrence of *Arthrostigma gracile*, Dawson, in the Lower Old Red Sandstone of Perthshire," *Proc. R. Physical Soc.*, Edinburgh, vol. xii., 1893, p. 102.

GENERAL RELATIONS OF THE PSILOPHYTALES

It was only in 1917 that the Psilophytales were first recognised as a distinct class of plants, based on the genus *Rhynia* and the manifestly allied, though less perféctly known *Psilophyton*. Not many years before, the very existence of *Psilophyton* itself, as a definite type of plant, had been doubted by competent authorities. Dawson's reconstruction is now confirmed in essentials, and his plant turns out to be one example of an important group. The new position has been reached through the discovery of the petrified plants of Rhynie and their brilliant investigation by Kidston and Lang ; the way had been to some extent prepared by Halle's work on good carbonised specimens from East Norway.

We now have three genera (of Middle, if not Lower Devonian age) of which the structure is pretty completely known, while other plants less favourably preserved, such as *Psilophyton*, *Arthrostigma*, and *Sporogonites*, fall into line with them. Various other fossils of the earlier Devonian or *Psilophyton* Flora no doubt belong to the same class of plants, but it would take us too far to consider them here, for the interpretation of these comparatively obscure forms is often difficult. An admirable account of the Devonian Floras and a discussion of their evolutionary significance will be found in the posthumous work by the late Dr. Arber, already referred to.

There can be no doubt that the Psilophytales constitute a distinct phylum of Vascular Cryptogams, previously unknown or unrecognised. So far, at least, as the Rhyniaceae are concerned, it would be impossible to associate the plants with any other Class ; in fact they differ more from the groups hitherto recognised than these do among themselves. The absence of both roots and leaves, the simple anatomy and histology, and the sporangia terminal on the branches, are characters separating the Rhyniaceae widely from other Pteridophyta. *Asteroxylon*, both in morphology and anatomy, is more complex, and had clearly made a great advance ; we have already considered the reasons which justify its inclusion in the Psilophytales. The strange union of characters which this genus presents forbids its reference to any of the other established phyla.

It is quite clear that the Psilophytales are the simplest race of Pteridophytes, and considering their early geological age we may presume that they are also the most primitive. The question may even arise, at least in the case of the excessively simple Rhyniaceae, whether these plants are Pteridophytes at all. As Kidston and Lang point out, their vegetative body may just as well be termed a thellus as a stem. In external morphology the Rhyniaceae are perfectly comparable to some of the Algae, and those not the most highly differentiated of their Class. Such Red Seaweeds as *Furcellaria* and *Polyides*, or such Brown Seaweeds as *Pycnophycus*, are about on the same level morphologically as *Rhynia* or *Hornea*. Other Algae, however, such as *Polyzonia* and *Sargassum*, have differentiated leaves, as *Asteroxylon* has, though in the latter genus there is no longer much suggestion of Algoid habit.

The agreement with Algae is not confined to mere configuration, for the sporangia of Rhyniaceae, formed from the modified ends of branches, find their analogue in the stichidia (tetraspore-fruits) of many Red Seaweeds, *e.g. Plocamium*,[1] an analogy which is the more striking because the tetraspores of such Algae are now often regarded as homologous with the spore-tetrads of Pteridophytes. We must not, however, imagine that any affinity between Psilophytales and existing groups of Algae is suggested. The point is rather that the simpler Psilophytales, in their general morphology, had not advanced beyond an Algoid stage. As Kidston and Lang

[1] See Oltmanns, "Morphologie und Biologie der Algen," Jena, 1904, Bd. I., p. 661, Fig. 421.

put it, " The facts are consistent with the Rhyniaceae finding their place near the beginning of a current of change from an Alga-like type of plant to the type of the simpler Vascular Cryptogams."[1] The relation between the earlier Devonian Flora generally and the Algae forms the main thesis of Dr. Arber's discussion of the origin of Cormophytes ; he believed that we have, in the *Psilophyton* Flora, the actual transition from Thallophytes to Pteridophytes, from marine Algae to the early land plants.

At any rate we have learnt to recognise in the Psilophytales a group of plants, no longer hypothetical, but known to have actually existed, which brings us appreciably nearer to the starting-points of terrestrial plant-life. The evidence they afford clearly supports the hypothesis that land-plants arose from highly organised Algae of the sea.

The fascinating subject of the subaerial transmigration has recently been discussed in an able essay by Dr. A. H. Church,[2] who gives a vivid picture of the great change from sea to land life, as he conceives it to have occurred. His treatment of the question, which he is the first to seriously take in hand, is not the less valuable because he relies wholly on general arguments, in complete independence of any fossil evidence. The new palaeobotanical data, however, are fully in agreement with his main conclusions as to the well-differentiated transmigrant Algae which became the Archegoniate series. Dr. Church believes that the chief phyla of the Landplants were already marked out among the Algae of the sea, before the transmigration ; for example, he suggests that the Lycopods and the Ferns represent lines of descent which have run a wholly distinct course from the earliest times, even perhaps from the original Plankton

[1] Kidston and Lang, *l.c.* Part II. p. 622.
[2] "Thalassiophyta and the Subaerial Transmigration," *Botanical Memoirs*, No. 3, Oxford University Press, 1919.

phase of free-swimming Flagellates. It may be possible to test this daring polyphyletic hypothesis as more of the early fossil forms come to light; in the meantime it would be rash to reject it simply on the ground of the synthetic nature of such a plant as *Asteroxylon*, for the apparent union of Lycopod, Fern, and other characters in this type may after all admit of a different explanation.

It must, however, be allowed that the existence, in the older Devonian Flora, of so simple a race of vascular plants as the Psilophytales, suggests that they may have been the survivors of a common stock from which the other phyla, at least of Pteridophytes, were derived. Vascular plants in which the vegetative phase is the sporophyte, must, however simple, be classed as Pteridophytes. If the sporogonium-like fructifications of *Hornea* and *Sporogonites* are anything more than a parallel development to the true Bryophyte fruits, they, or at least the former, would suggest that the sporophyte of the Moss series owed its origin to reduction from an Algoid body.

While it is impossible to doubt that the Psilophytales, and especially the Rhyniaceae, represent by far the simplest types of Vasculares hitherto known, we cannot be absolutely certain that all their characters are primitive. It is possible that in *Rhynia* and *Hornea* some degree of reduction, perhaps connected with xerophytic habit, had already taken place ; the very sparse, though perfectly typical, stomata of *Rhynia* might be regarded as pointing in this direction. But, however this may be, the relatively primitive nature of the newly recognised Psilophytales phylum is well established.

INDEX

An asterisk indicates a figure on the page cited.

Abietineae, 72, 223
Alethopteris, 248
Algae and Psilophytales, 420
Amber, 10
Anachoropterideae, 352-356
Anachoropteris, 352-356, 359, 364
  affinities, 355
  lamina, 355
  pulchra. See *Anachoropteris rotun-
    data*
  rotundata, 356
    petiole, *353
    synangium, *354
Analysis of petrifactions, 9
Andreaea, 395
Angiopteris, 258, 259
Angiosperms, 4
Ankyropteris, 288, 289-303, 304, 309,
    352, 358, 360
  aphlebiae, 296, *297
  bibractensis, 297, *313
  Brongniarti, 289, 295
  corrugata, 289, *297, 300, *302, 314,
    319, 320, 321
    aphlebiae, 301
    dichotomous branching, 301,
      *302
    possible sporangia, 327
    roots, 302
    secondary thickening, 303
    stele, 301
  foliar bundle, 294, 297
  Grayi, 289, *290, *291, *293, *294,
    305
    axillary branching, 295
    leaf-trace, 291, *293, *294
    phloem, 292
    stele, 290
    xylem, 291
  pinnae, 299
  ramenta, 301
  scandens, 289
  westphaliensis, 297, *298
    possible sporangia, 327
  Williamsoni, 303, *313

Annularia, 36, 66, 67, 73
  brevifolia, *66
  radiata, 67
Annulus in Botryopteridaceae, 357,
    358
  in *Botryopteris*, *343, *344, *345
  in *Corynepteris*, 329
  in *Etapteris*, 325, *326
  in *Hymenophyllites*, 264
  in *Lygodium*, 262
  in *Oligocarpia*, *255, 263
  in Osmundaceae, 264
  in *Pteridotheca*, *265, *266
  in *Renaultia*, 259
  in *Senftenbergia*, *255, 262
  in *Sturiella*, *255, 260
" Antennae," 298
Anthocerotales, 394
Aphlebia, 249
  in *Ankyropteris*, 296, *297, 301
  in *Botrychioxylon*, 320
  in *Botryopteris*, 349
  in *Diplolabis*, 318
  in *Metaclepsydropsis*, 315
" Apolar," 298
Arber, Mrs. A., 158, 162
Arber, E. A. N., 364, 365, 385, 411,
    419, 421
Arber and Lawfield, 69
Arber and Thomas, 189, 205, 208
Archaeocalamites, 22, 33, 40, 44, 62-
    64, 65, 66, 69, 110
  fructification, *54, 62
  leaves, *63
  radiatus, *54
  root, 64
  sporangia, 62
  stem, 64
Archaeopteris, 264
  hibernica, 264
Archaeosigillaria, 184
Archegonia of *Lepidostrobus*, 168
  of *L. Veltheimianus*, *169
" Areola " of Osmundaceae, 264
Arran, Isle of, 125

Arthrodendron, 29, 66
Arthropityostachys Williamsonis, 71
Arthropitys, 17, 29, 37, 66
  bistriata, 25
Arthrostigma, 412, 417, 418, 419
  affinities, 418
  gracile, *417
  leaves, 417
Aspidiaria, 117
Asplenium, 248
Asterochlaena, 288, 306-309, 337, 413
  habit, 306
  laxa, 306, *307, *309
  leaf-traces, 308, *309
  petiole, 309
  stem, 306, *307
Asterophyllites, 31, 54, 66, 67, 102
  charaeformis, 35, *36
  densifolius, *68
  grandis, *36, 51
  stomata, 36
Asteropteris, 288, 309-311, 336, 337,
    357, 366, 413
  affinities, 311
  leaf-trace, 310
  noveboracensis, *310
  stem, 310
Asterotheca, 254, *255, 277, 329, 368
  synangia, 254, *255
Asteroxylaceae, 410
Asteroxylon, 243, 387, 397-416, 422
  affinities, 409-416
  anatomy, 398
  fertile shoots, *405, *406
  habit, 397, 408
  leaf-trace, 401
  leafy stems, *399, *400, 410
  Mackiei, 397-416, *398, *399, *400,
    *401, *402, *403, *404, *405,
    *406, *407
  relation to *Psilophyton*, 410
  rhizome, 397, *398
  sporangia and spores, *407
  sporangiophores, 404
  stele, *401, *402, *403
  stomata, *404
Astromyelon. See *Calamites*, roots,
    37, 39-40
Axillary branching, 360, 362
Azolla, 168

Bacteria, 182
Baily, W. H., 329
Bancroft, N., 347
Bear Island, 110, 180
Bennettiteae, 263
Benson, M., 32, 213, 313, 334, 349
Bensonites fusiformis. See *Stauro-
    pteris burntislandica*, 334

Bergeria, 117
Berridge, E. M., 170
Bertrand, C. E., 121, 205, 351
Bertrand, P., 288, 289, 298, 303, 304,
    306, 310, 312, 318, 322, 325, 329,
    351, 413
Binney, E. W., 8
Boodle, L. A., 360
Bothrodendron, 148, 172, 179-183, 191
  cones, 179-181
  kiltorkense, 180
  leaves, 179-180
  minutifolium, 179
  mundum, 120, 173, 236
    cone, *181
    stem, 180
  punctatum, 179
    cuticles, 182
  stem, 179
Botrychioxylon, 288, 314, 319-322, 361
  aphlebiae, 320
  leaf-trace, 321
  paradoxum, *320
  petiole, 321
  roots, 320
  secondary wood, 319
  stem, 320
Botrychium, 322, 358, 361
Botryopteridaceae, 245, 265, 287-364,
    365
  affinities, 356-364
Botryopterideae, 288, 337-352
  affinities, 352
Botryopteris, 337-350, 355, 357, 363
  antiqua, 349
    leaf-trace, 349
    petiole, 349
    stem, 349
  cylindrica, 345, *346, *347
    branching, 347
    leaf-trace, 348
    petiole, 348, 349
    possible sporangia and spores, 348
    rhizome, 348
    stem, 347
  forensis, 338-350, 357
    lamina, 342
    petiole, *342
    sporangia and spores, *343
  hirsuta, *338, *340
    leaf-trace, 341
    petiole, 341
  ramosa, *339
    roots, 341, 348
    sporangia and spores, *344, *345
    stem, 338
    xylem, 340
Bower, F. O., 263, 264, 366, 369
Boweria, 267

Bowmanites Dawsoni. See *Spheno-phyllum Dawsoni*, 89
Bowmanites Römeri, 96, *97, *98, 109
  bracts, 97
  sporangia and spores, *97, *98, 99
  sporangiophores, 98, 99
Bracts (*see also* Sporophylls), *Bow-manites Römeri*, 97
  Cheirostrobus, 104, *105
  Sphenophyllum, 89, *90, *91, 92, *93
Brongniart, A., 8, 30, 70, 121, 193, 246
Brown, Richard, 219
Bruckmannia. See *Calamostachys*
Bruckmannia Grand'Euryi, 52
Bryophytes, 394, 396
Burntisland, 9
Butterworth, John, 34, 276

Calamarieae, 13-72
  affinities, 70
  classification, 65-72
  fructifications, 43-65
  leaves, 33-36, 66-69
  nomenclature, 30
  roots, 37-40
  stem, 17-27
Calamites, 7, 46, 47, 102
  branching, 13, *24, 27-29
  cambium, 21
  communis, *23, 25, *27
  infranodal canals, 16, 42
  leaf-traces, 24
  leaves, 33-36, *35, *36, 66
  medullary casts, 14-17, 41, 42
  nodes, *22, *23, *33, *34
  pedunculatus. See *Palaeostachya vera*
  periderm, 26
  phloem, 21
  pith, 17, 28
  primary structure, *19
  protoxylem, *20, 32
  ramosus, 67
  rhizome, 69
  rootlet, *40
  roots, 37-40, *38
  secondary wood, 24, 31
  stem, 17-27, *18, *19, *20, *22, *23
  Suckowii, *15, *16
  vascular bundles, 21
  wood, 20
Calamitina, 65
Calamocladus, 34. See *Asterophyllites*
  charaeformis, 35
  grandis, 36, 51
  longifolius, 51
Calamodendreae, 70
Calamodendron, 30, 37, 40, 66, 69
  intermedium, *30

Calamopitys, 29
Calamopitys, Williamson. See *Arthro-dendron*
Calamostachys, 43-53, 56, 58, 59, 67, 71, 94, 104, 108
  axis, 44
  Binneyana, *44, *45, *46, *48, *49, *50, 74
  bracts, 46
  Casheana, *frontispiece, 48, *51, 65
  Grand'Euryi, 52
  Ludwigi, 51
  ramosa, 67
  sporangia and spores, 47-50
  sporangiophores, 47
Calcareous nodules, 10
Calciferous Sandstone Series, 83, 102, 126, 163
Calcium carbonate, 8
Calopteris dubia. See *Anachoropteris rotundata*, 354
Calymmatotheca, 260
Campbell, D. H., 366
Cancellatae. See *Clathraria*, 191
Carboniferous, 4
  lower, 5
  upper, 5
Cardiocarpon anomalum, 175
Carruthers, W., 51, 52
Cash and Hick, 37
Casts, medullary. *See* Medullary casts
Caulopteris, 268
Cheirostrobeae, 102-109
Cheirostrobus, 102-109
  affinities, 108
  bracts, 104
  cones, *103
    axis, 103, 106
  pettycurensis, *103, *105, *106
  sporangia and spores, *103, *105, 107
  sporangiophores, 104, 105, 107
  sporophylls, 104
Chorionopteris gleichenioides, *354. See also *Anachoropteris*
Church, A. H., 421
Cingularia, 44, 59-62
  bracts, 60
  Cantrilli, 62
  sporangia, 61
  sporangiophores, 60
  typica, 59, *60, *61
Clathraria, 190, *194
Clepsydroideae, 336
Clepsydropsis, 288, 303-306, 309, *313, 357
  affinities, 304
  antiqua, 303
  habit, 306
  petioles, 303

Clepsydropsis (contd.)—
    roots, 305
    stem, 304
Club-mosses. *See* Lycopodiales
Coal, 8
    balls, 10
        analysis, 9
    Flora, 6
    leaf, 182
Coal-measures, 5
    lower, 17
    upper, 17
Coenopterideae. *See* Primofilices
Columella in *Hornea*, 390, *391, *392,
    394
    in *Sporogonites*, 396
Cone in *Archaeocalamites*, 62
    in *Bothrodendron*, 179, 180, *181
    in *Bowmanites Römeri*, 96-99
    in *Calamostachys*, 43-53
    in *Cheirostrobus*, 103-106
    in *Cingularia*, 60-62
    in *Equisetites*, 73
    in *Equisetum*, 64
    in *Lepidocarpon*, 174
    in *Lepidostrobus*, 155-169
    in *Macrostachya*, 65
    in *Mazocarpon*, 213
    in *Miadesmia*, 177
    in *Palaeostachya*, 54-59
    in *Pseudobornia*, 110
    in *Sigillariostrobus*, 208-213
    in *Spencerites*, 169-173
    in *Sphenophyllum*, 92-96, 99, 100,
        101, 102
Conifers, 71, 135
Corda, A. J., 270, 354
Corynepteris, 261, 288, 328, 329, 355,
    359
    synangia, 329
Cotta, B., 350
Cretaceous formation, 4
Crossotheca, *255, 260, 262
    sporangia, *255
Cryptogams, Vascular, 12
Culm Flora, 245
Cuticle, *Bothrodendron*, 182
Cyatheaceae, 247, 368, 370
Cyathotrachus altus, 254, 355
Cycadales, 212
Cycadofilices, 245
Cycadophyta, 4, 365

Dactylotheca, 247, *255, 258
    dentata, *247
    sporangia, *255
Danaea, 259, 368
Danaeites, 259
    synangia, 259

Davallia, 248
Dawson, Sir J. W., 310, 371, 382, 383,
    385, 410, 417
Dawsonites arcuatus, 385, 415
Devonian, 5, 245
    Early, Pteridophytes, 371-422
    Flora, 371
    Lower, Flora, 415
Dimorphic Fronds, 260
Dimorphism, 358
Dineuroideae, 336
Dineuron, 288, 311-312, *313, 314,
    336, 337
    ellipticum, 311
    petiole, 312, *313
    pteroides, 311
Diplolabis, 288, 316 - 318, 319, 337,
    355, 362
    aphlebiae, 318
    esnostensis, 316
    forensis, 316
    habit, 317
    leaf-trace, 317
    petiole, 318
    rhizome, 317
    Römeri, *313, 317
    roots, 317
    sporangia and spores, 318
    stem, 317
Diplotmema, 248
Diploxylic, 195
Diploxylon, 203
Dipteridineae, 368
Distichi. See *Psaronius*, 270
Dixon Fold, 218
Dukinfield, 219

Endarch bundles, 132
Eocene, 4
Equisetales, 13-74, 99, 109, 110, 244
    Mesozoic, 72-74
Equisetineae, 13
Equisetites, 73
    arenaceus, 72
    Burchardti, 73
Equisetum, 13, 19, 21, 23, 24, 28,
    36, 43, 44, 47, 64, 69, 73, 104
    Hemingwayi, 64
Etapteris, 288, 322-328, 337, 344, 357,
    358
    di-upsilon, *313, 322, 324
    Lacattei, 322, 324, *326
    petiole, 322-325
    phloem, 323
    pinnae, 323
    Scotti, *313, 322, *324
    shorensis, 322, 324
    sporangia and spores, 325-328, *326
    Tubicaulis, 322, 323

Etapteris (*contd.*)—
  xylem, 323
Eucalamites, 65
Eupodium. See *Marattia*, 258
Eu-Sigillaria, 189, 235
Eusporangiatae, 251, 364, 366, 370
Exarch bundles, 132

Farmer and T. G. Hill, 271
Favularia, *187, 189
Ferns, 244-370
  anatomy, 268-286. *See also* Botryopteridaceae
  classification, 369
  fronds, 246-250
  fructifications, 250-267. *See also* Botryopteridaceae
  Mesozoic, 368
  recent, 244
  summary, 365-370
  " Filament," 299
Filicales. *See* Ferns
Filices. *See* Ferns
Fischer, E., 60
Fronds, dimorphic, 260

Galium compared with *Sphenophyllum*, 102
Gaspé (Canada), 382, 417
Germinating spores in *Stauropteris*, *334
Gleichenia, 250
Gleicheniaceae, 263, 368
Gnetaceae, 71
Gnetopsis, 71
Göppert, H. R., 31, 270
Gordon, W. T., 88, 154, 169, 288, 312, 317, 319, 356, 404
Gradatae, 370
Grammatopteris, 350, 357
  leaf-trace, 350
  petiole, 350
  Riggoloti, 350
  stem, 350
Grand'Eury, C., 14, 34, 64, 68, 154, 155, 277, 327
Grand'Eurya, 256
  Renaulti, 256
  sporangia, 256
Greensand, lower, 4
Gwynne-Vaughan, D. T. *See* Kidston, R.
Gymnosperms, 12

Halle, T. G., 73, 240, 359, 383, 395, 415, 418
Halonia, 150-155, *151, *153
  morphology, 155
Hapalopteris, 259
  schatzlarensis, 267

Harvey-Gibson, R. J., 141
Hawlea, *255
  synangia, *255
Helminthostachys, 358, 361
Hemitelia capensis, 250
Heterosporeae, 370
Heterospory in *Calamostachys Casheana*, 48
  in *Lepidostrobus*, 174
  in *Macrostachya*, 65
  in *Palaeostachya*, 55
  in *Selaginellites*, 240
  in *Sigillaria*, 209
  in *Sphenophyllum*, incipient, 96
Hick, T., 34, 233
Hickling, G., 53, 57
Hill, T. G., 140
Hornea, 382, 387-395
  anatomy, 389
  columella, 390-394, *392
  habit, 387
  Lignieri, 387-395, *387, *388, *389, *390, *391, *392, *393
  morphology, 388
  rhizome, *387, *388
  sporangia and spores, 389, *391, *392, *393, *394
  stem, *389, *390
Horsetails, 13, 33, 40
Hovelacque, M., 133, 140
Hymenophyllaceae, 264, 301, 360, 364, 368
Hymenophyllites, annulus, 264
  quadridactylites, 264

Impressions, 7
Incrustation, 6
Indusium, 345
Infranodal canals of Calamites, 42
Integument in *Lepidocarpon*, *175, *176
  in *Miadesmia*, *177, *178
Isoëtes, 112, 116, 136, 141, 142, 157, 162, 165, 169, 210, 237, 242
  Hystrix, 140
Isosporeae, 369

Jeffrey, E. C., 280
Johnson, T., 180
Jurassic, 4, 73

Kaulfussia, 253, 258, 259
Kidston, R., 62, 64, 101, 138, 147, 154, 164, 179, 183, 205, 208, 209, 210, 211, 260, 264, 288, 349, 418
Kidston and Gwynne-Vaughan, 278, 286, 336, 363
Kidston and Jongmans, 69
Kidston and Lang, 371, 386, 410, 416, 420

Kisch, Mabel H., 134
Knorria, 117
Kubart, B., 353, 355

Laggan Bay, 125
Lang, W. H., 173, 361
Leaf-scars, Lepidodendron, *115, *116
　Sigillaria, 186-191, *187, *188, *189
Leaf-trace, Ankyropteris, 291, 301
　Asteropteris, 310
　Asteroxylon, 401
　Botrychioxylon, 321
　Botryopteris, 341
　　antiqua, 349
　　cylindrica, 347, 348
　Calamites, 24
　Diplolabis, 317
　Grammatopteris, 350
　Lepidodendron, 122, 131
　Metaclepsydropsis, 314
　Psaronius, 272
　Sigillaria, 195
　Sphenophyllum, 86
Leaves, nature of, 413
Leiodermaria, *189, 190
Lepidocarpon, 163, 174-176, 242
　embryo-sac, 174
　ligule, 175
　Lomaxi, *174, *175, *176
　megaspore, 174
　prothallus, 175-176
　" seed," 174-176
　sporangium and spores, 174-176
　Wildianum, 176
Lepidodendreae, 111-183
Lepidodendron, 7, 108, 111-146, 179,
　202, 203, 219, 235
　aculeatum, 120, 137
　branching, 143-146
　brevifolium. See Veltheimianum
　cambium, 134
　elegans, *113
　esnostense, 142
　fuliginosum, 120, 122, 124, 137,
　　145, 152, *153, 234
　habit, 112-118
　Harcourtii, 120, 121, *123, 159
　Hickii, 120, 122, 139, 142, *143,
　　152
　intermedium, 120, 137
　leaf-base, *116
　leaf-scars, *115, *116
　leaf-traces, 122, *127, 131
　leaves, 138-143
　ligule, *116, *139, 140, *141
　macrophyllum, 120
　mundum. See Bothrodendron
　　mundum
　obovatum, 137, 152

Lepidodendron (contd.)—
　Ophiurus, *114, 155
　parichnos, *116, 138, *139
　parvulum, 120
　periderm, 123, *128, *129, 132
　pettycurense, 119, 120, 138
　phloem, 131
　pith, 119
　rhodumnense, 119
　secondary thickening, 119, 120, 124
　selaginoides, 119, 120, *129, *130,
　　*135, 140, *144
　stele, 119, 125
　stem, 118-138
　stomata, *143
　vasculare. See L. selaginoides
　Veltheimianum, *115, 120, 126,
　　*128, 140, 146, 148
　wood, 120, 121, 129
　Wunschianum, 120, 124-126, *127,
　　150, 196
Lepidodendron and Lepidophloios,
　111-146
Lepidophloios (see also Lepidodendron),
　117, 121, 138, *139, *141, 150
　fuliginosus. See Lepidodendron
　　fuliginosum
　laricinus, 154
　ligule, *139, *141
　scoticus, 120, *151, 154
　Scottii. See L. scoticus, 154
Lepidostrobus, 155-169, *157, 173,
　380, 391
　archegonia, 168, *169
　axis, 158
　Bailyanus. See Bothrodendron kil-
　　torkense
　Brownii, 156, 158, 159
　foliaceus, sporangia and spores,
　　*167
　heterospory, 162, 174
　Hibbertianus, *156
　kentuckyensis, 159
　ligule, 160
　oldhamius, 158-163, 174
　Olryi. See Bothrodendron, 179
　prothallus, *168
　sporangia and spores, 156-169
　sporophylls, 156-164, 174
　Veltheimianus, *163, *164, *165,
　　*166, 167, *168, *169
　archegonium, *169
Leptosporangiatae, 251, 366, 370
Lias, 73
Lignier, O., 334, 336, 413
Ligule, Lepidocarpon, 175
　Lepidodendron, *116, 140-142
　Lepidophloios, *139, *141
　Lepidostrobus, 160

Ligule (*contd.*)—
  Miadesmia, *177, *178
  Sigillaria, 188, *189
Lomaria, 249
Lomax, J., 112, 120, 152, 176, 180, 319, 350
Lycopodiaceae, 106
Lycopodiaceous fructifications, seed-like, 173-179
Lycopodiales, 111-243
Lycopoditeae, 239-241
Lycopodites, 240
Lycopodium, 111, 140, 156, 179, 239, 240, 242, 388, 391, 400, 401, 412
  cernuum, 173
  Selago, 183, 412
Lycopods, 13, 109, 244, 416
  affinities, 241-242
Lyginopteris, 260, 262
Lygodium, 262

Mackie, Dr. W., 372, 397
Macrostachya, 64-65, 70
  infundibuliformis, *65
Marattia, 368
Marattiaceae, 248, 251, 256, 258, 259, 261, 262, 271, 278, 329, 356, 364, 365, 368
Marattiales, 366
Marsiliaceae, 370
Maslen, A. J., 39, 160
Matonia, 368
Matonineae, 368
Mazocarpon, 210, *213-217, 391
  affinities, 216
  axis, 213
  pettycurense, 216
  shorense, 213, *214, *215
    prothallus, *168
  sporangia and spores, 213-216
  sporophylls, 213
Medullary casts. *See* Casts, medullary
Megaphytum, 268
Megasporangia and megaspores. *See* Sporangia and spores
Mesarch bundles, 132
Mesozoic, 5
  Equisetales, 72-74
  Ferns, 368
Metaclepsydropsis, 288, 312-316, *313, 317, 321, 336, 337, 357, 358
  aphlebiae, 315
  duplex, *316, 319
  habit, 312
  leaf-trace, 314
  paradoxa, 316
  petiole, 315
  pinnae, 315

Metaclepsydropsis (*contd.*)—
  rhizome, 312
  roots, 314
  stem, 314
Miadesmia, 177-179, 239, 241, 242
  axis, 177
  ligule, 177, 178
  membranacea, *177, *178
  " seed," 177-179
  sporangia and spores, 177-179
  sporophylls, 177
Microsporangia and microspores. *See* Sporangia and spores
Miocene, 4
Mixtae, 370
Mollusca, 10
Myriophylloides, 37

Naiadita, 241
Nathorst, A. G., 110
Neocalamites, 73
Neuropteris, 248
Noeggerathia, 263
Nova Scotia, 219

Old Red Sandstone, 372
Oligocarpia, *255, 263, 365
  annulus, 263
  robustior, 264
  sporangia, *255
Oligocene, 4
Oolitic, 4
Ophioglossaceae, 322, 358, 361, 362, 364
Ophioglosseae, 251, 263
Ophioglossites, 263
Ophioglossum, 322
Osborn, Mrs. E. N., 304
Osmunda, 279, 368
  cinnamomea, 280
Osmundaceae, 264, 278-286, 345, 358, 362, 364, 368
  annulus, 264
  distribution, 286
  leaf-trace, 279, 282, 285
  roots, 286
  stem, 278-286
Osmundites, 278
  Carnieri, 280
  Dowkeri, 279
  Dunlopi, 279
  Gibbiana, 279
  Kolbei, 280, 286
  leaf-traces, 279
  phloem, 279
  schemnitzensis, 279
  skidegatensis, 279, *280, 286
  stem, 279
  xylem, 279

Palaeo-Marattiales, 367
Palaeopteris. See Archaeopteris
Palaeostachya, 43, *54-59, 60, 67, 72
  axis, 56
  bracts, 54, 58
  gracilis, 54
  pedunculata, *55
  sporangia and spores, 58
  sporangiophores, 54-59
  vera, 56, *57, *58
Palaeozoic, 4
Parichnos, Lepidodendron, *116, 138, *139, 140
  Sigillaria, 188, *189, 199
Pecopteris, 246, 256, 258, 260, 262, 277
  densifolia, 256
  dentata. See Dactylotheca
  exigua, 261
  intermedia, 260
  oreopteridia, 256
  Pluckeneti, 262
Periderm, Ankyropteris, 302
  Bothrodendron, 181
  Botrychioxylon, 321
  Calamites, 26, 40
  Lepidodendron, 123, *128, *129, 132
  Sigillaria, 196, 199, *204, 206
  Sphenophyllum, *81, 82, *87, 88
  Stigmaria, *222, *225
Permian, 4, 72, 75, 112, 306
Petrifactions, 6, 8
  analysis of, 9
Pettycur. See Burntisland
Phylloglossum, 111, 173, 238
Phyllotheca, 73
  deliquescens, 64
Pinakodendron, 183, 241
  Ohmanni, 183
Plankton, 421
Polypodiaceae, 369
Polystichi. See Psaronius, 270
Pothocites, 64
Potonié, H., 139, 335
Preservation, modes of, 6
Primofilices, 364, 365, 367
Prothallus, 168
  Lepidocarpon, *175-*176
  Lepidostrobus, *168, *169
  Mazocarpon, *168
  Miadesmia, 178
Protocalamites pettycurensis, 21, *32
Protocorm, 388, 393
Psaronius, 262, 268-278, 365, 367
  affinities, 278
  brasiliensis, 270, *272
  classification, 270
  leaf-trace, 272
  Renaulti, 276, *277
  roots, *275

Psaronius (contd.)—
  root-zone, 270, 273-*275
  steles, 271, 273
  stem, 271
Pseudobornia, 110
  ursina, 110
Pseudoborniales, 110
Psilophytales, 243, 336, 371-422
  affinities, 419-422
  characters, 386
Psilophyton, 371, 417, 419
  Flora, 421
  Goldschmidtii, 415
  princeps, 382, *385, 410
  relation to Asteroxylon, 410
  relation to Rhynia, 382-387
  rhizome, 384
  spines, 411
Psilotaceae, 75, 244
Psilotales, 412, 416
Psiloteae, 112
Psilotum, 239
Pteridophytes, Early Devonian, 371-422
  and Thallophytes, 421
Pteridospermeae, 71, 264
Pteridosperms, 245, 249, 262, 264, 365
Pteridotheca, 265
  annulus, *265, *266, 267
  seriata, 267
  sporangia and spores, *265, 267
  Williamsonii, *265, *266, 366
Ptychocarpus, 252, 354
  synangia, 252, *253
  unitus, 252, *253
Ptychopteris, 268
Purbeck strata, 4

Rachiopteris cylindrica. See Botryopteris cylindrica
  duplex. See Metaclepsydropsis
  hirsuta. See Botryopteris hirsuta, 339
  insignis. See Ankyropteris corrugata
  ramosa. See Botryopteris ramosa, 339
Ramenta, Ankyropteris corrugata, 301
Ranunculi, 76
Renault, B., 8, 10, 28, 37, 62, 70, 78, 86, 142, 182, 195, 199, 201, 207, 231, 234, 288, 325, 338, 350, 361
Renault and Grand'Eury, 197
Renaultia, Stur. See Sturiella, Weiss, 259
Renaultia, Zeiller, *255, 259
  annulus, 259
  sporangia and spores, *255
Renier, A., 149

Rhacopteris, 263
Rhaetic formation, 73
Rhizocarps, 370
Rhizome of *Asteroxylon*, 397, *398
  of *Botryopteris cylindrica*, 348
  of *Calamites*, 69
  of *Diplolabis*, 317
  of *Hornea*, *387, *388
  of *Metaclepsydropsis*, 312
  of *Psilophyton*, 384
  of *Rhynia*, 372
Rhizophore, 239
Rhynia, 371-387, 419, 422
  anatomy, 376
  branching, 373
  Gwynne-Vaughani, 372, *373, *375, *376, *377, *378, *379, *380, *381, 411
  habit, 372
  major, 372, *374, *382, *383, *384
  morphology, 372
  relation to *Psilophyton*, 382-387
  rhizome, 372
  sporangia and spores, 380, *382, *383, 384
  stomata, *377
Rhyniaceae, 396, 410, 416, 419, 422
Rhynie (Aberdeen), 372
Rhytidolepis, *188, 189, 203, *204, 208, 209
Roof nodules, 10, 11
Rootlets, *Calamites*, *40
  Stigmaria, 226-234, *225, *229, *230, *232, *233, *234
Roots, *Ankyropteris*, 296, 302
  Archaeocalamites, 64
  Botrychioxylon, 320
  Botryopteris, 341, 348
  Calamarieae, 37-40, *38
  Clepsydropsis, 305
  Diplolabis, 317
  Lepidodendreae. See *Stigmaria*
  Metaclepsydropsis, 314
  Osmundaceae, 286
  Psaronius, 273-276, *275
  Sphenophyllum, 86-88, *87
  Stigmaria, 217-239
  Tubicaulis, 351
Röragen (Norway), 383, 395, 417
Rudolf, K., 278

Saarbrücken, 184
Sahni, B., 305, 312, 336
St. Helens, 219
Salvinia, 238
Salviniaceae, 370
Sandstone, Calciferous Series, 83
  New Red, 4
  Old Red, 5, 372

Sarcopteris Bertrandi, 264
Schizaea, 364
Schizaeaceae, 262, 364, 370
Schizoneura, 73
Schizopteris, 327
  pinnata, 328
  and *Schizostachys*. See *Etapteris*
Schizostachys frondosus, 328
Scolecopteris, 256, 277, 354
  elegans, 258
  polymorpha, 256, *257
  synangia, 256, *257
Scott, Rina, *167, *168, *177, *178, *332, 333, 334, *344, *345
Seam nodules, 10
Seaweeds, Brown, 420
  Red, 420
Secondary rocks, 4
Secondary thickening in *Arthrodendron*, 29
  in *Ankyropteris*, 302
  in *Botrychioxylon*, 319
  in Calamarieae, 70
  in *Calamites*, 17, 24
    roots, 37
  in *Calamodendron*, 30
  in *Cheirostrobus*, 108
  in *Lepidodendron*, 119, 125, 134
  in *Metaclepsydropsis*, 314
  in *Psaronius* roots, 276
  in *Sigillaria*, 195
  in *Sphenophyllum*, 80
    roots, 88
  in *Stigmaria*, 222
    rootlets, 232
Secretory organs in *Bensonites*, 334
  in *Lepidodendron*, 124
  in *Psaronius*, 276
  in *Sigillaria*, 199
"Seed," *Lepidocarpon*, *174, *175, *176
  Miadesmia, *177, *178, 179
Seed-like Lycopodiaceous fructifications, 173-179
Selaginella, 116, 140, 142, 156, 159, 161, 162, 164, 169, 173, 237, 238, 240, 242
  Kraussiana, 223
  oregana, 141
  rupestris, 141
  spinosa, 111, 222, 241
Selaginellites, 240
  elongatus, 241
  heterospory, 240
  primaevus, 241
  Suissei, 240
Senftenbergia, *255, 261, 365
  annulus, 262
  sporangia, *255, 261

Seward, A. C., 56, 121, 137, 364
Seward and A. W. Hill, 125, 126, 196
Shore, Littleborough, 11
Sigillaria, 7, 124, 146, 147, 148, 179, 184-213, 216
  affinities, 196, 212
  anatomical structure, 193-208
  branching, 193
  Brardi, *189, 191, 197, 234
  cone-scars, 188, 211
  cortex, 196
  discophora, 212
  elegans, 205, 211.   See S. *Menardi*
  elongata, 205
  fructifications, 208-213
  habit, 184-193
  heterospory, 209
  latifolia, *200
  leaf-scars, 186-191
  leaves, 201-203
  lepidodendrifolia, 185
  mamillaris, *188, 206
  Menardi, *194, 197
  parichnos, 188, 189, 199
  periderm, 196, 199, 206
  reniformis, 184, 203
  (*Rhytidolepis*), *204
  scutellata, *206
  secondary thickening, 195
  spinulosa, 191, 197, *198, *200
  stem, 184-201
  stomata, 202
  tesselata, *187
  wood, 195
Sigillariopsis, 208
  Decaisnii, 207
  sulcata, *207, 216
Sigillariostrobus, 209-213, 216
  Crepini, 210
  nobilis, 209
  rhombibracteatus, *211
  sporangia and spores, 210
  sporophylls, 210
  Tieghemi, 209
Silicic acid, 8
Silicified specimens, 8
Silurian, 5
Simplices, 370
Sinnott, E. W., 281, 412
Sollas, I. B. J., 241
Solms-Laubach, Graf, 3, 8, 52, 96, 140, 234, 271, 274, 276
Spencerites, 169-173, 242
  insignis, 170, *171, 210
    axis, 172
    sporangia and spores, 170-172
  majusculus, 172
  spores, *166
  sporophylls, 170

Spermophyta, 12
Sphagnum, 390, 394
Sphenophyllales, 21, 75-110, 112, 244
Sphenophylleae, 75-102
Sphenophyllostachys, 96
Sphenophyllum, 75-102, *76, 106
  bracts, 89, *90, *91, 92, *93
  cambium, 82
  charaeforme, 95
  cone-axis, 92
  cuneifolium, 77, 92, 95
  Dawsoni, 88, *90, *91, *93, *95, 108, 109
  fertile, 87, 99, *100, 109
  fructifications, 88-101
  habit, 76, 102
  insigne, 83, *84, 87
  leaves, 76, 85
  majus, 100, *101
  myriophyllum, 83
  periderm, *81, 82, *87, 88
  phloëm, 82
  plurifoliatum, 78, *80, *81, *82, 83, 87
  quadrifidum, *79
  roots, 86, *87
  saxifragaefolium, *77
  speciosum, 77
  sporangia and spores, 90-94
  sporangiophores, 90-94
  stem, 76, 86
  stomata, 94
  tenuissimum, 100
  trichomatosum, 101
  verticillatum, 96
  wood, 78, 83
Sphenopteris, 248, 249, 259, 266
Sporangia and spores, *Archaeocalcmites*, *54, 62
  Botryopteris, *343, *344, *345
  Bowmanites Römeri, *97, *98, 99
  Calamostachys, *47-*50
  Cheirostrobus, *103, *105, 107
  Cingularia, *61
  Crossotheca, *255
  Dactylotheca, *255
  Diplolabis, 318
  Grand'Eurya, 256
  Hornea, 389, *391, *392, *393, 394
  Lepidocarpon, *174-*176
  Lepidostrobus, *156-*169
  Mazocarpon, *213-*216
  Miadesmia, *177, *178, 179
  Oligocarpia, *255
  Palaeostachya, *54, *57, *58
  Pseudobornia, 110
  Pteridotheca, *265-*267
  Renaultia, *255
  Rhynia, 380, *382, *383, *384

Sporangia and spores (contd.)—
  Senftenbergia, *255, 261
  Sigillariostrobus, 210, *211
  Spencerites, *166, 170-172, *171
  Sphenophyllum, 88-101, *90, *91,
    *93, *95
  Stauropteris, *332, *334
  Urnatopteris, *255
Sporangiophore, 43
  Archaeocalamites, 62
  Asteroxylon, 404
  Bowmanites Römeri, 98
  Calamostachys, 47
  Cheirostrobus, 104
  Cingularia, 60
  Palaeostachya, 54, 59
  Sphenophyllum, 90, 94
Sporogonites, 391, 395-397, 419, 422
  affinities, 396
  columella, 396
  exuberans, 395
Sporogonium, 390
Sporophylls, Cheirostrobus, 104
  Lepidocarpon, 174
  Lepidostrobus, 156-164
  Mazocarpon, 213
  Miadesmia, 177
  Sigillariostrobus, 210
  Spencerites, 170
Stangeria, 249
Starling-stones. See Psaronius, 269
Stauropteris, 288, 329-337, 356, 358,
    408, 413-415
  affinities, 334-337
  burntislandica, 329, 333
  oldhamia, 329, *330, *331, *332,
    *334
  petiole, 329-332, *330, *331
  phloëm, 329
  pinnae, 330
  sporangia and spores, *332, *334
  xylem, 329
Stenzel, K. G., 270, 289, 319
Stephanian Flora, 245
Stephanospermum, 71
Stigmaria, 126, 181, 185, 217-239,
    242
  affinities, 218
  anatomical structure, 221-236
  axis, 221-226
  branching, 218
  cortex, 224
  ficoides, *186, 217-234, *218, *222,
    *224, *225, *229, *230, *232,
    *233, *234
  flexuosa, 234
  habit, 217-221
  morphology, 236-239
  periderm, 225

Stigmaria (contd.)—
  rootlets, 220, 226, 233, *225, *229,
    230, *232, *233, *234
  branching, 232
  secondary thickening, 222-232
  wood, 221, *235
Stigmarian clay, 220
Stigmariopsis, 235
Stipitopteris, 276
Stomata, Asteroxylon, *404
  Calamites, 36
  Lepidodendron, *143
  Rhynia, *377
  Sigillaria, 202
  Sphenophyllum, 94
Stopes, Marie C., 40, 350
Strasburger, E., 258
Strobilus. See Cone
Stur, D., 256, 261
Sturiella, *255, 260
  annulus, 261
  synangia, *255
Stylocalamites, 65, 69
Sub-Sigillariae, 189, 235
Sutcliffe, W., 11
Swamp Flora, 6
  Great Dismal, 6
Synangia, 366
  Asterotheca, 254, *255
  Chorionopteris, *354
  Corynepteris, 329
  Cyathotrachus, 254, 355
  Danaeites, 259
  Hawlea, *255
  Ptychocarpus, 252, *253
  Scolecopteris, 256, *257
  Sturiella, *255
Syringodendron, 192, 199

Tansley, A. G., 335, 414
Telangium Scotti, 262
Tertiary Plants, 4
Tetrastichi. See Psaronius, 270
Thallophytes and Pteridophyta, 421
Thamnopteris, 279, 281-284, 313, 317,
    362
  leaf-trace, 282, *285
  Schlechtendalii, 281, *282, *283,
    *285
  stem, 281
  xylem, 281
Thoday, D., 96
Thomas, H. Hamshaw, 34, 51
Thursophyton, 411
Tmesipteris, 239
Todea, 279, 368
Tovarkovo cuticles, 182
Tracheotheca, 381
Transmigration, sub-aerial, 421

Tree Ferns, 268
Trias, 4, 72
Trichomanes, 360
Trizygia, 77
Tubicaulis, 350-352, 357
  Berthieri, 351
  petiole, 351
  primarius. See *Zygopteris*, 319
  roots, 351
  Solenites, 350
  stem, 351
  Sutcliffii, 351

Ulodendron, 147-150, *148, 212
  and *Halonia*, 147-155
  morphology, 149
Underclay, 185
Urnatopteris, *255, 260
  sporangia, *255

Vascular cryptogams, 5
Velum. *See* Integument
Volkmannia, 54
  Dawsoni. See *Sphenophyllum*, 89

Watson, D. M. S., 120, 254
Wealden Flora, 4, 73
Weiss, C. E., 59, 65
Weiss, F. E., 153, 231, 234, 235
Westphalian Flora, 245
White, D., 184

Wieland, G. R., 4
Wild, G., 14, 176
Williamson, W. C., 8, 37, 41, 56, 83, 88,
  118, 121, 125, 203, 218, 223, 299
Witham of Lartington, 8, 120

Xanthorrhoea, 193
Xenophyton, 237
  radiculosum, 233
Xerophytic habit, 202

Zalessky, M., 155
Zalesskya, 279, 317, 362
  diploxylon, 281, 284
  gracilis, 281, 284
Zeiller, R., 88, 95, 147, 179, 185, 208,
  210, 240, 244, 246, 250, 261, 264,
  270, 328
Zeiller and Renault, 328
Zobel, A., 96
Zygopterideae, 288-337, *313, 356,
  401, 413
  petioles, *313
  relationships of genera, 336-337
Zygopteris, 288, 295, 318-319, 337, 363
  elliptica. See *Etapteris*, 325
  Kidstoni, 311
  petiole, 319
  primaria, 319
  Römeri. See *Diplolabis*, 316
  Tubicaulis. See *Etapteris*, 322, 323

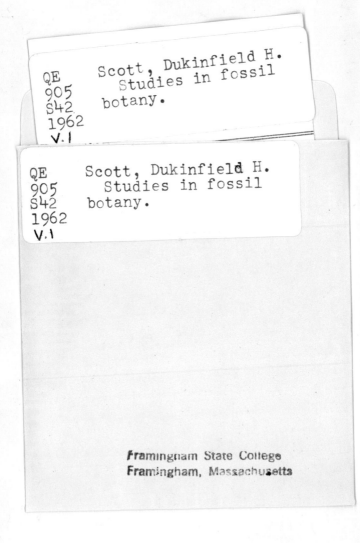